ABOUT THE AUTHOR

A retired professor of historical geography, Ronald Rees taught at the University of Saskatchewan and, as adjunct professor, at Mount Allison University, New Brunswick. He has written books on the landscape and settlement of the Canadian Prairies, on the United Empire Loyalists who settled in the Maritime Provinces of Canada, and on garden history. He was born in Skewen and has most recently been writing about Wales. He is currently working on a history of mining and mining settlement in the western region of the south Wales coalfield. He lives in St Andrews, New Brunswick.

HEROIC SCIENCE

SWANSEA AND THE ROYAL INSTITUTION OF SOUTH WALES 1835-1865

Ronald Rees

WALES BOOKS
GLYNDŴR PUBLISHING

2005

First published in 2005 by Welsh Books (Glyndŵr Publishing)
Porth Glyndŵr, Higher End, St Athan,
Vale of Glamorgan, CF62 4LW.
www.walesbooks.com

ISBN 1 903529 16 6

*This publication was assisted by a grant
from the Welsh Books Council.*

Cover design: Welsh Books Council.

Printed and bound in Wales by
Dinefwr Press, Rawlings Road
Llandybie, Carmarthenshire, SA18 3YD

To
Matthew Rees
Geologist, Companion and Aide

ACKNOWLEDGEMENTS

I am indebted to Richard Morris for his generous transmission of the thirty-six volumes of the Lewis Weston Dillwyn Diaries; to Professor Eric Mills of Dalhousie University for the loan of microfilms of the Alder-Norman Correspondence; and to Cathy Talbot for copies of typescripts of the entries (then works-in-progress) on William Dillwyn (1743-1824) and Lewis Weston Dillwyn (1778-1855) for the Dictionary of Quaker biography.

For their many kindnesses and services, I also owe debts of thanks to Bernice Cardy, Curator of the Swansea Museum, to Michael Gibbs, Librarian at the Museum, to Jennifer Sabine of the Royal Institution of South Wales, and to Tom Sharpe of the Department of Geology of the National Museum of Wales. I am also greatly indebted to Mary Doon, librarian at the St Andrews Community College, for her fine skill in locating sources of research materials, and for the despatch with which, through a remarkably efficient interlibrary-loan system, she delivered them to me.

CONTENTS

PUBLISHER'S PREFACE 9

FOREWORD 11

THE SETTING 15

THE SCIENTISTS

John Henry Vivian FRS 1785-1855 23
Metallurgist, Mineralogist
Leader of the World Copper Industry

Lewis Weston Dillwyn FRS 1778-1855 43
Pioneer Botanist, Zoologist
Manufacturer of Fine Porcelain ('Swansea China')

John Gwyn Jeffreys FRS 1809-1885 76
Conchologist
Pioneer of Deep Sea Dredging

Sir Henry De la Beche FRS 1796-1855 115
Geologist
First Director of the Geological Survey of Great Britain

Sir William Edmond Logan FRS 1798-1875 150
Geologist
Founding Director of the Geological Survey of Canada
Canada's Most Acclaimed Scientist

Thomas Williams MD FRS 1818-1865 182
Physician
Polymath and Pioneer Microbiologist

William Robert Grove FRS 1811-1896 204
Physicist, Jurist
Inventor of the Fuel Cell

THE 1848 BRITISH ASSOCIATION MEETING IN SWANSEA 235

BIBLIOGRAPHY 244

PUBLISHER'S PREFACE

This was an exciting time for Wales, when Swansea and Swansea scientists were leaders in the Scientific Revolution spreading across Europe and America. At this same time Wales could claim other notable scientists – Richard Phillips (mentioned in this text, *'Britain's best-known and most able chemist'*), Alfred Russel Wallace (*arguably the real pioneer of Darwinism*), and the great David Hughes (*the first man to transmit and receive radio waves and the pioneer of telephones*) – the list is seemingly endless of men who contributed to the advancement of thought and action. William Morgan (1750-1830) the nephew of *the most original thinker* Wales has ever known, Dr Richard Price, even invented the X-Ray, in the presence of Benjamin Franklin, 110 years before Roentgen. Along with also inventing the vacuum tube, he was the founding father of modern actuarial science! The parameters of these men knew no bounds. They were living on the edge of discovery.

At this time also, George Parry of Ebbw Vale invented a process that he sold and which became known as 'the Bessemer Process', and the invention of Sidney Gilchrist Thomas and his cousin Percy Gilchrist made the global breakthrough which led to the modern steel industry (see *'100 Great Welshmen'*). Yet this is a relatively unexplored and unknown area of history – we are interested in battles and relationships, but shy away from areas that we regard as 'difficult'. Bill Bryson with his recent book 'A Short History of Nearly Everything' has really helped many people to come to an accommodation with the fundamentals of science. The exciting fact about that particular book, is that is has been written by a non-scientist, who can then act as a bridge to those of us whose education in that realm is lacking. We can see from Bryson that even now men are reaching out into the dark to find reasons for certain processes, much like the 'gentleman-scientists' in this book.

This is a book that demonstrates how one particular part of a small region of a small country could become a centre of activity for European science. Swansea has to be proud of its role in scientific history, and it should never be forgotten. Ronald Rees has produced a superbly researched book, which will stand the test of time, and it is hoped that his association with our publishing house is a long and fruitful one.

Terry Breverton

FOREWORD

On the eve of the eighteenth annual meeting of the British Association for the Advancement of Science in Swansea, the magazine and newspaper correspondents who had gathered for the occasion expressed surprise and, in a few cases, astonishment at the choice of venue. Even allowing for the Association's policy of taking science to distant corners of Britain, Swansea seemed an almost frivolous choice. In 1848 the town had no rail connections, no university, college or medical school and it was, as the president of the Association (the Marquis of Northampton) remarked, 're-mote from the metropolis, remote from the chief seats of learning, remote also from those great highways of communication'.[1]

The Great Western Railway would not connect Swansea with Gloucester and London until 1850. Particularly upset with the absence of a railway was the correspondent for the *Literary Gazette*. He noted that in a place renowned for the making of metal 'its most wonderful uses and lightning rapidity are unfelt, and from the speed of the racer or swallow we seem to sink to the pace of the porpoise or sloth. Still, patience and progress going hand in hand, even the longest journey, like life, comes to an end'.[2] Just as disgruntled was the correspondent for the *Illustrated London News*. He arrived after a rail journey to Bristol and a 'somewhat tedious' channel crossing to Swansea.

Others had come even more tediously by overnight coach from London and Birmingham, crossing the Severn by the unpredict-able New Passage, near the present-day Severn Tunnel, in an open boat with sails. On a good day the three-mile crossing took an uneventful and disarming half-hour but on a bad one, against a powerful ebb tide and contrary winds, it could be a knuckle-biting, hours-long trauma. Even travellers accustomed to the crossing could be unnerved. In 1833 Sarah Vivian pleaded with her husband: 'I entreat you *not* to cross by the New Passage if as bad as today. Life is too precious and above all yours'.[3] The mail coach left London at 8.55 p.m. and, travelling through the night, reached Swansea at 1 p.m. the following day. The Bristol-Swansea coach left Bristol at 8 a.m. and arrived in Swansea at 7 p.m.

The quickest route from London and the Midlands was by rail to Bristol and steam packet to Swansea. Travellers could leave London or Birmingham in the early morning and be in Bristol in good time for the six-hour steam packet crossing to Swansea. Travellers who wished to avoid the six-hour crossing could take the shorter three-hour crossing to Cardiff and come on to Swansea by coach. Michael Faraday, for whom no river or channel crossing was short enough ('I dare not trust my hand in rough waters') wrote to his friend and fellow physicist William Robert Grove for directions for the fastest route by land. The 1848 visit would be his third to Swansea and he must have hoped that since the last, fifteen years earlier, the journey had been quickened or the road shortened.[4]

Because of the difficulties of access, not even local reporters were convinced that reason and logic had much to do with the British Association's decision. Regional or national loyalty demanded some support from the *Cardiff and Merthyr Guardian* but its approval was couched in a grudging negative: 'In determining the locality of its meeting the Council of the Association has been, we may feel assured, uninfluenced by caprice'.[5] Judging from 'the tenor of the remarks' made at the meeting, it also questioned whether some of the officers of the Association and some of the principal delegates had not anticipated a failure. Swansea, too, had its sceptics or 'croakers'. When the scientists began to gather in respectable numbers they were roundly rebuked by the *Cambrian*: 'We know now that notwithstanding all the croaking, that this Swansea meeting will be a good one and that the British Association is *not* in its decrepitude'.[6]

For most people outside Wales, Swansea in the middle of the nineteenth century had one claim to distinction: it smelted most of Britain's copper. Copper was to Swansea, the *Cambrian* proudly intoned, what coal was to Newcastle and silk to Lyons. Up the Tawe Valley and away from the town stretched a chain of smelters that produced more than half of Britain's copper and a fair proportion of the world's. This industrial distinction alone would have attracted the British Association, whose mandate was to promote technology as well as science, but for those who had kept abreast of developments in the natural and the physical sciences Swansea had far more to offer than long experience in the handling and processing of ores and metals.

During the first half of the nineteenth century, as the historian of the University College of Swansea noted, the town bred, nurtured, or sheltered a 'veritable galaxy of talent' – a group of scientists of national and, in a few cases, international importance.[7] No fewer than seven of them were elected, either during or shortly after their Swansea days, fellows of the Royal Society. Five, too, were among the eleven founding members of the Philosophical and Literary Institution, the forerunner of the Royal Institution of South Wales (RISW). Admittedly, entry to the Royal Society in the mid-nineteenth century was far easier than it is today but for a remote provincial town of twenty-five thousand people to have produced several fellows was no small achievement.

In 1850, two years after the British Association meeting, a special correspondent for the *Morning Chronicle* described Swansea as a society distinguished by two or three leading minds all with European reputations.[8] He cited the physicist William Robert Grove, inventor of the fuel cell, the botanist Lewis Weston Dillwyn, and the conchologist and marine zoologist John Gwyn Jeffreys. He might also have added Henry De la Beche and William Edmond Logan, two of the century's great field geologists, who had strong connections with the town.

The symbol of this scientific eminence was the Royal Institution of South Wales, an elegant Palladian building that housed behind its pillared and pedimented front a library, museum and lecture hall. Built in 1838-39, it predated by more than thirty years the first college of the University of Wales and by more than seventy years the National Library. With no distinguished philosopher among them and only one well-known physician, the members could not claim, as did the intelligentsia of Edinburgh and Glasgow, to have re-created the ethos of fifth century Athens, but in a society in which science had as yet no reckoning in the national genius the Royal Institution was a beacon.

What follows is a series of linked portraits. The first is of the town, for no matter how talented its practitioners science needs a context, and in the first half of the nineteenth century Swansea probably was the only town in Wales that could have sustained a scientific community.

The scientists, seven in all, were all members, and in several cases founding members and officers, of the Royal Institution of South Wales. They formed friendships, and in some cases lifelong associations, and because in the first half of the nineteenth century there was a common language of science they were able to follow developments in related fields. Chemists could communicate with mineralogists and geologists, botanists with geologists and palaeontologists, and physicists with physicians. And because of the broad use of the vernacular in scientific writing all, to some extent, could communicate with laymen and lay women. By 1848 four of the seven had moved onto larger stages, both national and international, but all except William Logan, who was directing the first geological survey of Canada, returned for the British Association meeting. They were instrumental in bringing the meeting to Swansea and the Royal Institution and, as if to acknowledge a debt to what for some was their *alma mater*, they promoted the event, helped to organize it, and chaired most of the major sessions.

NOTES

1. Presidential address to the 18th annual BAAS meeting, Swansea 1848.
2. *Literary Gazette* (12 August 1848).
3. Averil Stewart, *Family Tapestry* (London, 1961), 121.
4. Dafydd Tomos, Michael Faraday in *Wales* (Denbigh, 1977), 167.
5. *Cardiff and Merthyr Guardian* (12 August 1848).
6. *Cambrian* (11 August 1848).
7. David Dykes, *The University College of Swansea: an Illustrated History* (Stroud, 1992), 34.

THE SETTING

An 1848 sketch of Swansea, made from a daguerreotype looking toward the harbour and the mouth of the Tawe, shows a town being taken over by, in Oliver Goldsmith's phrase, 'trade's unfeeling train'. Around the harbour and the mouth of the river, in the middle distance, are terraces of well-proportioned Georgian and Regency houses in what was still the most fashionable quarter of the town. Among them, but not clearly discernible in the sketch, is the Royal Institution of South Wales. Beyond the houses are the sands of the shore and the Burrows where there were parks, pleasant coastal walks and across the river – although no longer in use by 1848 – a racetrack.

In the foreground, however, and dominating the scene, are the dark, densely packed row houses of the shopkeepers, industrial workers, and clerks which are beginning to crowd the elegant rows around the harbour. In the harbour itself, and the bay beyond, there are coasting vessels and pleasure boats but most of the shipping is commercial and oceangoing. Anchored in the harbour and tied to the wharves are barques recently returned from Cuba and Chile with cargoes of metal-rich copper ore to be piled in storage sheds and barged upstream to the calciners and smelters in the copper works. Within fifteen years of the date of the sketch the Burrows will be doekland. The Royal Institution and a few of the terraces will survive but many of the houses and most of the parks, gardens and walks will have made way for two new docks and a railway terminal.

By 1848 Swansea was thoroughly reconciled to a future of industry and trade, but for about a century, from 1720-1820, it had harboured a dream of elegance: the town longed to be a resort.[1] In 1850 a special correspondent for the *Morning Chronicle* noted crossly that an ornamental inscription commemorating Beau Nash, who had been born in the town in 1674, was of far greater pretension than the memorials announcing the birthplace of Goethe in Frankfurt, or of Rubens in Cologne.[2] When Daniel Defoe visited in 1720 he found a small but busy coaling port of about 1500 people handily situated for business and trade.

He also noted that the spirit of Beau Nash was already abroad. Nash applied his talents for fashion and organization to Bath and Tunbridge Wells, but by 1720 the burgesses and aldermen of his home town were already advertising 'styptick and restorative waters' capable of curing or counteracting consumptions – 'if not too far gone' – dropsies, palsies, rheumatisms, haemorrhages and fluxes.[3] As it happens, Swansea had no mineral springs and therefore no real prospect of emulating Bath or Tunbridge Wells, but it had all the attributes of a successful seaside resort. The harbour was attractive and it opened into a majestic bay that to the west gave onto the open and beckoning lands of Gower. None of these assets escaped the aldermen and burgesses and they were endorsed by English travellers, who saw in Swansea Bay a rival to the great Bay of Naples.

When choosing a summer retreat away from the noise, smells and diseases of the town or city, the wealthy and the well to do looked for healing airs and waters in addition to attractive surroundings. With no science of medicine to draw on, and no understanding of the mechanisms of infection, the only prophylactics honest physicians could recommend were fresh air and exercise and healing waters, either for bathing in or drinking. Few towns had mineral waters but many physicians considered seawater, either drunk or bathed in, to be almost as therapeutic. The great champion of salt-water therapy was Dr Richard Russell who thought it especially effective in curing diseases of the glands. Following the publication of his book on the subject in 1750, the English, as Cowper put it, rushed headlong to the sea. Visitors who arrived in Swansea without their Russell could turn to a companion work by William Turton, a local physician, on the therapeutic powers of hot and cold seawater baths.

Determined that Swansea should receive its share of seaward-rushing tourists, the Corporation took the initiative in developing and promoting the town. Through the enclosure acts of the 1760's it came into possession of the small Burrows, a tract of open, common land immediately south of the town bounded by the river to the east and the bay to the south. To attract summer visitors, developers and benefactors were encouraged to apply

Swansea, 1848.

for leases to build lodging and rental houses and to lay out parks, gardens and coastal walks. First to oblige was the Duke of Beaufort, the lord of the borough and manor of Swansea, who laid out at his own expense walks, paths and gardens. With investment from the Corporation, bathing houses, bandstands, a theatre and, in the Crymlyn Burrows on the far side of the river, a racecourse, duly followed. Development of what, in effect, was a new town remained piecemeal until 1810 when the Corporation approved a plan that included new or remodelled parks and gardens, and a new Guildhall and assembly rooms, the latter to be designed by William Jernegan, a leading English architect. A decade later, the Burrows was the most fashionable area in the town.

Most visitors to the spas and early seaside resorts expected to be edified as well as entertained, and they required newspapers, magazines, journals and books. Books were expensive and in short supply, but for a small fee they could be borrowed from a variety of subscription libraries. By 1815 there were six in Swansea. Most stocked cheap romances and sensational autobiographies – the 'slopshops of literature' – but in one there was a subscription reading room that offered three London daily papers and various provincial journals.

17

For serious readers, summer as well as year-round, there was the Glamorgan Library financed by seasonal or annual subscriptions from its readers. Its aim was to build up a stock of nonfiction books for the cultivated reader and the gentleman scholar. To keep romances at bay, one of the library's rules specified that 'novels . . . be excluded.' Classical novels were exempt but they surrendered the shelves to books on philosophy, natural history and topography.[4] By 1804 the town also had an English newspaper, the *Cambrian,* the first in Wales. Its owners and backers – one of which was the Corporation – were very clear about its role. As well as serving the needs of English visitors, it would bring the language of commerce and trade to Swansea, already the most Anglicized town in Wales, and expose its readers to the ideas and aspirations of a wider world.

The other major and, as it turned out, more lasting string to the town's economic bow was the copper trade. Swansea and copper smelting, as historians have pointed out, were made for each other. Cornwall, on the far side of the Bristol Channel, had high grade copper ore and Swansea had coal of smelting quality. In the eighteenth century it took three tons of coal to smelt one ton of copper ore so the logistics were simple: the ore came to the coal. Although large fortunes were made from copper smelting, the trade, for a town wishing devoutly to be a resort, had one serious drawback: it produced mountains of furnace waste and clouds of toxic, evil-smelling smoke.

The town learned its lesson early. In 1720, it allowed a group of Quaker merchants and businessmen to build a copper works on the river just inside the northern boundary of the town. The prevailing winds in Swansea blow from the southwest and on most days they funnelled the smoke up the narrow valley away from the town. But the Westerlies, though steady, are not trade winds and from time to time they backed to the north and east and sent smoke and fume onto the town. Copper-smoke even once every fortnight was more than the townsfolk could tolerate and when the lease of the works expired in 1764, at the very time when the town was eyeing the development of the Burrows, the Corporation rejected the application for renewal and assigned the site to a pottery.

Whatever Swansea's social aspirations, copper ores and Tawe

valley coals were inseparable and no municipal ordinance could keep the smelters at bay. Denied access to the town, they simply moved upriver into the lower valley; by 1850 this was a forest of chimneys and a wasteland of slag. But as long as the works remained small and the winds steady, and beach-bound rail passengers were prepared to ignore the last mile or two of their journey, the works were no threat to the hotel and boarding house owners. For the first twenty or thirty years of the nineteenth century, copper smelting and tourism were able to co-exist. The Corporation built parades, walks and bathing huts in the Burrows while a mile or two inland coppermen from Cornwall, London, Bristol and Anglesey built calciners and smelters. At first they used Cornish ores but when these were no longer enough they went farther afield to Cuba, Chile and Australia. The workers lived in a string of connected villages built around the copper works while most of the owners settled west of the town on large, smoke-free estates overlooking the bay. 'Straggling villas rising immediately to view', they had appropriately romantic names: Marino, Verandah, Sketty Lodge, Woodlands, Lilliput Hall.

In 1848 Swansea was a prosperous community of some twenty-five thousand people increasingly dependent on the copper trade and its associated industries. In a watershed editorial in 1822 the Cambrian conceded that if it came to a choice between tourism and copper smelting then the latter would win hands down.[5] Swansea itself was widely regarded as the leading town in Wales, the 'natural Metropolis' according to some. It was also the most cosmopolitan of the Welsh towns and, by definition in the context of the nineteenth century, the most progressive. Industrialized, predominantly English-speaking, outward looking and, despite the absence of a railway until 1850, in one of the more accessible parts of Wales, it was an outlier of invention and progressive thought.

Like the industrial towns of northern and middle England, it had been energized by the new techniques in manufacturing and by new ideas and new blood. Factory owners and professional men studied the climate, minerals, and flora and fauna of their localities and took a new or renewed interest in history and archaeology. With few universities available, and none offering comprehensive instruction in the natural or the physical sciences, it was an age of self-taught amateur scholars. With an enthusiasm that we can only marvel at, they formed select reading groups and founded philosophical and literary societies with libraries, reading rooms and lecture halls. In England towns such as Newcastle, Manchester, Derby and Liverpool were exemplars of this burgeoning intellectual life; in Wales, however, Swansea stood alone.

NOTES

1. For the development of Swansea as a resort see David Boorman, *The Brighton of Wales, Swansea as a fashionable seaside resort 1780-1830* (Swansea, 1986).
2. *Cambrian* (14 June 1850).
3. Daniel Defoe, *A Tour through the Whole Island of Britain* (London, 1745). Quoted in J. R. Ross, *Letters from Swansea* (Llandybie, 1969), 31.
4. Janet Thomas, *Swansea as a Fashionable Watering Place 1787-1820* (Swansea, 1983) 17-20; Tom Ridd, 'Swansea's Parks and Public Libraries', *Glamorgan Historian*, 6 (1970) 105-115.
5. *Cambrian* (15 June 1822).

THE
SCIENTISTS

JOHN HENRY VIVIAN FRS
1785-1855

Metallurgist, Mineralogist
Leader of the World Copper Industry

On the eastern edge of the campus of the University College of Wales, Swansea, is a mansion house in the chimneyed and turreted Tudor style. On its flanks are large exotic pines and in front a double terrace and a broad, curving lawn that sweeps down to the bay. The house is now the administrative centre for the College. West of it, in what was once part of the estate, are the library, laboratories and lecture halls, functional buildings of moulded cement, brick, aluminium and glass. Were he to return, the former owner and builder of the mansion house, John Henry Vivian, might take exception to the campus architecture but he would be delighted that the house in which he studied, wrote, organized his mineral collection and entertained some of the most distinguished scientists in the land, should have been chosen, in 1920, as the nucleus of the new university college. In Swansea, no other site would have been nearly as appropriate. John Henry Vivian was an icon: Swansea's leading industrialist during the first half of the nineteenth century, an accomplished scientist and fellow of the Royal Society and, for more than twenty years, the town's dedicated and unopposed Liberal MP.

He is now regarded as a native son but, like most of the early industrial entrepreneurs in Wales, his origins were elsewhere. He was born in Truro in 1785, the son of John Vivian and Betsy Cranch, both children of the manse. John Vivian's two younger brothers followed paths expected of minor Cornish gentry and became fellows of Exeter College, Oxford. John's interests, however, were in commerce and trade. Truro then was the organizing centre for the Cornish copper mining industry and by the end of the eighteenth century John Vivian had interests in every branch of it. By turns, he was an agent for smelting companies who needed Cornish ores, a supplier of materials to miners and mine owners, a partner in the Miners' Bank of Truro, deputy-governor of the Cornish Metal Company, and Vice-Warden of the Stannaries, the mining districts of Cornwall.[1]

John Henry Vivian was the second of John and Betsy Vivian's three sons. The youngest, Thomas, died when he was only 21, the eldest, the stellar Richard Hussey, became a celebrated soldier. After Truro Grammar School and spells at Harrow and Exeter College, Richard Hussey flirted with a legal career but when still only eighteen he found his metier: the army. Purchase, petition, patronage and a flair for soldiery brought him a series of commissions and by 1808, at age 24, he was a lieutenant-colonel in Spain. Under Wellington he was first a colonel and a brigade commander then, after a bloody engagement during the closing stages of the Peninsular War in which he was shot in the shoulder, a major general.

At Waterloo he commanded a brigade of cavalry with such panache that he was praised by Wellington and thanked formally by both houses of Parliament. Decorations from the Emperor of Austria and the Tsar of Russia followed and fellow Cornishmen feted him at a grand dinner in Truro's Assembly Rooms. His portrait, which hangs prominently in the stairway of the Royal Institution at Truro, is a study in self aggrandizement: in the uniform of a brigade commander, Richard Hussey poses theatrically in front of the near-wild horse (barely restrained by an orderly) he rode at Waterloo.

Although siblings, Richard Hussey and John Henry could hardly have been less alike. John Henry also engaged Napoleon, but in conversation not battle.[2] On a Grand Tour in 1814/1815 he visited Elba where, dressed in the uniform of the Militia of Cornish Miners, he spent an hour with the Emperor. Earlier in Vienna he had met the Empress Marie Louise and the little Prince Imperial, Napoleon's wife and son. Vivian spoke fluent French. Napoleon questioned him about the Cornish terrain and the Cornish economy, the state of the roads and bridges in the Alps, southern France and Italy, progress at the Congress of Vienna, and the character of nations as expressed in their soldiery. He thought the English soldiers when drunk were ungovernable but the French in a similar state were 'doux et tendre'. An attending equerry remarked that he had seldom been present at such an agreeable interview.

Sir Richard Hussey Vivian.   *John Henry Vivian.*

On receiving a letter summarizing the audience, and noting Napoleon's interest in roads and bridges, Richard Hussey, now a Major General, showed it to the Prime Minister, Lord Liverpool. Liverpool ignored the warning and two months later Napoleon escaped.[3] A year or two before his death, in 1855, John Henry also posed for a portrait, a modest monochrome drawing. Puck-like, seated, and wearing a dress coat and a tall hat, he smiles benignly at the artist, J. H. Lynch. His mother's shy, introverted temperament was clearly his. Betsy Cranch, as the writer Averil Stewart noted, was 'a gentle daughter of the rectory' and on her death her husband remarked that 'a more benevolent meek spirit never ascended to the Father of spirits.'[4]

From his father, on the other hand, John Henry inherited an aptitude for business. Like Richard Hussey, he attended Truro Grammar School but following this he rejected the classical high road to Harrow and Exeter College – the Oxford choice of most West country men – in favour of commerce and language studies at Marburg in Germany. From Marburg he went on to the Mining Academy of the University of Freiburg in the Erzegebirge (Ore Mountains) to study metallurgy, chemistry, mathematics and mineralogy. He had set his sights on a career in the copper trade. There would be no college of chemistry in England until 1846 and no school of mines until 1851. The chemical arts might fill the national coffers, as the provost of Oriel (Edward Copleston) remarked in the 1820s, but they could never take precedence over 'that intellectual laboratory, where the sages of Greece explored the hidden elements of which man consists'.[5]

Young Englishmen apprenticed through practice alone, depending on itinerant lecturers for any theoretical instruction. Any sustained instruction required a move abroad. By going to Germany Vivian followed a trail blazed in 1786, and retraced in 1793 and 1798, by the geologist and mineralogist John Hawkins, a fellow Cornishman.[6] In Germany, a technical and scientific education carried no stigma. Hawkins's tutor in mineralogy and geology, Abraham Gottlob Werner, was also Vivian's. Werner was the most celebrated mineralogist and geologist of his day and a gifted teacher. Vivian's instructor in chemistry and metallurgy was Wilhelm August Lampadius, best known for his discovery of carbon disulphide and the introduction of gas lighting to Germany. Lampadius studied science at Goettingen and until his appointment to Freiburg in 1794 he worked as a chemist in iron and steel plants.

For Vivian, his meeting with Werner and Lampadius was providential. Werner was the son of a mining and iron working family and he, like Lampadius, could bring to the lecture hall his experience of the foundry and the factory. Werner's father managed an iron works in Bunzlau. As a small child, when scarcely able to speak, Werner is said to have amused himself by breaking down pieces of sandstone and marl and he could be bribed into good behaviour by the promise of a glance at his father's collection of minerals.[7] After a spell at the works, as an assayer and bookkeeper, he enrolled in the Mining Academy at Freiburg, then a small and little-known school for training miners and mining engineers. From there he went on to mining law at the University of Leipzig where, bored with law, he published an essay on the external characteristics of minerals that, in effect, proved to be a method of classification. His system rested on the observation that external characteristics reflected internal chemistry and, the corollary of this, that chemical composition should be the basis of any mineral classification. Although much modified, Werner's system remains the basis for the hand identification of minerals. Werner had no microscope. The essay created a stir and it led to an invitation to teach mining and mineralogy at his old school in Freiburg.[8]

Few appointments have been as inspired. As a teacher Werner was a sensation. He attracted students from all parts of Europe and, with help from Lampadius, raised Freiburg's status from an academy to a university. Just as Linnaeus brought order and method to the study of botany, so Werner systematized the study of mineralogy and geology. He insisted upon accurate observation in the field, the use of precise terminology, and the systematic classification of rocks and minerals. His lectures, however, were far from narrow disquisitions on the fine points of mineralogy and geology. He had eloquence and charm and, like all gifted teachers, he delighted in making associations and connections. Former students described how, from a few specimens arranged seemingly at random on a table before him, he would launch into mesmerizing extrapolations, establishing connections between rock type, topography, soils, the distribution of population and the character and wealth of nations.

A few samples of stone suitable for building might trigger a lecture on the history of architecture, and a few pieces of iron or copper ore on one of the classical metal ages. He was as much sorcerer as teacher and to students of all ages and at all stages he was irresistible. Among his best-known students were Alexander von Humboldt, the famed geographer, and Frederich Mohs, the author of a scale of hardness for minerals. Even established scientists attended his lectures, some of whom learned German for the purpose. Werner was also an excitable enthusiast. A present of diamond crystals from John Hawkins delivered by the Welsh naturalist and travel writer Thomas Pennant made him almost mad with joy: 'Hi, hi, hi, il pense de moi, comme il est bon, comme ce joli hi hi hi' was, Pennant reported, repeated at least fifty times.[9] Georges Cuvier, the renowned French zoologist, left this impression of Werner's drawing power:

> *At the little Academy of Freiberg, founded for the purpose of training mining engineers and mine captains for the mines of Saxony, there was renewed the spectacle presented by the universities of the Middle Ages, for students flocked thither from every civilized country. One saw men from the most remote countries, already well advanced in years, men of education holding important positions,*

27

engaged with all diligence in the study of the German language, that they might fit themselves to sit at the feet of this 'Great oracle of the sciences of the earth'.[10]

Although a stickler for method and accuracy, Werner was not averse to speculation. He asserted that the rocks of the crust were formed, the oldest more than a million years ago, by precipitation from a turbid ocean that once enveloped the earth. The earliest rocks (granite, gneiss, porphyry etc.) were entirely of chemical origin and the most recent (sandstones, shales, limestones etc.) of sedimentation or mechanical deposition. The various skins or layers ('like the rind of an onion') so formed he labeled and described as precisely as he had the minerals in his cabinets. Although he had never set foot outside Saxony, he asserted that these same rock formations could be found in all parts of the world, in the same order and exhibiting the same characteristics.

The universality, and the theory which underpinned it, were soon dismissed as yet another fantastic cosmogony, but the concept of identifiable layers of rock arranged in regular succession brought a vestige of order to seeming chaos, and it is now regarded as the springboard for the great stratigraphical exercises of the first half of the nineteenth century. Because of the critical role of the sea in Werner's suppositions, supporters of the theory – which became the subject of a famous controversy – were labelled 'Neptunists'. They were opposed, and ultimately defeated, by 'Vulcanists' who sought a fiery origin for the igneous and metaphorphic rocks. But at the turn of the nineteenth century, Werner's views ruled. He was, as one of his critics remarked, a kind of geological pope. He also had the backing of a literary pope, Goethe, who rejected the violent vision of the Plutonists as a wilful disturbance of the picture of a fair earth. The comforting Neptunian vision he gave to Faust, the hellish Plutonian vision to Mephistopheles.

In addition to the public lectures, which were free to students from Saxony, Vivian received private instruction from Werner. Students from outside Saxony paid a 'moderate' fee for each course but there is no suggestion in Vivian's references to Freiburg that he paid extra for his private lessons. Werner was extremely well paid and in 1804/5 Vivian and a Mr. Chevenix were the only English students at the Academy. Vivian wrote subsequently that he would always be grateful for Werner's 'great attentions' while he was a student, and for his generosity and attentiveness during a subsequent visit to Freiburg in 1815. Under Werner's tutelage, he also began his mineral collection. As a student and, in 1815, tourist, he visited mines and smelting plants in and around Freiburg as well as others in Hungary, Poland, Austria, and other parts of Germany. In a French-controlled district of the Harz Mountains he was forced, England and France being at war, to pass himself off as an American.

He also visited at least one other mining academy, at Schemnitz in Lower Hungary, and wrote detailed notes on the courses of instruction at it and at Freiburg. For the courses at Freiburg he had nothing but praise. Mining and metallurgical students studied for three years, the mining students under the direction of a board of miners who insisted that they make frequent excursions underground. Instruction was free because the sovereign, as was the custom in other European states, derived substantial revenues from the mines. The Academy at Schemnitz, on the other hand, which had neither a Werner nor a Lampadius, pleased him less.

In the curriculum for mining students, mineralogy came under the rubric of chemistry, a subservience that Vivian thought unwarranted. Just as disturbing, for a diligent private collector of minerals, was the Academy's mineral collection. Subject to cannibalization by larger and more important museums in Vienna, the collection was 'incomplete and carelessly arranged'. But the saving grace for instruction in mineralogy and geology was that it followed the Wernerian system.

Vivian published these observations in an article written for the first volume (1814) of the *Transactions of the Royal Geological Society of Cornwall*.[11] The papers on the academies at Freiburg and Schemnitz were in support of a resolution by the Society to establish a mining academy and a chair for a Professor of Mineralogy and Geology. Through its auspices, classes were offered in several Cornish towns but there would be no permanently housed Cornish school until the opening of the Camborne School of Mines in 1859. Like John Hawkins, who preceded him at Freiburg, Vivian thought mining practices in Cornwall were primitive. He acknowledged that on the continent, where all metallic minerals belonged to the state not to the landowner, there was greater incentive for governments to establish mining academies. But until there was an academy in Britain the kind of instruction – in the practice of mining and metallurgy as well as in the theory of chemistry and mineralogy – that he had received in Germany would not be available. It meant that Vivian was unusual, if not unique, among British industrialists and it is no accident that he was probably the first to enlist laboratory science in an effort to modify heavy industrial operations.

For that same volume of the *Transactions,* he also wrote technical papers on salt mining in Poland and Austria, and on methods of preparing arsenic and cobalt in works in Saxony and Bohemia.[12] Both papers were written at the request of John Ayrton Paris M.D, one of the founder members of the Cornish Geological Society, Humphry Davy's first biographer, and the inventor of the thaumatrope.[13] Cobalt had recently been found in Cornwall and Cornish works were having difficulty making arsenic from arsenical pyrites or white mundic, the term preferred by Cornish miners. Vivian visited the salt mines at Salzburg in the fall of 1814, when travelling from Vienna to Italy via the Tyrol, and those at Wielitska the following summer.

Salt mines are like no others and, like most visitors, Vivian was astonished by them. The Wieletska mines, which had been worked for about six hundred years, were on the north side of the Carpathians about eight miles from the city of Cracow. Access to the principal mine was by a wide staircase that descended about two hundred feet to a spacious chapel, replete with altar, monk-like figures performing mass, worshippers at prayer, crucifixes and ornaments. All were hewn or carved from solid salt and all appeared to be of great antiquity. In the chapel, as throughout the mine, he was unprepared for the hard surfaces and the extremely dry air, stripped of all humidity by the moisture-absorbing salt.

From the chapel another stairway led to the levels or galleries from which the salt was being cut. The galleries were perfectly straight and regular, eight or nine feet in height and nearly as many in width. The ceilings were supported by immense tree trunks piled horizontally in cross layers or, more commonly, by arches of salt. Strewn throughout the bottoms of the galleries were large blocks of salt and casks filled with small pieces of salt that fell during the cutting and dressing of the blocks. At the bottom of the mine was a lake, large enough to be crossed by boat, and with sufficient surrounding floor space to accommodate an orchestra and an audience. The ceiling was also high enough to allow fireworks and illuminations. Music and fireworks were entertainments for the Emperor of Russia who visited the Wielitska mine on his way to the Congress of Vienna in 1814.

Vivian's earlier visit to the town of Hallein, about eight miles from Salzburg, had been just as captivating. He and his companion were first kitted out 'a la Saxonne', in local mine wear, and made to descend the mine 'in a most singular and ludicrous manner'. The mineshaft was a steep incline and, holding onto a rope, they slid down in a toboggan-like apparatus 'at a pace that was most agreeable'. Several persons, he added, could descend in a string, the one resting on the shoulders of the other. In this way they descended through three shafts, upwards of nine hundred feet. In the second shaft they were obliged to throw their bodies completely back to prevent themselves from going too fast. The ascent, in a carriage on wooden rails drawn by a man and two boys was just as agreeable as the descent. At Hallein the salt was so adulterated with clay that it could not be cut and marketed as blocks of pure rock salt. To remove the clay from the salt, the underground chambers were filled with water from the surface and the water, once saturated, was siphoned to boiling houses in Hallein and the salt separated by evaporation. The insoluble clay fell to the bottom of the chamber where, once the water had been drawn off, it was tamped down and the chamber re-filled. At each filling the chambers throughout the salt-producing districts rose a few inches.

On his way home from Freiburg in 1805 John Henry visited his brother Richard Hussey, then quartered at Ipswich. While there Lord Anglesey, Richard's friend and patron, pressed him to take a commission. But for John Henry, despite an attachment to the Cornish Miners' Militia strong enough that he took its uniform to Elba, there was to be no military interlude. While he was in Germany his father, John Vivian, had been making other plans. Frustrated by the smelters' control of the price of copper ore, he had begun moving his capital from mining into smelting. In 1800, through a joint venture with the Associated Miners of Cornwall, he bought an interest in a smelting works at Penclawdd, a village on the Llwchwr estuary about seven miles west of Swansea.

When John Henry returned from Freiburg in 1806 John Vivian directed him to Wales where, still only 21, he was appointed manager of the Penclawdd works. But within a year both father and son, uneasy about the prospects at Penclawdd, began to look around for a site for a new works. Shipping in the shallow Llwchwr estuary could be treacherous and Penclawdd was some distance from the sources of coal. For their new site they settled on Hafod, then a picturesque village on the west bank of the Tawe just above Swansea. To steer the enterprise, John Vivian created a new company, Vivian & Sons. He kept half the shares for himself and divided the other half between John Henry and the absent Richard Hussey whose interest in the company seldom rose above its ability to pay his gambling debts.[14] In manufacturing, John Vivian's practice was to produce at full capacity and sell as cheaply as possible. The Hafod was the largest smelting works in the kingdom and within fifteen years it had cornered fifteen percent of the British market. With his brother permanently absent and his father resident in Truro, John Henry Vivian was the de facto leader of the copper industry not just in Britain, but the world.

Although Vivian was quiet and retiring, his success and inescapable prominence in Swansea demanded a way of life that matched his status. In 1816 he married Sarah Jones, the eldest daughter of Arthur Jones of Flintshire and Reigate, Surrey. Through his mother, Arthur Jones inherited the Priory, a large estate at Reigate on the Brighton River and while there he had become a gambling friend of the Prince Regent. He sold the Priory and came to live in Swansea where his wife had relatives and where his daughter met John Henry Vivian. After the marriage the Vivians rented Marino, an elegant but modest villa overlooking the bay on the fashionable west side of the town. Within a year the Vivians had bought the freehold and begun a process of extension and remodeling that converted modest Marino into a mansion house of late mediaeval or Tudor design. Mock Tudor and Gothic were then the height of fashion. Marino disappeared behind a Gothic façade of vertical windows and pointed arches, and beneath a thicket of Tudor turrets, pots and

Singleton Abbey.

chimneys. There was also a change of name. The Vivians bought an adjacent forty-two acre farm owned by the Singleton family and they applied the old farm name to the new house. Marino became Singleton Abbey, the suffix an acknowledgement of the ecclesiastical origins of late Gothic design.

As well as housing the Vivians and their nine children, Singleton was also a setting for John Henry's collections of rocks and minerals, and stuffed birds and animals. The Hafod had capable managers and Vivian was able to indulge his scientific interests. His association with Werner gave him early entry to the Geological Society of London of which he was an honorary member from its foundation in 1807. The Society had begun as a gentleman's social and dining club with the purpose, as set out in its original manifesto, 'of making geologists acquainted with each other, of stimulating their zeal, of inducing them to adopt one nomenclature, of facilitating communication of new facts, and of contributing to the advancement of geological sciences'. The first chairman and the first president of the Society, George Bellas Greenough, had also studied with Werner. It is unlikely that Vivian attended many of the monthly dinners and meetings but he kept abreast of developments in mineralogy and geology. He continued to collect and classify minerals, and some five hundred from his collection were given 'distinguished notice' in the first volume of the transactions of the Cornish Geological Society.

One, 'Vivianite', a hydrated iron phosphate in the form of prismatic crystals probably found in Cornwall, was named after him. First to confirm its identity, and record its description in the scientific literature, was Abraham Werner, in 1816/17. At Singleton Vivian set up cabinets of rocks and minerals classified according to Wernerian principles and he is said to have corresponded with Werner until the latter's death, in 1817. If so, it may well have been a one-sided exchange because Werner, an enthralling speaker, disliked writing. In his latter years dislike turned to repugnance and on his death several hundred unanswered letters were found in his apartments.

But what brought Vivian to the attention of the scientific world, and in turn brought the scientific world to Swansea, were not his geological and mineralogical interests but a problem at the works. Before copper ore can be smelted, the sulphur and other impurities in the ore have to be burned off, or calcined. Unmodified, the process produces clouds of acrid, white smoke virulent enough to scour glass and kill plants and grazing animals. Upwind from Hafod, trees and shrubs withered, grasses turned yellow, and cattle, sheep and horses developed deformities so peculiar to the smoke districts that they acquired a name, 'effryddod' (deformity caused by 'smoke sickness'). The problem was not specific to the Hafod, but as the largest copper works in the Tawe Valley it was the prime target for aggrieved farmers and landlords. Even before the opening of the works, apprehensive landlords, aware of the destructive power of the smoke, issued warnings to the Vivians. After the opening, warnings turned into lawsuits. The earliest of them the Vivians were able to divert, but in 1820 an aggrieved landowner managed to get an indictment for common nuisance upheld by a Cardiff Grand Jury. If successful, it could have closed not only the Hafod but all the copper works in the Tawe valley.

There was, of course, little prospect of any Glamorgan jury allowing a handful of disgruntled farmers and landowners to injure Swansea's golden goose and the Vivians could, with impunity, have let their accuser have his day in court. But, in a letter to his father, John Henry acknowledged that landowners and farmers had 'ample cause for complaint' and ought to be compensated. Yet he also realized that to yield in this one case would be to trigger an avalanche of grievances not only against the Hafod but against every copper works in the valley. In theory every copper smelter could be indicted, or sued for damages. To protect the industry, two approaches were possible: they and their fellow smelters could either seek legal protection from actions the courts might regard as gratuitous or malevolent, or they could look for ways to reduce the damage caused by the smoke.

For Vivian the decision was an easy one. In 1820 experimental science was just getting into its stride and, with his background in chemistry and metallurgy, it must have seemed inconceivable that it would not solve the copper smoke problem. To attack the smoke on a broad front, he suggested a competition and the award of a prize of a thousand pounds to anyone who could devise a method for removing the destructive gases. Subscriptions were invited and the money quickly raised. Vivian himself and the company, Vivian and Sons, contributed a hundred pounds each, an amount matched only by the Swansea Corporation. At a meeting in the Town Hall in October 1821 the terms of the contest were set out. The proffered solutions had to work under factory, not just laboratory, conditions and to claim the prize all the poisonous gases had to be eliminated. The most lethal to plants and animals was one of the smallest in volume, sulphurous acid gas, the 'great enemy' as Vivian was to describe it. The judges were a mix of trained scientists and practical men: the botanist Lewis Weston Dillwyn, ironmasters Anthony Hill and William Crawshay of Merthyr, and Davies Gilbert, chemist and vice-president of the Royal Society. Davies Gilbert was a Cornishman and, like the others, known to John Henry Vivian.

Although provoked by the indictment, Vivian had been attentive to the smoke problem since his arrival in Wales. At Penclawdd, where he was not threatened with lawsuits, he had experimented with the design of flues hoping, by making the smoke pursue a tortuous course, to tease the impurities out of it. At some expense, and against the resistance of workers reluctant to adopt any changes that impeded movement or interfered with their work in any way, he persisted with the experiments at Hafod. But he quickly concluded that the solution to the smoke problem lay in chemistry, not mechanics, and after consulting his father he decided to seek expert help. As a metallurgist of some standing and a prominent industrialist he was able to approach – the phrase is his father's – the most 'knowing heads' in Britain: Richard Phillips, Michael Faraday, and Sir Humphry Davy. All three were chemists even though Faraday preferred to be called a natural philosopher, a title he considered more appropriate for someone who strove to understand natural processes. Davy, then president of the Royal Society, was one of thirteen founder members of the Geological Society of London and, like Davies Gilbert, he was a fellow Cornishman and friend.

Davy and Faraday need no introduction but Richard Phillips has been largely forgotten.[15] He was born in London, the son of James Phillips, a printer and bookseller whose grandfather, William Phillips, a Quaker, had moved from Redruth in Cornwall to take over a Swansea copper works. James Phillips sired two remarkable sons, William, a renowned geologist and mineralogist and Richard, the best-known chemist of his day. Richard Phillips apprenticed with William Allen, a well-known Quaker chemist and pharmacist at Plough Court, Lombard Street, London. Allen's pharmacy was a training ground for East End talent and also a theatre for social and political reform. Allen, an FRS, and a member of the Mineralogical Society lectured in chemistry at Guy's Hospital. Phillips's association with Allen and his attendance at Humphry Davy's immensely popular lectures and demonstrations at the Royal Institution drew him to analytical chemistry. In 1806 a paper on the mineral content of the hot springs at Bath brought him national attention. Other papers on other natural waters followed.

Phillips proved to be an able and extremely engaging lecturer and he travelled the country speaking to philosophical and literary societies. He also wrote popular articles on chemistry for the *Penny Encyclopaedia* and after 1821 he was the editor of the *Annals of Philosophy*, a scientific journal. When the *Annals* became the even more prestigious *Philosophical Magazine,* in 1826, he was one of the joint editors. He was a founder member of the Askesian Society and an early member of the Geological Society of London, the latter the product of a merger of the Askesian

Society and the British Mineralogical Society.[16] In 1839 he was appointed chemist and curator of the Museum of Economic Geology, London, an arm of the newly formed Geological Survey used for the display of economic minerals and the analysis of rock and soil samples. In 1841 Phillips was also prominent in a movement to create the Chemical Society of London, the world's first national association of chemists, and in 1870/71, a year before his death, he served as its fourth president.

One of science's greatest debts to Phillips was his encouragement and support of Michael Faraday during the latter's apprenticeship at the Royal Institution. He urged Faraday to write for the *Annals of Philosophy* and he was the moving spirit in Faraday's election to the Royal Society, only a year after his own election in 1822. Faraday, in turn, considered Phillips the 'prince of chemical critics'.[17] The gregarious Phillips and the more reserved and retiring Faraday became close friends. Phillips had a keen sense of the ridiculous and, according to one fellow chemist, a 'ready power of repartee'. They were qualities that appealed to Faraday who would complain whenever he was long absented from them. 'I have refrained from writing', he wrote in 1828, 'in the obscure hope that I might have a laugh with you this summer but I have been obliged to laugh without you so far and must still endeavour to be cheerful notwithstanding your absence'.[18] The Swansea project, in which he and Faraday were to be the on-site chemists and the elder Davy an adviser, was their second collaborative venture in the world of industry. The first was a legal case, in which they represented an insurance company in an action brought against it by a sugar-baking firm, whose factory had been destroyed by fire.[19]

Faraday first visited Hafod during a walking tour of Wales in 1819. He approached Swansea from the north-east and, like all nineteenth century travellers, he felt bound to comment on the pall of sulphurous copper smoke that hung permanently over the lower valley just upstream from Swansea. He was more restrained than George Borrow, the most celebrated nineteenth century walker in Wales, but in his diary he could not resist a mischievous aside. He dubbed the ferryboat, in which he crossed the Tawe into the town, the *Charon of Swansea*. Vivian was away from the town at the time but his plant manager, Roger Morgan, showed

Faraday through the works so that by the end of his visit to Swansea Faraday was familiar with processes of smelting and the destructive nature of copper-smoke. As if to anticipate Vivian's appeal for help with the smoke problem, at Hafod he wrote extensive notes.

In July 1822 he and Phillips were invited to stay at Singleton: 'I fancy,' he wrote, 'we are going to a large mansion, and into high company'.[20] Phillips and Faraday spent a fortnight at the house, each content in the other's company but the retiring Faraday found the interminable Singleton dinners irksome and found ways to avoid some of them. On Sunday evenings they were followed by the playing of sacred music in the drawing room, a custom that had no appeal for Faraday who was a Sandemanian. Faraday seldom mentioned his religion but in a letter from Singleton he intimated that if sacred music on a Sunday evening was the practice of 'regular people' then he was pleased not to be one of them. A devoted husband, he wrote frequently and at length to his wife, Sarah, prompting Mrs Phillips to suggest to her much less attentive spouse that he ask for a copy of one of Faraday's letters so that he might learn to write love-letters of similar length and ardour. In one of his letters home Faraday wrote of 'working very hard . . . at the copper works, and with some success. Our days have gone on just as before. A walk before breakfast; then breakfast; then to the works till four or five o'clock, and then home to dress for dinner. After dinner tea and conversation'.[21]

At Hafod, Faraday and Phillips analyzed the composition of the smoke, assigning the toxins to five distinct categories.[22] The most pungent, penetrating and toxic of the gases was the notorious sulphurous acid gas that they reckoned to be not more than one twenty-eighth part of the whole. At Hafod they analysed and measured both the solid deposits in the flues, and those in solution in water troughs after the smoke had been made to pass through steam chambers, and shower chambers of plain water and of water charged with lime, soda and nitre. Phillips returned in October to conduct further experiments with shower chambers and the following January Faraday analysed the effects of steam treatments. The steam treatments and the shower chambers removed the solid particles and many of the constituent gases from the smoke but the great enemy, sulphurous acid gas, was untouched. Faraday's immediate response was to consume the gas inside the furnace, 'don't let it escape', but it would be forty years before this would be practicable.[23] An experiment in a neighbouring works, in which furnace smoke was made to pass through ignited charcoal, did in fact eliminate the sulphurous acid gas but they pointed out that the method, which consumed forty-five tons of charcoal per week, would use up the available wood in Glamorgan in less than a year.

Davy also stayed at Singleton, but as an adviser only he would have spent less time at Hafod. He and Vivian were keen huntsmen and spent much time shooting birds at Singleton and in Gower. In December 1823, Sarah Vivian recorded in her diary, 'Sir Humphry came to stay with us on the 16th and remained until the 30th. He enjoyed our Welsh woodcock shooting exceedingly'.[24] Davy himself made no secret of his fondness for shooting woodcock and there is a suggestion that he timed his visits to coincide with the season. In a letter to Vivian thanking him for sending several brace of woodcock to London he deeply regretted that he had not been present at their demise. In return, Davy sent by coach a haunch of venison and a recently killed cock pheasant that he thought should arrive in the right condition.

When hunting at Singleton, Davy wore a red hatband, possibly as protection against Vivian's father-in-law Arthur Jones who on one hunt shot the keeper in the leg. Vivian's problem at the works also brought to Swansea another renowned and very practical chemist, William Hyde Wollaston, who liked to spend part of each year visiting works and factories. He was Secretary of the Royal Society in 1806 and would have been President had he not voluntarily made way for Humphry Davy. In December 1822 Wollaston stayed with Lewis Weston Dillwyn and spent a morning cockshooting with Dillwyn and John Henry Vivian at Penllergare. The following day Dillwyn, who was a judge in the competition to suppress copper-smoke, drove him to the Hafod works to meet Sir Humphry Davy.

At the final meeting of the Subscribers to the Fund for Obviating the Smoke, in December 1822, the committee delivered its report. There was no prizewinner. Sulphurous acid gas remained at large. As expected John Henry Vivian, who had spent more than six thousand pounds on experiments, received the highest praise. Faraday deposed, as he would in an 1833 copper-smoke trial at Carmarthen, that Vivian had done everything possible to suppress the smoke. Davies Gilbert on the other hand, who had been prevented by ill health from attending at Swansea, damned with faint praise. In a letter to Vivian, he applauded the motivation for the Hafod experiments but pointed out that the experiments themselves merely demonstrated 'the utter inapplicability of what might be termed laboratory resources, to the great scale of actual Copper Works'. Modifications founded on a 'correct theory of chemistry . . . supported by minute experiments', he continued, could have no place in the rough and ready world of heavy industry.

A more aggressive man than Vivian might have pointed out that Gilbert's censure contradicted the mandate of the Royal Society (of which Gilbert was then a vice-president) to encourage the introduction of 'useful mechanical inventions and improvements' and, through lectures and experiments, 'the application of science to the common purposes of life'. In a public debate, Faraday would undoubtedly have taken issue with Gilbert but in a letter to Vivian (1826), in which he inquired if he had discovered any new substances in his furnaces, he conceded that discontinuities between the laboratory and the factory were inevitable. 'Things sometimes happen in the large way that cannot occur in the small and your operations are so great that they must occur now & then with you'.

In spite of his failure to eliminate the most toxic of the gases, and thus claim the prize, Vivian would get his reward in other ways. For the benefit of the judges of the Fund and others interested in the smoke question, Vivian wrote a sixty-page report explaining in detail the nature of the experiments at Hafod and the modifications, entailing great expense, made to the flues and stacks. He accompanied this with an essay outlining the stages involved in the production of copper, from the shipping of the ore to the refining and toughening of the finished metal.[25] In the essay Vivian gave away few trade secrets, but it was the first account in Britain of the calcining, smelting and refining processes, normally the subject of shamanistic-like secrecy, by a trained scientist. Richard Phillips thought well enough of it to ask Vivian if he might publish it in the *Annals of Philosophy*, and Faraday thought so well of Vivian that he asked if he might nominate him for a fellowship in the Royal Society. Humphry Davy seconded the nomination and, with such heavyweight support, it was duly carried.

Although a fellowship in the Royal Society was not the prize then that it would become later in the century, the essay alone may not have won Vivian the necessary votes. The fellowship can be taken as a reward for his general achievements, among them his accomplishments in mineralogy and his early membership and support of the Geological Society of London. In 1808, within a year of the founding of the Society, he presented it with a collection of rocks and minerals classified and arranged under Werner's tutelage at Freiburg. But his greatest contribution to science and technology were his efforts to bring together the worlds of heavy industry and experimental science.

To do so he applied the lessons learned at Freiburg, where mining and metallurgical students moved freely between the classrooms of two of the most renowned mineralogists and chemists in Europe and local mines and smelters. In Britain, acceptance of that kind of interchange between science and industry would have to wait until the Great Exhibition of 1851, and not until the 1870s would schools and colleges provide advanced instruction in scientific and technical subjects. Fittingly, it was Vivian's son and successor at Hafod, Henry Hussey Vivian, who did so much to bring instruction in the applied sciences and foreign languages to Wales. It was largely through his efforts, and the Government's recognition of the limitations of purely prag-matic and craft approaches to training, that Swansea acquired its first Technical School, in 1895, a year after his death.

Earlier he had led the movement to bring a University College to Swansea against the rival claims of Cardiff, and when the movement failed he generously agreed to become the College's first treasurer. As treasurer and, later, vice-principal, he urged the establishment of a professorship in applied mechanics. Swansea had to wait until the 1920s for its University College, but the delay was providential. Singleton Abbey would adorn any campus but that it should have been the home of an FRS who brought Swan-sea to the attention of the most prominent scientists in Britain is one of those satisfying conjunctions that might suggest that design occasionally impinges on the random commerce of life.

NOTES

1. Averil Stewart, *Family Tapestry* (London, 1961), 116.
2. 'An Interview with Napoleon', Stewart, *Family Tapestry*, appendix, 211-217.
3. Stanley Vivian, *The Story of the Vivians* (Truro, 1989), 51.
4. Stewart, *Family Tapestry*, 117.
5. Hannah Gay, 'East End, West End: Science, Education, Culture and Class in Mid-Victorian London', *Canadian Journ. History*, XXXII (1997), 425-53.
6. Sir Arthur Russell, Bart, 'John Hawkins, F.G.S., F.R.H.S., F.R.S., 1761-1841, A Distinguished Cornishman and Early Mining Geologist', *Journ. Royal Inst. Cornwall*, New Series, 2, 2, (1954), 98-106.
7. Sir Edward Bailey, *Geological Survey of Great Britain* (London, 1952), 2.
8. Sir Archibald Geikie, *The Founders of Geology* (London, 1905), 201-235.
9. Russell, 101.
10. Bailey, *Geological Survey of Great Britain*, 6.
11. John Henry Vivian, 'A sketch of the plan of the Mining Academies of Freyberg and Schemnitz', Trans. *Royal Geol. Soc. Cornwall*, 1 (1814), 70-77.
12. John Henry Vivian, 'Remarks on the Salt Mines of Wielitska in Poland, and of Salzburg in Germany', *Royal Geol. Soc. Cornwall*, 1 (1814), 155-167; and 'Observations on the processes for making the different Preparations of Arsenic', *Trans. Royal Geol. Soc. Cornwall*, 1 (1814), 61-76.
13. An optical toy that worked on the eye's ability to retain an image for a fraction of a second after the object is gone. Retention of vision is the basic principle of animation.
14. Stanley Vivian, 50.
15. Colin Russell, 'In the Service of Government', *Chembytes – e-zine, Royal Soc. Chemistry* 2001.
16. The Askesian Society was a learned society, founded in 1796, for the purpose of reading and discussing scientific papers.
17. Ibid., 4.
18. Frank A. J. L. James, *Correspondence of Michael Faraday*, Vol. 1 (London, 1991), 465.
19. The issue was whether a new process, involving the heating of whale oil and introduced without the knowledge of the insurers, increased the risk of fire.
20. Dafydd Tomos, *Michael Faraday in Wales* (Denbigh, 1973), 153.
21. James, *Correspondence of Michael Faraday*, 1, 284.
22. John Henry Vivian, *Results of Experiments made at the Hafod Works by Messrs. Phillips and Faraday, July and August, 1822*.
23. In the 1860s Moritz Gerstenhofer patented a furnace that burned the sulphur, and a condenser that converted the furnace gases into sulphuric acid.
24. Stewart, 120-21.
25. John Henry Vivian, 'An Account of the Process of Smelting Copper', *Annals of Philosophy* 113-14 (1823), 69-95, 1823.

LEWIS WESTON DILLWYN FRS
1778-1855

Pioneer Botanist, Zoologist
Manufacturer of Fine Porcelain ('Swansea China')

During the closing ceremonies of the 1848 meeting of the British
Association in Swansea, Charles Cardale Babington, who would
become Professor of Botany at Cambridge, conferred on Lewis
Weston Dillwyn the ultimate scholarly accolade: the paternity of
his chosen discipline. Dillwyn, according to Babington, was the
father of English botany and one of the heroes of British zoology.[1]
Dillwyn then was a venerable figure in his seventieth year and
Babington was moving a vote of thanks in Dillwyn's house for his
host's services as chair of the zoology and botany section of the
meeting. Immoderate praise was the order of the day and the
audience at Sketty Hall chorused its approval.

No botanist today would regard Dillwyn as the father of English
botany but few would deny him a place at the high table of early
nineteenth century British naturalists.[2] He was the author of important works in botany and conchology and in his day he had
the ear of every prominent natural scientist in the land. No sojourn
in London passed without visits to the Royal, Linnaean or Geological Societies, or meetings with Sir Joseph Banks, Sir Humphry
Davy, the chemist William Hyde Wollaston, or the botanist William
Jackson Hooker; none to Oxford without a call on William Buckland, the first Professor of Geology; and none to Bristol or Bath
without geological rambles with the Reverend William Daniel
Conybeare and Henry De la Beche. At Bristol, too, he and De la
Beche were regular visitors to the city's Philosophical and Literary
Institution. Dillwyn's credentials as a naturalist were formidable
and they opened all doors.

He was born at Ipswich in 1778, the son of William Dillwyn, an
American-born descendant of a Hertfordshire family who emigrated

43

Lewis Weston Dillwyn.

to America in 1699, and Sarah Weston. William Dillwyn, who was a Philadelphia Quaker, visited England in 1774 and returned to settle in 1777. He became active in the anti-slavery movement and was one of an informal committee of six London Friends who offered to finance Thomas Clarkson's seminal essay on the African slave trade in 1786.[3] He was also one of seven Quaker members of a nonsectarian committee, assembled in 1787, to campaign for abolition. One of the other Quaker members was the printer and publisher James Phillips, father of the chemist Richard Phillips whom John Henry Vivian had engaged in an effort to eliminate the toxins in copper-smoke. From his Lombard Street shop James Phillips printed and published abolitionist books and essays, including Thomas Clarkson's essay on the slave trade. In 1777 William Dillwyn married 'Sally' Weston whom he met at the Tottenham Meeting House. They lived at Higham Lodge, Walthamstow, and had seven children of whom Lewis Weston was the eldest.

For such a prominent and gregarious figure, surprisingly few details have survived of his early life. At ten he was a boarder at Josiah Forster's School, a Friends school in Tottenham that – the grammar schools being closed to them – attracted Quaker boys from all parts of the country. There he befriended the naturalist Joseph Woods, his senior by two years, who would become an authority on roses and author in 1850 of the *Tourist's Flora*, a descriptive catalogue of the flowering plants and ferns of western Europe. For an orthodox English family with means, Oxford or Cambridge would have been the natural destination for an academically gifted son but, as a Quaker, Dillwyn could not have matriculated.[4]

The professions also, in a denominational sense, were closed shops so young Quakers were directed to industry and trade. To learn the rudiments of the linen trade, in which his father had an interest, and to improve his then delicate health, Dillwyn was sent to a drapery in Dover on the benign, smoke-free south coast of England. When he returned to London, to work in his father's linen warehouse in Gracechurch Street, he met and courted Mary Adams, also known as Mary Llewellyn, the natural daughter of Colonel John Llewellyn, a wealthy west Glamorgan landowner. Mary Adams was John Llewellyn's only child and, provided she married with issue, his designated heir.

Whether the Dillwyns knew of Mary's prospective fortune is not known, but as David Painting, the biographer of Mary's granddaughter Amy, has intimated, William Dillwyn's purchase of the lease of the Cambrian Pottery in Swansea during the engagement may have been more than a coincidence.[5] The pottery was for his son but, as a safeguard, he retained the services of the previous owner, George Haynes, who for the next eight years managed the works. For the twenty-three year-old Lewis Weston, who seemed only marginally more interested in pottery than he was in linen, the arrangement was ideal. It provided an income and gave him the freedom to collect and classify plants and shells and cultivate friends and associates in the scientific communities of London and Oxford. Dillwyn was an inveterate networker 'who longed with an ambitious fondness', his associate Dr Thomas Williams remarked, 'to cultivate the friendship of the lettered and scientific men of every country'.[6]

Dillwyn's first systematic study of plants dates from 1798 when he and Joseph Woods botanized in Dover. Dillwyn was twenty and Woods twenty-two. 'During his residence at Dover', Woods wrote, 'I paid him a visit and well recollect the pleasure we had in rambling over the country, and finding many plants which were then unknown to us. I apprehend that it was during this residence at Dover that he first applied himself to botany, but what fixed his attention to that science I do not know. Probably his intimacy with the three brothers Forster had something to do with it'.7

In March 1801 a catalogue of rare plants found in the environs of Dover, prepared by Dillwyn, was read to the Linnaean Society and in October of the same year Dillwyn contributed a notice, published in the sixth volume of the *Transactions*, of the discovery of the *Sisymbrium murale* in the neighbourhood of Ramsgate. He followed this, in 1802, with the first fascicle of *British Confervae*, his most important work and one that clearly engaged his imagination. Dillwyn had been drawn to the thread-like algae, that grow in freshwater ponds and pools, by their delicacy and their beauty: 'the most beautiful and curious of the order of vegetables to which they belong'. His entries contain frequent lyrical passages. The *Conferva Atra* is a 'rare and beautiful species' while the 'elegant' *Conferva Glomatera* 'delights in the purest waters, and . . . adorns the most limpid streams in Europe'. Some species were also useful. When dried, the *Conferva Bullosae* could be used as wadding while in an emergency the *Conferva Rivularis* could be used for binding fractures. If kept wet it had, according to the ancients, the power to knit bones.

Yet in spite of their beauty and utility, the *Confervae* had been 'involved in such obscurity as to have been publicly termed "the opprobrium of botany."'8 One of the most beautiful species, the *Conferva Flexuosa*, found by his friend and associate Dawson Turner, had been gathered at Yarmouth from 'the rejectementa of the sea'. Linnaeus had adopted *Conferva* as the name for a genus but having named them he then, like most other botanical writers, ignored them. The first fascicle, which encompassed the ponds and pools around Dover, London and Yarmouth, Dillwyn completed with the help of Joseph Woods. Presented as the work of a young, unknown botanist, *British Confervae* begins humbly and disarmingly: 'I offer this work as no more than a set of drawings, whereby the species of this intricate tribe may be, in some measure, fixed; and which may at least serve as materials for the future labours of more able botanists'.

Dillwyn, however, had no intention of remaining unknown for long, or of making way for more able botanists. His list of collaborators is strikingly at odds with his stance as a diffident young scholar. It included Sir Joseph Banks, President of the Royal Society, whom he thanked for the use of his library and herbarium, and Dr Williams, Professor of Botany at Oxford, for providing access to the Dillenian Herbarium. Dillenius was one of only two previous botanists to write about *Confervae*. Four of the plates in the first fascicle were drawn by William Jackson Hooker, who would become the first director of Kew Gardens. Each of Dillwyn's twenty-five extant letters to Hooker begins with the salutation 'My Dear Hooker'.

British Confervae took twelve years to complete, the sixteenth and last fascicle appearing in 1814. It included both the already known and newly discovered species of *Confervae*, the latter of course getting the greater attention. Each plant in the fascicles is represented by a plate accompanied by notes on the plant's distinctive features. Toward the end of the exercise, Dillwyn told his publisher, the Quaker William Phillips, that to make the work as comprehensive as possible he had written to every British botanist who might have an interest in *Confervae*. His hope was that from fear of being left out of the study they would 'rummage up and send in all the information in their power'. His thoroughness and persistence paid off. His predecessors in the field had found about three-dozen species of *Confervae*; in the succeeding ten years Dillwyn identified 88 and by 1814, when the last fascicle appeared, he had described and illustrated 167 species.

In 1804, at age twenty-five, and before even half of *British Confervae* had appeared, he published, in conjunction with Dawson Turner (to whom he dedicated *British Confervae*), the two-volume *Botanist's Guide through England and Wales*. In the preface to the *Guide*, Turner, a banker, botanist and, in later life, antiquarian from Great Yarmouth, acknowledges his secondary role in the enterprise even though his name has precedence on the title page.[9] Dillwyn had conceived the work and collected most of the material before engaging in his partnership with

Turner. 'It is right to observe', wrote Turner, 'that the present work is indebted for its origin exclusively to Mr. Dillwyn'. Dillwyn had begun the compilation 'chiefly for his own use and amusement' and, persuaded by friends of its general usefulness, he worked it up into a two-volume book.

Although not lacking in confidence, in the later stages of the exercise he must have felt the need for a known and well-connected co-author. Turner was a fellow student of algae and author of *A Synopsis of British Fuci* that he would follow with the *Natural History of Fuci*, 1809-1819. He was already a Fellow of the Royal Society and in 1815 his eldest daughter, Maria Turner, would marry William Jackson Hooker, the future director of Kew Gardens.[10] Dillwyn's reward for his efforts was election to fellowships in the Linnaean Society in 1806 and, for his work on *British Confervae*, the Royal Society in 1804. He was not yet thirty.

Based on the Linnaean system, the 755-page *Guide* was a major work of compilation and organization – 'proofs of great industry and labour', as his associate Dr Thomas Williams remarked. The authors make no higher claim. In the preface, they describe it as a work whose 'very nature precludes all display of knowledge or investigation, and forbids us to look for credit beyond that of careful and industrious compilers. . . Our responsibility, as authors, is confined to the mere circumstance of having faithfully copied and properly arranged, the materials before us, a task we have endeavoured to fulfil with as much accuracy as can be fairly expected in a work of this nature.' Although Dillwyn had botanised in southern and southwestern England and south Wales, the *Guide* was a product of the library rather than the field. With help from Turner and Joseph Woods – who worked in the London libraries – he abstracted from the botanical literature all the references he could find to each plant. The legacy of this, and Dillwyn's other compilations, was a remarkable botanical library: a collection of about a thousand volumes, illustrating the development of botany from the sixteenth to the nineteenth century, that in 1928 was acquired by the National Library of Wales.[11]

Dillwyn and Turner's *Guide* was the first attempt at a comprehensive catalogue of the rarer plants of England and Wales. It is organized by county, each in its alphabetical order. The only concession to topography or terrain is a brief description of the county's dominant physical features. Thus the entry for Anglesey reads: 'Anglesea, although divided by only a narrow channel from the vast ridge of Caernarvonshire mountains, contains in itself no remarkable elevation or diversity of surface. Its antiquities and mineral treasures have long rendered it an object of curiosity to the traveller'. This most fleeting of topographical descriptions is followed by a list of the plants peculiar to the county and brief notes on their locations and habitats. Included in the preamble to each county are acknowledgements of the naturalists whose aid, either through books or correspondence, the authors had enlisted. The number of entries for each county and the degree of detail depended entirely on the number of naturalists who had lived there, or visited it, and how fully and how accurately they had recorded their observations.

In England, not surprisingly, Cambridgeshire was one of the most 'botanized' counties. Well populated, the seat of an ancient university, and with a great variety of soils and topography – chalky hills, extensive heaths, bogs and rich cornlands – it sustained a rich and varied flora that had been thoroughly documented. The Cambridgeshire entries took up twenty-nine pages. For Bedford-shire, on the other hand, they had no great expectations, but thanks to the 'unwearied activity' of a single naturalist, Dr Abbot, they were able to choose from a list of 1,225 species.

Welsh counties, on the whole, fared badly. Most favoured was Caernarvonshire with thirty-one pages of entries; its mountains appealed to both naturalists and tourists. For Breconshire, how-ever, the authors could muster only two pages and twenty entries, and for equally unfashionable and even more remote Cardigan-shire and Carmarthenshire a mere twenty-six and fifteen entries respectively, fewer than four pages in all. Neither of the two latter counties warranted a topographical description. The authors allowed that they could have added to the entries for Breconshire and some of the other Welsh counties had they been able to rely on the records of travellers who had visited them.

The most prominent culprit was Mr. Evans, the author of popular tourist guides to Wales. Evans professed to have made his tours chiefly for botanical purposes with a view to publishing a book on the flora of Wales, but after covering some of the same ground Dillwyn found that the plants were not always in the sites he assigned to them. Evans' guides were very popular, and likely to be reprinted, leaving Dillwyn and Turner to hope that future editions would amend those inaccuracies 'of which Naturalists now have cause to complain'.

There is nothing in the two volumes of Dillwyn's and Dawson's *Guide* that might pass as today's plant geography. Some of the plants listed were peculiar to, or characteristic of, the counties in which they are listed, and there are thumbnail descriptions of habitat: 'moist shady places', 'moist rocks near a river', 'among thickets on the north side of Garreg Wen rocks', 'in dry meadows near Llanidan', 'in peat pits not uncommon'. But the relationships between plant types, topography and climate then being analyzed by Alexander Von Humboldt can be inferred at best. At worst, habitat is ignored, replaced by locations only. These, however, are not without charm: 'in a wheatfield and in an adjoining coppice called Marget', 'very abundant in Colonel Johnes woods', 'in a wood at Hafod near a gate'. In a gesture to utility, Dillwyn and Turner suggest that comparisons of the 'vegetable productions' of the various counties might offer clues as to how well they might be suited to new ways of farming and, with no explanation offered, to manufacturing.

Dillwyn's responsibilities at the Cambrian pottery were never heavy enough to be onerous or to seriously interfere with his work in botany. During the period of Haynes's management, 1802-09, he completed the *Botanist's Guide* and continued work on *British Confervae*. His influence on the pottery, according to E. Morton Nance, is discernible only in the decoration of the pots.[12] Under Dillwyn's ownership, paintings of flowers became more precise; each plant was shown separately and flowers, leaves, stems and seedpods were all painted accurately and in their correct proportions. Dillwyn's good fortune extended even to the aptitudes and affinities of one of the decorators. In 1803 the pottery hired as a 'draftsman' the mercurial and multi-talented William Weston Young.[13]

Like Dillwyn, the Bristol-born Weston Young was a Quaker (whose mother was also named Sarah Weston) and a keen naturalist. He was also of Dillwyn's age, twenty-six to Dillwyn's twenty-four. The temptation to use Young as both field assistant and illustrator of *Confervae* proved irresistible and in the 1809 fascicle (compendium) Young is credited with having made the drawings for nearly half of the 115 engraved and coloured plates. In the attributions he is described variously as 'My friend W. W. Young' and 'an ingenious artist from Swansea'. To make the drawings, Young had to go into the woods and fields and, on at least one occasion, he discovered a new species of *Conferva*. In the notes to plate 63 (*Conferva Dissiliens*) Dillwyn wrote that it had been found 'on reeds and other aquatic vegetables in a Ditch on Cromlyn Bog near Swansea', and that 'this species, which has not, I believe, been heretofore described, was first discovered by my friend and draftsman, W. W. Young.' Dillwyn reserved his warmest praise for Plate 102 (*Conferva Youngana*); 'The present species was first discovered (on limestone rocks near Dunraven Castle, Glamorganshire) by Mr. William Young A.L.S. in honour of whom I have named it, as a token of my private friendship, and as a public acknowledgement of the assistance which this work has received from his accurate pencil'. By December 1806 Young's dedication to the work, as Dillwyn's annotation affirms, earned him an associate membership of the Linnaean Society.

Young's role at the pottery has intrigued historians. He was part-employee and part-friend and when not out in the field or working on drawings for *British Confervae* he must have decorated the opaque china for which the factory is renowned. In 1855 the catalogue of an exhibition of British pottery and porcelain at the Museum of Economic Geology in London gave some prominence to Young's work at the Cambrian Pottery. The founder and director of the museum, Henry De la Beche, was Dillwyn's son-in-law and, presumably, he was responsible for the pages on Swansea ware. He described Young as the draftsman and natural historian employed by Dillwyn to decorate the opaque china with 'birds, butterflies, and shells, drawn from nature'. The scientific names of the specimens were written on the inside of the pieces.

For more than a century the romantic assumption was that Young was simply Dillwyn's graphic arm, drawing and painting from nature under instructions from the master naturalist. But in 1959 Owen Harding, a young Cambridge graduate and an amateur lepidopterist pointed out that some of the butterflies attributed to Young as 'drawn from Nature' were extinct in Britain by the beginning of the nineteenth century. Young's butterflies were either copied from book illustrations or from preserved specimens, and what was true of butterflies might also have been true of some of the birds and insects.[14]

Dillwyn's factory is known best for a delicate, often translucent, and beautifully decorated porcelain, known to the world as 'Swansea China'. It was produced for just three years, between 1814-1817, and it represents the one period when Dillwyn seems to have been genuinely interested in the works. The unlikely conjunction that led to this event was Dillwyn's friendship with Sir Joseph Banks, the great naturalist and president of the Royal Society. In 1813 William Billingsley, the leading flower painter at the famed Derby porcelain factory, and his son-in-law Samuel Walker, who was also a skilled potter, decided to set up a porcelain factory in south Wales. They leased a house and land alongside the Glamorganshire canal at Nantgarw, a village about ten miles above Cardiff, and with a loan of 600 pounds (more than double the amount of their own capital) from William Weston Young, began building kilns.

Their objective was to produce a soft-paste porcelain that would rival the exquisite porcelain of the state-backed factory at Sevres, France. The paste, a mixture of alkaline and aluminium silicates and bone ash, was made from a formula whose exact proportions Billingsley and Walker kept secret. The bones were burned and ground in an adjoining mill powered by a leat running from the canal to the river Taff. In porcelain manufacture, however, the devil is in the firing. High temperatures are needed to produce perfect porcelain and in the firings at Nantgarw nine out of ten pieces could shiver (i.e. crack) or lose their shape. Repeated failures soon exhausted Billingsley and Walker's scant capital, forcing them, in 1814, to apply for Government funds to build new furnaces.

Their application, for a grant of five hundred pounds, to the Committee of Trade and Plantations (the present Board of Trade) they justified on grounds of the French Government's subsidy to the Sevres factory. The Committee replied that there was no equivalent British fund to draw upon, but the application and the samples of Nantgarw porcelain that accompanied it came to the attention of its most distinguished member, Sir Joseph Banks, who happened to be a collector of oriental porcelain. Although so disabled at the time of the application that he had to be carried to his carriage, he kept in close touch with the Committee's affairs and when able to walk he could often be seen in Christie's auction rooms. On seeing the memorial and the samples of Nantgarw porcelain that accompanied it he thought immediately of Dillwyn, whom he knew owned the Cambrian Pottery, and wrote to ask if he would mind inspecting the ailing works.

Dillwyn, possibly encouraged by Weston Young, had already considered manufacturing porcelain in Swansea so within days of receiving Banks's letter he visited Nantgarw. After inspecting the operation he concluded that the breakages were due not so much to defective kilns but to a paste that was too 'glassy' to withstand great heat. But in order to persuade Billingsley – who was convinced that the fault lay in the kilns – to move his operation to the Cambrian pottery he offered to build new ones. The manoeuvre is spelled out in a letter from Dillwyn to Henry De la Beche: 'My friend, Sir Joseph Banks, informed me that two persons, named Walker and Beely [either an alias used by the secretive Billingsley or a homely abbreviation of his surname], had sent to government, from a small factory at Nantgarw . . . a specimen of beautiful china, with a petition for their patronage, and that, as one of the Board of Trade, he requested me to examine and report upon that manufactory. Upon witnessing the firing of a kiln at Nantgarw, I found much reason for considering that the body used was too nearly allied to glass to bear the necessary heat . . . The parties, however, succeeded in making me believe that the defects in the porcelain arose entirely from imperfections in their small trial kiln, and I agreed with them for a removal to the Cambrian Pottery, at which two new kilns, under their direction, were prepared'.[15]

Elated at the prospect of producing fine porcelain, Dillwyn wrote enthusiastically to his father-in-law, Colonel Llewellyn: 'I never have done a better day's work in my life. I am to be put into immediate possession of every circumstance relative to the making of porcelain, and the entire management, both as to the scale and the manner in which the manufactory is to be carried on is without restriction, to be placed at my discretion'.[16] At Swansea, however, experiments to strengthen the porcelain without reducing its translucency and whiteness were only partly successful and in 1817, three years after embarking on the project, he had to fulfill a commitment made in 1815 to Colonel John Llewellyn.[17]

Dillwyn had promised that on Llewellyn's death he would undertake the stewardship of the Penllergare estate until his son, John Dillwyn Llewellyn, who was also Llewellyn's son-in-law, attained his majority. A condition of the trust was that he remove himself from the works. Accordingly, on Colonel Llewellyn's death in 1817, he sold the lease of the pottery to Timothy Bevington, his partner for the past eleven years and moved from his home, The Willows, on the edge of town, to Penllergare (the spelling used by the Dillwyns, the Welsh is 'penllergaer', meaning the head place of the fort). Billingsley and Walker returned to Nantgarw and with an additional eleven hundred pounds from Young, and another thousand from ten anonymous backers whom Young had persuaded to invest, they fired the kilns. The new Nantgarw venture was no more successful than the old and one April day in 1820 Billingsley and Walker walked out leaving Young holding the lease and a large quantity of undecorated porcelain.

The failure of the porcelain venture spelled the end of Dillwyn's interest in the pottery. Except for filling the role of steward of a 14,000 acre estate, he was now free to pursue his interests. He began a diary and, having married outside the faith and renounced his formal Quakerism, he was able to involve himself in politics and local affairs. Officially he was an Anglican, albeit a reluctant one who found ceremony and sermons an inadequate substitute for silent witness. He still, however, maintained close ties with the Tottenham Quakers and when in London he attended meetings. One Sunday in April 1818 he and his sisters arrived too late for a seat at the Tottenham meeting, so they took a walk with William Phillips the Lombard Street printer and bookseller and publisher of *British Confervae*. In London, too, he was free to attend book auctions, browse in book and shell shops, and visit his favourite societies and natural scientists.

After breakfast with the naturalists William Leach and Georges Cuvier at the British Museum in June 1818, he noted in his diary 'How sweet a little science tasted after so much bustle of an opposite nature'. In November 1819 he visited Banks at his house in Soho Square for three hours and saw the only live Toucan that was ever in England. The Toucan was very tame and ate liberal helpings of bread and milk. On 6 April 1820 Dillwyn called on Banks in the morning and went to the British Museum at two where he met Leach and Dr. Goodall, the Provost of Eton. Having the museum all to themselves – it was the Easter holiday – they did not leave until ten.[18]

During these years, too, his interests shifted. After completing the last fascicle of *British Confervae*, in 1814, Dillwyn concentrated on conchology and entomology. He collected both shells and insects and when in London or Bristol he would frequently spend entire days examining both private and institutional collections and visiting shell shops. In 1817 he published, in two thick octavo volumes, the *Descriptive Catalogue of Recent Shells, arranged according to the Linnean method,* which he dedicated to Sir Joseph Banks who was then president of the Royal Society. The impulse behind the undertaking seems to have been an absolute intolerance for disorder. When arranging a small cabinet of shells with the help of a Gmelin edition of Linnaeus's *Systema Naturae* he found that the same species occurred under two or three different names and that in many instances the same name was used for two or three different species. Other conchologists might have regretted the confusion and moved on but for Dillwyn nothing less than a complete revision would satisfy. The revised catalogue of five thousand names and synonyms of shells and some fifteen thousand references to English and continental authors ran to a thousand pages.

Dr. Thomas Williams, who wrote an admiring biographical essay on Dillwyn, marveled 'at the tenacity of memory which enabled one man in so brief a period of study, to grasp such a vast multitude of particulars, to retain the names and definitive characters of so many species, so subtly to detect fallacies amid alleged affinities, and indicate resemblances amid opposed dissimilitudes, in fact, to chart, with the lucid intuition of genius, the grounds of a new classification of objects in an unexplored province of research'.[19] Dillwyn dedicated the catalogue to his 'venerable friend' Sir Joseph Banks and in the preface acknowledged his debt to him: 'Without the use of Sir Joseph Banks's extensive library, no writer on natural history can hope to attain any tolerable degree of perfection, and the advantages which the author has been permitted to derive from the liberal use of it, demands the public expression of warmest thanks'.

In 1823 another major compilation followed: Dillwyn's index to

Martin Lister's *Historia Conchyliorum*. Lister was a prominent English physician, and one of the physicians to Queen Anne, but he is chiefly remembered for his studies in natural history. Lister's book, listing and illustrating all the shells then known, was the first attempt at a systematic classification of molluscs. Made up from nearly a thousand unnumbered plates with one or more figures per plate, and published in various issues between 1685 and 1692, it became the standard work. Lister presented the plates and his shell collection to the Ashmolean Museum, Oxford, and in 1770 the Clarendon Press published a second edition. Except for frugal descriptions and indications of locality engraved on each of the plates there was no accompanying text and no index. The shells were divided into discrete groups but without a coherent text or an index the work was difficult to use.

In 1821, the University decided to republish the plates but with an index. Dillwyn, who was known to all the Oxford naturalists, seemed the obvious choice as indexer. In December 1821 he examined Lister's plates and papers at the Ashmolean and by November of the following year he had completed the assignment. The index alone ran to forty-eight folio pages but, in addition, Dillwyn annotated many of the illustrations and provided references to related literature. It was so thorough and painstaking an exercise that a grateful University offered him a DCL (Doctorate of Civil Law) one of the University's most prestigious degrees, but for reasons not disclosed Dillwyn declined. For a gregarious, public figure he was strangely shy of honours. In 1819 the poet W. S. Millard wrote to ask if he might dedicate to him a poem on botany but this overture, too, he declined.

Dillwyn's interest in molluscs led inevitably to a study of the fossil record. Of all fossil remains, shells in general were the best preserved and therefore natural subjects for geological and palaentological research. In November 1822, after visiting chalk-pits in Sussex, he spent an evening with Gideon Mantell, the Lewes physician and palaeontologist. He submitted, in the form of a letter to Sir Humphry Davy, a paper on fossil shells that was read before the Royal Society in June 1823 and published in the following issue of the Society's *Philosophical Transactions*. In the context of Dillwyn's oeuvre, which is a byword for extreme caution, the paper was remarked on for its speculative tendency, a quality of mind which, as Thomas Williams noted, was 'peremptorily suppressed' in Dillwyn's other writings.

In the paper Dillwyn advanced the proposition that extinct and living creatures of comparable anatomical structures would probably have similar habits and habitats, however widely separated they might be in time. It follows from this that if, in stratified rocks, one layer is much like the next then the fossil material found in them will be similar. Any change in the mineral composition of the layers, however, would indicate changes to the environment and signal striking differences in the fossil species. He concluded with the assertion that if this line of inquiry were to be extended then the accumulated analogies between living animals and fossil remains would throw much light on changes that the surface of the planet has undergone.

In a second letter he referred to the 'gradual approximation which may be observed in our British Strata, from the fossil remains of the oldest formations to the living inhabitants of our land and waters'. In other words, the younger the strata the greater the affinities between living and extinct species. According to the geologist F. J. North, Dillwyn's observation of a succession of species, involving the extinction of some and the survival of others, anticipated the thought of the geologist Charles Lyell and even that of Darwin himself.[20] This was, however, Dillwyn's only known venture into speculative territory and is an intimation of what he might have achieved had he been more adventurous. As a scholar he was the soul of caution: a Gradgrind who protected himself with a shell of unimpeachable fact – with works, as Thomas Williams put it, that were indestructible monuments of slowly garnered truths. Dillwyn was an observer, a collector and classifier, not a theorist. When chided for his conservatism his standard reply, delivered jocosely, was Newton's 'hypotheses non fingo.' In both his conversation and his writings, lamented Williams, there was nothing of the poetic and, despite his association with the production of beautiful porcelain, apparently little feeling for the arts.

Fiction, Williams noted, he tended to dismiss with contempt and after a visit to the London Opera in 1826 he confessed to being 'mightily pleased when it was over'. As a combustible romantic himself, Thomas Williams admired Dillwyn's discipline and application but he drew the line at his dismissal of invention and imagination. In the end, Dillwyn's failure to employ them, Williams concluded reluctantly, condemned him to the intellectual foothills, 'coiling around his soul a cramping *cordon*, which shackled the natural growth of . . . his masculine mental frame, the dwarfed dimensions of which alone made him less than the greatest men of his times'.

In Dillwyn's defence, it should be said that there seems to have been very little in the practice of botany at the turn of the nineteenth century to encourage the poetic or the imaginative faculty. Dillwyn arrived on the British botanical stage when, according to historians of botany, the spirit of scientific inquiry and research had been driven into the wings. Centre stage belonged to the Linneans. Exhausted by complicated and prolix systems of classification, eighteenth century British botanists fell upon Linnaeus's *Systema Naturae* (1737). Linnaeus showed that flowering plants could be classified according to the number of their male and female parts, the stamens and pistils respectively. The system is sometimes described as the sexual system. At the same time he revived and clarified binomial nomenclature which assigned all plants to a genus and a species, each describable by a single Latin word. With Latin as its lingua franca, the system could be applied universally.

It brought order and clarity to the study of plants and steered botany in the direction of modern science by severing its ties to superstition and herbalism. The system triggered a resurgence of interest in plants and their names and laid the foundations of taxonomy, the science of naming and classifying plants.[21] For many, however, taxonomy became an end in itself, reducing much of British botany at the turn of the nineteenth century to an exercise in naming and classification. Critics of the system argued that energies that ought to have been employed in studying the physiology, chemistry, general morphology, and medicinal properties of plants were used to commit lists of names to memory. According to the Cambridge botanist J. Reynolds Green, the Linnaean system, by offering 'a certain finality', was a soporific that stifled inquiry. Neither Linnaeus nor any of his immediate pupils, he continued, ever made a single discovery of any importance and they did nothing to establish botany upon sound philosophical principles. Green conceded that Linnaeus was a master in the art of description but questioned whether he had a true understanding of vegetation.[22]

Equally dismissive was the twenty year-old Alfred Russel Wallace. His criticism was triggered by a lecture at Neath, in April 1842, by J. E. Bicheno, on the virtues of the Linnaean system.[23] The lecture, 'so uninteresting, and so utterly unlike what such a lecture ought to be', consisted in the enumeration of the whole series of Linnaean classes and orders illustrated by coloured figures on cards about the size of ordinary playing cards. The natural system Bicheno rejected as unsuitable for beginners. 'All this', wrote Wallace in his autobiography, 'was opposed to views I had already formed'. While he conceded that any classification was better than none, in 'a vast number of cases [the Linnaean system] grouped together plants which were essentially unlike each other; and that for all purposes, except the naming of species, it was both useless and inconvenient'. In a review of the lecture, the young Wallace limned a natural system of classification to demonstrate 'the much greater interest' such a system gave to the study of botany. Wallace's system called for a detailed study of plant anatomy that allowed for the recognition of what he described as 'the real affinities under very diverse external forms'.[24]

Another severe critic of the Linnaean system was John Lindley, the first Professor of Botany at London University and for many years editor of the *Botanical Register*. On Linnaeus himself his views were mixed. He admired the clarity of his mind and the precision of his language but lamented his lack of invention and his legacy. In his inaugural lecture at London University, April 1829, he described him as 'a person exactly adapted to the state of science of the time in which he lived . . . Nature had gifted him with logical accuracy of reasoning and a neatness and perspicuity of expression'. In that same lecture Lindley dismissed the sexual system as 'a positive and serious evil' but later softened his criticism, objecting to it 'not . . . because it is artificial . . . but because it is superficial.'[25] Lindley was one of the chief English proponents of a natural system, based on the affinities of plants then being promoted by French and other continental botanists. Isolated from the continent and the main streams of European thought by the Napoleonic wars, Britain had missed important developments in the study of the anatomy, morphology, and physiology of plants.[26] Lindley also noted that by reducing botany to a study of the obvious external characters of plants the Linnean system diverted attention away from Von Humboldt's ideas on plant geography, already widespread on the continent but only just beginning to penetrate Britain.[27]

Like Linnaeus, who classified not only plants and animals but minerals and even diseases, Dillwyn seems to have been a compulsive classifier. There is no evidence, however, that he submitted as slavishly to the Linnean system as Dr George Shaw (1751-1813), a founder member and vice president of the Linnean Society, and Keeper of Natural History at the British Museum. Shaw went through his shell collection with a small hammer, breaking all those that did not fit Linnaeus's diagnoses.[28] Even so, Dillwyn seems to have been unable to observe any set of natural phenomena without organizing the parts into genera and species, and on the death of his father he destroyed hundreds of letters from his correspondence that had not been sorted and classified. 'The indiscriminate keeping of Letters', he noted in his diary, 'I find to be equally useless & troublesome, and within the last week I have burned many hundreds'.[29] He spared only complete collections, one of which was a collection of his own letters that William Dillwyn had kept bundled.

Equally frustrating to him were books that predated the *Systema Naturae*. Writing to Sir William Hooker in 1835 he noted that much of his leisure for the past twenty-five years had been given to raising and acclimatizing East Indian and Australian shrubs. He had consulted the extensive literature and found that the most valuable work was van Reede tot Drakenstein's *Hortus Malabaricus* (1678-1703), consisting of 12 folio volumes and 794 plates. Written before the *Systema Naturae*, its nomenclature was unclear and had since been further muddied by references to the plates in the 150 years of botanical writing following its publication. With the help of the Linnean Society's library and Carl Loddiges' famous nursery of rare and exotic plants he compiled a review of the references, from 123 titles, printed the results and circulated them among students of oriental botany (1839). It was yet another example, as the admiring Thomas Williams remarked, of his subject's 'extraordinary aptitude for the systematic collocation of particulars'.

Classifiers of any persuasion had obvious appeal to Dillwyn. Of particular appeal, however, was Luke Howard, the classifier of those most amorphous and ephemeral of natural phenomena: clouds. As a student of Linnaeus, Howard gave clouds the Latin names (cirrus, cumulus, nimbus and stratus) that we still use today. Howard was a retail chemist, a member of the Askesian Society, and a fellow Tottenham Quaker to whom Dillwyn looked for answers to weather phenomena that puzzled him: 'Last Wednesday Eve', he wrote to Howard on 23 October 1820, 'on my return from London my own carriage met me at Witch Tree Bridge and in passing over Llangafelach (*sic*, Llangyfelach) Hill . . . I was struck by a fine object which was new to me . . . It was a Lunar Rainbow in the North West which appeared in front of a dark cloud when the moon was nearly full was shining brightly in the opposite direction; it had all the Colors of a common Rainbow but they were much fainter and a whitish cast was diffused over the whole. The Arc was very large and perfect, and appeared at one end visible over a Heath which was almost close to my carriage but I could not help fancying it was flatter at the top . . . I enjoyed the sight for about five minutes without thinking of the moon when in the twinkling of an eye she became darkened by a cloud and the whole was over. The weather before was and has since continued to be very unsettled and stormy both as to wind and rain and the sudden tempests which have arisen in the past eight days have proved highly dangerous to navigators of the Bristol Channel.'[30]

Other objects of Dillwyn's collecting and classifying zeal were insects. In Bristol and London he could spend entire days examining collections and when at home he was easily beguiled by his own. On 8 January 1820, a day free of all social and business commitments, he spent from five in the morning until eleven at night arranging his collection.[31] Beetle collecting in the 1820s was a national obsession but Dillwyn's interest had less to do with fashion than his eclectic interest in the natural world and his gift for close observation. 'Without ever having made of Entomology a *principal* study, it was my amusement, for several years, when walking in the neighbourhood, to collect Coleopterous Insects [beetles], and to make memoranda of the situations in which they were found, and of any circumstance relating to their habits or specific characters that appeared to be worth notice'.[32] From these observations came a monograph, circulated privately, on the Coleopterous insects found in the neighbourhood of Swansea.

Over half the ninety-seven species he had found were then unknown to science. In the monograph he acknowledged his debt to a talented young naturalist, John Gwyn Jeffreys, who had introduced him to many species and helped write and arrange the notes.[33] From these we learn some of the curious pleasures and passions of beetle collecting. He owed to Jeffreys the observation that in the autumn of 1828 the Coleopterous insects in the Crymlyn Burrows, a favourite haunt of both men, were hibernating un-usually early. A much larger debt was Jeffreys' examination of the habitats of the *Cercyon ruficorne*: 'in horse dung and putrid fungi common, and Mr Jeffreys has found it under stones and decayed leaves and moist places'.

After 1818, the year in which he began his diary, Dillwyn divided his time between his botanical, conchological and ento-mological interests, and his duties as landlord, county magistrate and, after 1834, MP. All dovetailed nicely. His public duties took him around the district and the county and, as MP, periodically to London, where he could keep up his contacts at the Royal, Linnaean, and Geological Societies. Penllergare House and later Sketty Hall, the 'ideal marine villa' overlooking the sea on the

Sketty Hall.

edge of the Vivian estate to which he moved after the marriage of his son, were open house to the naturalists of London, Oxford and Bristol. Penllergare he described as an 'Inn of Science' ready to welcome any scientist whose interests drew him to south Wales. Among the notable guests were the botanist Robert Brown, librarian to the Linnean Society and Sir Joseph Banks, Sir Roderick Impey Murchison, president of the Geological Society, Sir Humphry Davy, the chemist Richard Phillips, and the eccentric and engaging William Buckland, reader in mineralogy and the first professor of geology – or undergroundology as he preferred to call it – at Oxford.

When in west Glamorgan, Buckland stayed either with the Dillwyns or with the Talbot sisters at Penrice Castle in Gower. In Oxford, however, Dillwyn stayed at the Star rather than in Buckland's legendary quarters at Christchurch. His rooms, approached through a doorway in the wall of the Christchurch quadrangle, were a combination of museum and menagerie. Visitors were confronted with a short, wide staircase covered with fragments of rock and fossils, an immense tortoise, and a stuffed wolf. Once the stairs had been negotiated they had to contend with a living and dining room in which not a table, chair or a square yard of floor was free of rock and mineral specimens. Among these wandered animals as small as a guinea pig and as large as a hyena or a bear. The hyena he kept so that he could compare teeth marks on modern and fossil bones.[34] Few could visit them without recording their impressions in prose or verse but in his diary Dillwyn is disappointingly silent.

In the field Buckland travelled in a carriage that had been strengthened to carry loads of rocks as well as a small furnace and the implements with which to assay and analyse rocks and minerals. When at Penllergare he and Dillwyn geologized in the surrounding countryside. Dillwyn had been a corresponding member of the Mineralogical Society from its inception in 1799 and an honorary member of the Geological Society from 1807, the year of its foundation. Corresponding members were people living outside London who could transmit to the Society from time to time characteristics of the local geology revealed by the opening of quarries and the sinking of shafts and wells. There was at the time great interest in the carboniferous series and Dillwyn worked on a classification of fossilized coal plants to determine whether there were differences between the plants of the upper and lower coal measures. When in Oxford Dillwyn unfailingly attended Buckland's lectures in mineralogy. He was present at his inaugural lecture in February 1822, and during the following month, when he worked on the index for Lister's conchology, he attended six more.

Buckland's lectures, which were strictly extracurricular and attracted as many dons as students, were as colourful as his rooms. When not geologizing at Penllergare or Sketty Hall the two naturalists sometimes shot rooks, the nests as well as the birds because Dillwyn thought it important to destroy the eggs. Nineteenth century sensibilities were not ours. Even uncommon birds and animals were shot and stuffed without apology. Buckland, too, was not above experimenting with wildlife. In November 1825, after attending one of Buckland's lectures, Dillwyn helped him bury 24 toads in his garden at Christchurch. To test their longevity in holes where air was excluded, Buckland prepared two large blocks, one of Heddington and the other of Pennant stone, with twelve holes in each. The blocks were buried, the toads placed in the holes, and the holes covered with glass.[35] Dillwyn did not record the results.

Buckland's most notable visit to Swansea was in January 1823. The previous summer two amateur archeologists from Port Eynon, Daniel Davies and John Davies, respectively a surgeon and a clergyman, found two large molar teeth and a partly-buried section of the trunk of an elephant or mammoth in a cave near Paviland farm in southwestern Gower, about fifteen miles west of Swansea.[36] Goat's Hole cave and its bones were known to farmers but the cave was so difficult to get at – at high tide the cave opened onto a wave-swept cliff – that the bones had never been examined. Excited by their find the two amateurs reburied the trunk for its protection and informed Lady Mary Cole and Mary Theresa Talbot, two well-known, but also amateur, naturalists who lived at Penrice Castle six miles east of Paviland. Lady Mary Cole was a botanist and horticulturist and her sister Mary Theresa Talbot a geologist and palaeontologist. A few years earlier they had written to Buckland about bones from their own collection found in 1792 in a limestone fissure at Crawley rocks near Oxwich Bay, and at Buckland's request they had sent a selection to Oxford.

The two women informed Dillwyn of the new discovery at Paviland and at the end of December he drove his phaeton to Penrice. He, Miss Talbot and John Traherne spent two days in the cave and, so Dillwyn recorded in his diary, 'brought away a great quantity of Bones' which they stored in the museum at Penrice Castle.

The collection consisted of the re-excavated tusk, a large part of the skull to which it belonged, as well as several baskets of teeth and other bones. Dillwyn then wrote to Buckland whom, he assumed, had already been told of the discovery. In a letter to Lady Mary Cole, Buckland asked her 'whether there really has or has not been a Discovery of a New Cave full of bones in your neighbourhood. Mr Dillwyn in his short letter and alludes to it as a thing notorious to me, and as if understanding that I was coming into Glamorganshire immediately to examine it, whereas I know nothing at all about the matter and never heard of it, but by Mr Dillwyn's letter . . . be so kind therefore as to oblige me with a line to clear up the obscurity which at present hangs over this matter. I should gladly have come into Glamorganshire at this time with Sir H. Davy and Dr. Wollaston, had I not been under the necessity of preparing immediately my account of the German Caves I have visited in the past summer for my book which is forthcoming at Murrays in a month or 2'.[37] He went on to ask if the cave could be closed until he was able to examine it. At the time Buckland was working at Kirkland Cave, a newly discovered hyena den near Kirby Moorside, Yorkshire.

Buckland arrived on 18 January 1823 and he, Dillwyn and John Traherne were 'engaged together geologically nearly all day'. Three days later Dillwyn and Traherne were joined by Miss Talbot and together they 'went . . . to meet Buckland who had gone early to Goat Cave near Paviland and from thence we went to look at Hound's Hole and Deborah Cave'.[38] Buckland described the Paviland Caves in *Reliquae Diluvianae*, published in 1825. 'Two large caves (Goat Hole and Deborah Cave) facing the sea, in the front of a lofty cliff of limestone which rises more than 100 feet perpendicularly above the mouth of the cave, and below them slopes at an angle of 40 degrees to the water's edge'.[39] Hound's Hole was a small fissure that lay about 150 feet west of Goat Hole, invisible from the land side and accessible only at low water. Goat's Hole was about fifteen feet wide and extended inward for about seventy feet. The floor of Goat's Hole was covered with a mass of diluvial loam of reddish yellow colour mixed with angular fragments of limestone and containing sea shells and fragments of the bones of animals and birds in which bones, teeth etc were intermixed.

Like all serious geologists, Buckland dismissed estimates of the age of the earth and the origins of mankind arrived at by a literal exegesis of Genesis. But as a clergyman raised in the Anglican tradition as well as reader in geology at a university indifferent to science, he was under some pressure to find evidence in the geological record that would corroborate the Biblical account, metaphorically if not literally. The most promising and least controversial avenue pointed toward the Mosaic Flood. Although he would later recant, he subscribed to the widely held Deluge theory that ascribed the haphazard arrangement of loosely compacted materials on large parts of the earth's surface to the catastrophic consequences of the Flood. To gather evidence in support of the theory, he travelled throughout Britain and in 1823 he published a book, *Reliquae Diluvianae* (Relics of the Flood), with the uncompromising subtitle: *Observations on the organic remains contained in caves, fissures, and diluvial gravel, and on the other geological phenomena, attesting the action of a universal deluge.*

In 1821 quarrymen had stumbled upon a cavern in Yorkshire, Kirkland Cave, filled with the bones of animals which had not been represented on the Ark. Buckland concluded that they had been destroyed by the raging floodwaters of a universal deluge c.6000 BC. In the foreword to *Reliqiuae Diluvianae* he reassured the Lord Bishop of Durham (Shute Barrington), who had encouraged the study, that his investigations 'had produced conclusions . . . affording the strongest evidence and leads us to hope that it will no longer be asserted . . . by high authorities that geology supplies no proofs of an event in the reality of which the truth of the Mosaic records is so materially involved'. He also thanked his Lordship for noticing his efforts both to draw the University's attention to geology and, so as not to cause offence, for combining it with subjects thought to be more strictly academical.

At Paviland, Buckland's investigation unearthed a partial human skeleton, missing the large bones on the right side, the cranium and the vertebrae. The bones were held in a mass of ruddle or red ochre (iron oxide) which had stained them red. Accompanying them were handfuls of shells, fragments of rings, and small ivory rods which had been buried in the red earth with the body. In the field, Buckland identified the skeleton as male, suggesting that the bones were those of a customs officer murdered by smugglers. By the time of the publication of *Reliquiae Diluvianae* later that year, however, both the sex of the skeleton and its provenance had been changed. Prompted by the perforated shell necklaces, Buckland now identified the ochre-stained skeleton as that of a female who had been buried with ornaments made from bone, antler and – to get around the problem of coexistence with pre-Ark mammoths – fossil ivory. The skeleton's supposed sex and the red staining of the bones provided a ready-made title: The Red Lady of Paviland.

A later excavation in 1912 by Professor Sollas, the then current occupant of the chair once held by Buckland at Oxford, changed the sex of the Red Lady yet again. Sollas declared the skeleton to be that of a male and, with no church dogma to contend with, of prehistoric provenance. New methods of dating and skeletal analysis identified the Lady as a young adult male who lived in the Stone Age about 15000 BC when the Gower Peninsula was just emerging from the grip of the Devonian glaciation. More recent research has pushed the date back even further, to about 18000 BC. Sea levels were much lower and the present-day coast was no more than a line of rocky bluffs overlooking a wide expanse of forest that stretched toward the river Severn. Rather than an inaccessible opening in a wave-swept cliff, Goat's Hole then was a convenient shelter on a hillside that overlooked a wide and, in part, wooded valley. The bones of bears, wolves and wooly mammoth were the remains of carcasses dragged into the cave by scavengers and predators.

Unable to accept the obvious conclusion that the skeleton was of the same age as the animal bones, Buckland declared that the Red Lady must have been buried in the cave at a much later date. To explain her presence in 'such a place' he suggested, somewhat ungallantly, that 'the remains of a British camp . . .on the hill immediately above the cave, seems to throw much light on the character and the date of the woman under consideration . . . and whatever may have been her occupation, the vicinity of the camp would afford a motive for residence, as well as the means of subsistence in what is now so remote and uninviting a solitude'. To account for the ivory artifacts found in association with the skeleton, he ingeniously suggested that they were made from fossil ivory found in the diluvial material washed into the cave at the time of the Great Flood. Today, Buckland's conclusion is usually a subject for ridicule but even as late as 1853 it was corroborated by no less distinguished a geologist than Henry De la Beche. In his *Geological Observer* he offered the opinion that 'had Buckland not employed needful caution, human remains . . . in Paviland Cave in Glamorganshire might have been regarded as proving the contemporary existence of man and of the elephant'.

Buckland's interest in bones that might substantiate the Biblical Flood persisted in spite of the accumulation of evidence to the contrary. In July 1831 he stayed with Dillwyn at Penllergare and examined Bacon Hole and Minchin Hole, Gower, in both of which hyena bones had been found. A year later, on 2 July 1832, Dillwyn and Gwyn Jeffreys drove to Caswell Bay to inquire about some bones that had been found in a cliff nearby. Within weeks, Buckland and his friend and fellow diluvialist William Daniel Coneybeare, who had heard reports of the discovery of a hyena den, were on the scene. The cave seems to have been destroyed subsequently by wave action but bones were removed from it. By 1830, however, Buckland and Conybeare, were finding it increasingly difficult to sustain the diluvial theory, having to produce more and more catastrophic floods to reconcile the geological record. In 1829 a paper delivered at the Geological Society drew, so Charles Lyell reported, 'such a sharp volume of musketry from all sides and such a broadside at the finale . . . as was enough to sink the *Reliquiae Diluvianae* for ever'. Conybeare's memoir, he continued, 'admits three deluges before the Noachian and Buckland adds God knows how many catastrophies besides so we have driven them out of the Mosaic record fairly'.[40] Needless to say, the projected second volume of *Reliqiuae Diluvianae* never materialized. In 1834 Buckland met Louis Agassiz, the great Swiss geologist, who ascribed to continental ice sheets and their meltwaters the effects once attributed to catastrophic floods. The flood-weary Buckland was an easy convert. A visit to Switzerland in 1838 quickly convinced him of the truth of Agassiz' thesis and 1840 found the two geologists in Scotland comparing notes on the effects of continental glaciation.

There is no evidence either in his diaries or elsewhere to indicate whether Dillwyn accepted or questioned Buckland's diluvial theory. Theories about the origins of man and the age of the earth might have interested him, but they were not his province and he was in any case hostile to speculation. His 'mental caste', as Thomas Williams pointed out, was 'strictly that of an observer'. By 1830, too, as affairs consumed more and more of his time, he was doing little original work. In 1834 he was one of two members for Glamorgan elected to the Reformed Parliament. It proved, as he admitted in a letter to Henry De la Beche, to be the 'most comfortless part of my existence'.[41] Thomas Williams described him as a liberal Whig but his political instincts, like his intellectual ones, were conservative. On the hustings in Bridgend in 1832 he confessed to a strong dislike of the ballot and he was opposed to the repeal of the Corn Laws, a measure that would have brought relief to urban and industrial workers but displeased landlords and farmers.

Like all Quakers he abhorred the slave trade but, to avoid anarchy, he thought emancipation should be gradual, and adopted only where it could be shown to benefit the slaves. When he retired from Parliament in 1841 he was offered a baronetcy to oppose the Tory interests in Glamorgan but this honour, too, he declined. He kept up his scientific contacts but he did little in the way of research. In 1840 he dashed off a history of Swansea which he admitted was 'altogether got up with too much haste . . . for a slow coach like me'.[42] It was sold at church bazaars to raise funds for the Infirmary.

The book is an aggregation, a cabinet of curiosities made up from loosely related items gathered over the years. Entries as various as ancient rights and laws, selections from corporate accounts, a listing of portreeves, and miscellaneous materials for a history of the town and neighbourhood lie beneath the same cover. There is no narrative thread, not even a table of contents, confirming Thomas Williams's worst suspicions of a mind lacking in invention and, possibly, powers of synthesis. Local reviewers were generous but the reviewer for *Archeologica Cambrensis*, while appreciating the effort, dismissed the product: 'The anti-quarian will praise the learning, industry and research that must have been exercised in its compilation – but we should be glad to hear of the whole being, at some future period, digested into a more ample and regular form'.[43] Despite his misgivings about the work, Dillwyn had fifty extra copies printed for distribution among friends. Such, too, was his reputation that seven Scottish universities ordered copies.

Dillwyn's last published work was a monograph, *Materials for fauna and flora of Swansea and Neighbourhood,* written for the British Association meeting in 1848 and presented to each of the botanical and zoological delegates. The gift of a work on the region for the delegates was a Continental practice that Henry De la Beche thought Dillwyn ought to introduce to Britain.[44] As a simple listing, with annotations, of plants, animals, insects and birds, Dillwyn dismissed it as a 'Bagatelle' but it has some of the charm of the *Botanist's Guide*.[45] There are notations of where particular plants, animals or insects were seen or found: 'on the walls of Oystermouth Castle', 'in a field near Drumau', 'in a boggy meadow at Penllegare'. But not all locations were salubrious. The indefatigable Gwyn Jeffreys found the *Dischirius cylindricus* 'under rubbish on the seashore' and the *Aleochara micans* 'in a dead dog on Crumlyn Burrows'. For one list of twenty-two species of beetle he was also indebted to Alfred Russel Wallace, a gift from Wallace's years in Neath.[46]

From Dillwyn himself we learn more of the collecting practices of nineteenth century naturalists. Under *Falco peregrinus* we are informed that 'One was shot on Fairwood Moor by Mr. L. L. Dillwyn'. In 1840 he also shot at different times two Lesser Spotted Wood-peckers, both in the woods at Ynysgerwn. In December 1825 Mr. Talbot shot a long-eared owl at Penrice, where the specimen is preserved. And the ever-inventive Weston Young assured him that by removing the egg of a wryneck from the bole of a tree and continuing to repeat the robbery every day that the bird was induced to lay 24 eggs.[47] The Swansea monograph would be his final publication and, as a parting flourish, Dillwyn asked De la Beche if it might be appropriate to include 'Vice President of the British Association' on the title page. Toward the end of his life he was not oblivious to honours.

The main achievement of his last two decades was his stewardship of the Royal Institution of South Wales. He and John Henry
Vivian had been founding members, in 1835, of the Philosophical
and Literary Institution, the Royal Institution's predecessor. The
Society's headquarters were on the second floor of a red brick
building in Castle Square that looked onto Wind Street; the landlord's grocery shop occupied the ground floor. Above the shop
there was space for a meeting room, a small library, and a museum
for exhibiting minerals, plants and stuffed animals. Within a year
the membership had increased from 20 to 172 and there had been
more than 700 visitors. Larger quarters were needed and in
January 1836 the members resolved to put up a new building
large enough to house a reading room and library, a lecture
theatre and a museum. A populous town that was 'seventh in the
kingdom in the extent of its trade', and 'surpassed by few in
intelligence', deserved nothing less.[48] By April 1838 the members
had raised three thousand pounds and opted for a site in the
Burrows donated by the Corporation. They also settled on a new,
unequivocal direction. In future the emphasis would be on
science, and to extend the range of the new institution's influence
to the whole of Wales they would seek royal patronage. John
Henry Vivian presented a note to Lord John Russell, one of the
principal Secretaries of State, in which he, Dillwyn and the geologist
William Edmond Logan pointed to Swansea's unmatched advantages for the pursuit of research in the natural and the physical
sciences.

Lord Russell and the Queen concurred and the Philosophical
and Literary Institution became the Royal Institution of South
Wales. Literature had been jettisoned and the new Institution
would march forward under the banner of science. 'In soliciting
the honor which has been conferred on the Society, its members
have bound themselves by a stricter obligation not to relax in
their steady and persevering endeavors to acquire and maintain
for the Institution the scientific character demanded by the title it
now bears'. The new building would be large enough for a
lecture room, a museum, a residence for the curator, and a reading room and lending library for members and subscribers. The
building committee settled on 'an attractive Grecian ornament': a
Palladian structure – *de rigueur* for Philosophical and Literary

71

Institutions – of 'chaste and elegant design' designed by the Liverpool architect Frederick Long.[49]

In his diary entry for 24 August 1838 Dillwyn described the laying of the foundation stone: 'At 12 I drove as President to a large public Breakfast [at the Assembly Rooms] given by the Building Committee and about 2 walked in procession and laid the first stone of the Royal Institution. It was accompanied by a Royal Salute of twenty-one guns, the ringing of bells, the cheers of a vast multitude and a prayer by Dr Hewson'. As President, Dillwyn was in the chair and in reply to a toast in his honour he asserted that the day was not far distant when Swansea as a burgeoning port in a mineral basin of vast and increasing proportions would be generally regarded as 'the Metropolis of Wales'.[50]

Dillwyn remained president of the Royal Institution until his death in 1855. He lectured from time to time on various aspects of natural history and, with his serious work behind him, he was able to bask in his reputation. His presidency coincided with the glory days of the Institution. Excited by the achievements of Victorian science, the public packed the lecture theatre week after week. For private scholars of modest means the library, which had several thousand volumes by 1840, was a godsend. Its most distinguished reader was Alfred Russel Wallace, co-author with Darwin of the theory of natural selection, who during the 1840s worked as a land and railway surveyor in the Neath Valley.[51] Some of the most distinguished scientists in Britain were flattered by honorary memberships, among them William Buckland, the geologist William Daniel Conybeare, and the chemist Richard Phillips.

On the day of his inauguration Phillips, who had been in Swansea examining a scheme to suppress copper-smoke at the Forest works, had been called back to London that very morning and his acceptance speech was read by Henry De la Beche who was then director of the British Geological Survey. During his address De la Beche referred to the 'abundance of talent in the various departments of knowledge which it was the object of the institution to promote'. One of the most eminent talents, of course, was Lewis Weston Dillwyn to whom William Buckland, at his inauguration in 1841, delivered an accolade as flattering as the one Dillwyn would receive at the 1848 BAAS Meeting: a 'fellow labourer whose name throughout the world, is enrolled amongst the most illustrious individuals, for half a century'.

NOTES

1. H. A. Hyde, 'Lewis Weston Dillwyn as a Botanist', *South Wales and Monmouth Record Soc.*, 5 (1963), 6-8.
2. Like Dillwyn, Babington was a taxonomist and systematist who built his career on the study of the detailed systematics (the morphology and external characteristics) of British and European floras. It was said of him that he would not release even a corner of the Herbarium for laboratory work. John Gilmour, *British Botanists* (London, 1944), 45.
3. 'William Dillwyn', *Dictionary of Quaker Biography*, 1743-1824 (London, Society of Friends), typescript, work-in-progress.
4. Graduates of Oxford and Cambridge were required to subscribe to the Church of England's Thirty Nine Articles.
5. David Painting, *Amy Dillwyn* (Cardiff, 1988), 4-5.
6. Soranus (Dr. Thomas Williams), *The Science and Scientific Men of Wales* (Tenby, 1855), 10.
7. Quoted in 'Lewis Weston Dillwyn, Esq.', *Proceedings of the Linnaean Society*, xxxvi-vii (1856).
8. Lewis Weston Dillwyn, *The natural history of British Confervae*, 16 Fasc. (London, 1802-1814).
9. Dawson Turner and Lewis Weston Dillwyn, *Botanist's Guide through England and Wales*, 2 Vols. (London, 1805).
10. David McClintock, *Companion to Flowers* (London, 1968), 90.
11. Through purchase from Sir C. V. Llewellyn, Llysdinam, 1928.
12. E. Morton Nance, *The Pottery and Porcelain of Swansea and Nantgarw* (London,1942), 72-3.
13. Elis Jenkins, 'William Weston Young', *Glamorgan Historian*, 5 (1969) 61-97.
14. Ibid., 74-75.
15. Quoted in Nance, *The Pottery and Porcelain of Swansea and Nantgarw*, 254.
16. Quoted in Elis Jenkins, 'Swansea Porcelain', *Glamorgan Historian*, 6 (1970) 116-147, ref. 123.
17. Banks was not pleased with the Swansea ware, finding it thicker and heavier than the French, its 'facture too glassy and its glaze too floating'. For details of Dillwyn's agreement with Colonel Llewellyn see Oliver Fairclough, 'Lewis Weston Dillwyn and the Cambrian Pottery', *Welsh Ceramics in Context*, ed. Jonathan Gray (Swansea, 2003), 215-228.
18. Diary, 6 April 1820. There is a three-volume calendar of the Dillwyn diaries, 1818-1852, in the library of the University College of Wales, Swansea. The 36 volumes of the original diaries are in the possession of the Dillwyn family.

19. 'Soranus', (Thomas Williams), *The Science and Scientific Men of Wales*, (Tenby, 1855), 13. See also the *Cambrian* 7 September 1855.
20. F. J. North, 'From the Geological Map to the Geological Survey', *Trans. Cardiff Naturalists Soc.*, 65 (1932), 42-115. Ref. 64.
21. Ellison Hawks, *Pioneers of Plant Study* (London, 1977), 238-9.
22. J. Reynolds Green, *A History of Botany in the United Kingdom from the earliest times to the end of the 19th Century* (London, 1914), 211-215.
23. Bicheno was a former secretary to the Linnaean Society and a friend of Dillwyn's.
24. Alfred Russel Wallace, *My Life; a record of events and opinions* (London, 1905), Vol. 1, 199-200.
25. Inaugural lecture, University of London April 30, 1829.
26. John Gilmour, *British Botanists* (London, 1944), 44-45.
27. William T. Stearn, *John Lindley: 1799-1865, Gardener-Botanist and Pioneer Orchidologist* (Portland, 1995), 73-89.
28. Hawks, *Pioneers of Plant Study*, 262.
29. Diary, 3 December 1826.
30. Calendar of the Diary, Vol. 1, Appendix 113.
31. Diary, 8 January 1820.
32. Soranus, 16.
33. Colin Matheson, 'Lewis Weston Dillwyn as a Zoologist', *South Wales and Monmouth Record Soc.*, 5 (1963), 9-11.
34. B. W. Richardson, *Thomas Sopwith* (London, 1891), 164.
35. Diary, 26 November 1825.
36. F. J. North, 'The Red Lady of Paviland', *Glamorgan Historian*, 3 (1966) 123-137; and Stephanie Swainston and Alison Brookes, *Paviland Cave and the 'Red Lady', the history of collection and investigation'* in Stephen Aldhouse-Green, *Paviland Cave and the Red Lady* (Bristol 2000) 19-47.
37. Quoted in North, 'The Red Lady of Paviland', 127. Wollaston and Sir Humphry Davy had come to Swansea to observe Faraday's and Richard Phillips's attempts to eliminate toxic gases from the copper-smoke at the Hafod works.
38. Diary, 21 January 1823.
39. William Buckland, *Reliqiuae Diluvianae* (London, 1823) 82.
40. Martin J. S. Rudwick, *The Meaning of Fossils* (London, 1972), 168.
41. NMW, De la Beche Coll., #457, Dillwyn to De la Beche, 19 Oct 1840,
42. Ibid., #456, Dillwyn to De la Beche, 23 August 1840.
43. *Archeologica Cambrensis*, 1, (1846).
44. NMW, De la Beche Coll., #463, 11 June 1848.
45. Ibid.
46. In a letter to Wallace, Dillwyn wrote: 'I am now working up a number of notes which for about half a century I have been collecting on our mammals, Birds and Fishes with the intent of printing a few copies for the convenience of the British Association and I may perhaps comply with a request to reprint my Bagatelle on the Coleoptera . . . In this case I shall be happy to notice the additions of which you have sent me a list and any particulars respecting this with which you may find leisure to favour me'. R. Elwyn Hughes, 'Alfred Russel Wallace; some notes on the

Welsh connection', *British Journ. Hist. of Science* 22, (1989) 401-418, ref. 411. See also Raymond Walker, 'The Dillwyns as Naturalists: Lewis Weston Dillwyn', *Minerva* XI (2003), 20-43, ref. 37.

47. There is more on Dillwyn hunting and collecting practices in Gerald Gabb, 'The Dillwyn Family in Mumbles', *Gower Journal* 51 (2000) 20-31.

48. Reports of the Swansea Philosophical and Literary Institution, 1835-38.

49. *Cambrian* (21 April 1838).

50. *Cambrian* (31 August 1838).

51. In January 1848 Wallace and his sister Fanny attended an evening gathering, or *Coversazione*, at the RISW organized by the Swansea Literary and Scientific Society. It was the first *Conversazione* ever to be held in Wales. Among the objects on display were a large collection of 'well-preserved' foreign birds, the 'splendid microscopes' of Dr. Thomas Williams and a collection of insects contributed by Alfred Russel Wallace. *Cambrian* (26 January, 1848).

JOHN GWYN JEFFREYS FRS
1809-1885

Conchologist
Pioneer of Deep Sea Dredging

In his essay on Lewis Weston Dillwyn, Thomas Williams's disappointment in his subject's failure to scale the intellectual heights is tempered by Dillwyn's shepherding of a brilliant young naturalist who did. From a fearless collector of beetles in Crymlyn bog, and an avid collector of shells in Swansea Bay, Gwyn Jeffreys rose to become an internationally renowned conchologist and a pioneer of deep sea dredging. As a naturalist and scholar, Gwyn Jeffreys in most ways was Dillwyn's opposite. Apart from an early interest in insects, which he may well have cultivated in order to please Dillwyn, he seldom deviated from conchology and the marine environment. Unlike Dillwyn, too, he was not averse to fiction and the arts; he had no fear of the imagination and he had great powers of synthesis. His achievements would surpass Dillwyn's but Gwyn Jeffreys never wavered in his admiration for, nor forgot his debt to, the man whom he regarded as his mentor and friend.

To Dillwyn's guidance, encouragement and influence he owed his first publication, an 88-page synopsis or catalogue of the *Testaceous Pneumonobranchous Mollusca* (air-breathing snails) of Great Britain that he would later fold into the first volume of his seminal work, *British Conchology* (1862-69). He wrote submissively to Dillwyn in September 1828: 'If you think that the following account of an interesting branch of our native Testacea, compiled from my own observations and a careful investigation of those authors who have written on the subject, will be found worthy of the notice of the Linnaean Society, I shall be glad to avail myself, with permission, of your medium in submitting it to that learned body'.[1] The synopsis duly appeared in the Society's *Transactions* and in 1830 Jeffreys was elected a fellow. He was

John Gwyn Jeffreys.

only twenty-one. Lewis Weston Dillwyn did not live to see the publication of the five-volume *British Conchology* but in 1830, the year of Jeffreys' election, he was in his middle-aged prime and he travelled to London to cast his vote.

Gwyn Jeffreys came from an old Swansea family and a line of solicitors that began with his great grandfather. He began collecting shells when a boarder at Swansea's Free Grammar School and was encouraged first by the Reverend Evan Griffith, the school's headmaster, and then by Lewis Weston Dillwyn. At school he excelled in classics and in his spare time he sorted, in a small room assigned to him by Evan Griffith, shells collected from the beach and from the crews of coasting vessels from Cornwall and the south of Ireland. At seventeen he began articling as a solicitor with a High Street law firm and ultimately became a partner. The law may have been his profession but molluscs, of both the land and the sea, were his passion. What had begun as a pastime or, as he put it, 'an inexhaustible source of pleasant and innocent occupation', became a consuming interest.[2] Like Dillwyn, he was an active and enthusiastic member of the Philosophical and Literary Institution and the Royal Institution that succeeded it. The first meeting of the provisional committee, responsible for the

Philosophical Institution's prospectus, was held at his house, and at the first general meeting in the town hall he was elected Honorary Secretary for a year. The following year he was nominated to the managing committee.

To exploit the wealth of scientific talent then available in the town, Jeffreys was one of several members keen to convert the Royal Institution into a learned society that would have some of the characteristics of a college or university. An undated, and apparently untested, resolution signed by L. W. Dillwyn and Committee aimed at raising the status of the Institution by distinguishing between members and subscribers. Members were to be held to one of the following conditions: hold a degree from a British or foreign university, be a fellow or a member of a college or distinguished society, or the author of a recognized scientific or literary work. Failing all of these, a member would have to demonstrate to the president and council his or her attainment of a satisfactory level in science. Members would meet once every fortnight to present papers and engage in debate on specified subjects. Subscribers, by contrast, would be mere onlookers, allowed to attend meetings and comment on the proceedings but not to participate in the discussions. Papers read at the meetings would be published in established scientific or literary journals or, failing these, the local press. In the flush of enthusiasm before the British Association's visit in 1848 Jeffreys also proposed that the Institution should seek incorporation as the 'Royal College of Wales'.[3]

In the decade following his synopsis on *Pulmonobranchous Mollusca* for the Linnean Society, Jeffreys published only one paper, but by 1840 he was well enough known as a conchologist and, no less important in the first half of the nineteenth century, well enough connected to be elected a Fellow of the Royal Society. 1840 was also the year of his marriage to Ann Janion Nevill, the daughter of Richard Janion Nevill of Llangennech Park, Llanelli. Richard Janion Nevill was one of south Wales's scholar entrepreneurs, owner of the Llanelli Copper Co., a Fellow of the Geological Society of London and a founder member of Swansea's Philosophical and Literary Institution. When not practising law, Jeffreys spent much of his time collecting living molluscs and the shells of dead ones, his 'workman's tools' as he would later describe them. As a collector he worked his way seaward, beginning as a schoolboy with molluscs from the land, beach and foreshore and then, as a young solicitor, dredging for shells and living creatures from a rowboat offshore. In the late 1830s and 1840s he made several expeditions to northwest Scotland and the Shetlands and wrote papers on both the molluscs and coastal formations.

As well as gathering his own specimens, Jeffreys also bought shells from fellow collectors and from the well-known London dealer George Brettingham Sowerby. His most important single acquisition, however, was the collection of William Clark of Bath. Clark's intention was to write a book on British molluscs but in 1835 he was 'so overwhelmed . . . with Publick and Private Concerns' that he despaired of completing it and had decided to pass the torch to 'more ardent and younger hands'. He did eventually summon up the necessary authorial energy and his *History of the British Marine Testaceous Mollusca* appeared in 1855. In 1839, however, convinced that he could not do the work, he prepared to sell his collection. 'I think I may state with perfect verity', he wrote in a letter to Sowerby, 'that my collection of shells is by far the most complete in the Kingdom . . . They are all named and arranged in the most accredited modern genera'.[4] At the same time, Clark also sold to Jeffreys an earlier and equally celebrated collection, that of Dr William Turton, author of the 'useful but unsystematic', as Jeffreys saw it, *Conchological Dictionary of the British Islands.*

At the end of his working life, Jeffreys probably had the largest private collection of shells in Great Britain. By his own count his British shells alone numbered in the tens of thousands, 'possibly 100,000'. To these he could add collections, which he supposed to be complete, of Mediterranean shells and Scandinavian marine shells. The Mediterranean shells included the collection of the German conchologist Heinrich Conrad Weinkauff who, for health reasons, spent much of his life in the Mediterranean. To his British, Scandinavian and Mediterranean collections, Jeffreys could also add collections from the Arctic and North America as well as deepwater shells obtained from dredging expeditions in various parts of the world. On his retirement, in a move said to have been even more shocking to British conchologists than the sale of the

Charles d'Orbigny collection to the British Museum had been to the French, Jeffreys sold them all to the Smithsonian Institution in Washington DC.

Like most collectors, Jeffreys was in thrall to the beauty of shells but he insisted that his British and northern European collections were the tools from which he fashioned his magnum opus, a comprehensive, five-volume study of British molluscs. He was called to the Bar at Lincoln's Inn in 1856, and appointed a Chancery counsel, but the larger legal stage, and the move to London that it entailed, had no apparent effect on his work in conchology. He continued to write papers and commentaries for scientific journals (more than thirty by 1860) and at his house in Kensington he embarked on the first volume of *British Conchology*, a study of the soft-bodied molluscs on land and in the surrounding seas. The first volume appeared in 1862 and the fifth, and last, in 1869. It was a massive achievement, the first volume of which was, as he acknowledged in the preface, the fruit of his relationship with Lewis Weston Dillwyn. 'When a mere youth, I was encouraged by my lamented friend, Mr Dillwyn, to commit to print what little I then knew of the subject comprised in the present volume'.

British Conchology is Gwyn Jeffreys' testament: part inventory of British molluscs, classified according to Linnaean principles, and part declaration of his views on their scientific, commercial and cultural importance. He admits to a greater interest in the shells than the soft, fleshy parts (the anatomy and physiology) of molluscs but insists that the study of conchology 'properly comprises the study, not only of the shell, but also of the whole animal'. In his maiden publication, for the Linnaean Society in 1828, he was critical of collectors and taxonomists who 'in the prevailing rage for classification' failed to examine the relationship between the anatomy and physiology of the animal and its shell. He was acutely aware of the importance of well-founded classification but he was adamant that *British Conchology* was to be regarded neither as an exercise in taxonomy nor as a narrowly conceived manual or textbook for naturalists, geologists and palaeontologists. His aim, rather, was to entice general readers into the net of natural history: to make conchology 'more an object of general cultivation than it has hitherto been'.

Like all attempts to popularize, *British Conchology* did not escape small fire from punctilious associates. In the first volume the Newcastle merchant and naturalist Joshua Alder thought there was 'perhaps rather too great a leaning towards the introduction of new views, and towards the opinion of French naturalists in opposition to our own'. The introduction, 'written in a very popular style', also gave him pause by seeming 'to embrace everything that can be said on the subject'.[5] On the introduction to the second volume, he is more sharply critical. It might do 'very well as an essay, but a great deal of it is not to the purpose. He makes rather a hobby of geology at present. Indeed, through the whole of the volume he makes his observations a medium for giving his opinion upon various subjects and displaying the extent of his reading. Many of the scraps of poetry are lugged in without adding anything to the illustration of the subject. There is a good deal of very pleasant gossip as well as much valuable information'.[6] By the third volume Alder has mellowed some-what, but still cavils: '[There is] more solid matter in this volume [but] at the same time I think there is more disposition to dilate on the subject more than is necessary, together with a more frequent use of the pronoun "I", which though in most cases I prefer to "we" may certainly be too obtrusive'.[7]

And perhaps most irritating of all for an expensive book on a specialist subject: 'Jeffreys informs me that it is selling well on account of the popular character he has given it'.[8] But in spite of what were perceived as lapses and idiosyncracies, on balance Jeffreys' associates responded generously. Alder allowed that 'no living naturalist could have done it so well' and that it was 'very well written'.[9] In a letter to Alder, fellow conchologist Alfred Merle Norman thought that Jeffreys, who had risen every morning at six, had produced a book which 'takes the lead, and which no conchologist can do without'. Norman also congratulated him for making the macological part, which dealt with the soft, fleshy parts of the molluscs, equal to the rest.[10] One of the gentlest reviews came from the *Cambrian*, his hometown newspaper, which thought the second volume 'at once an excellent compan-ion for a summer excursion to the seaside and a valuable book of reference for home study'. No writer on shells could ask for more.[11]

To make conchology intelligible or, as we might say today, accessible to lay readers Jeffreys attempted to cut through the thickets of nomenclature generally found in works on natural history. For the common cockle in 1860 there were no fewer than sixteen names and for the oyster fourteen. The record was held by a small freshwater bivalve with eighty names that covered five octavo pages. The redundancy arose partly through breakdowns in communication between British and continental naturalists during the Napoleonic and other wars. But even in peacetime communications were seldom easy enough to prevent duplication of species by zealous naturalists keen to elevate the status of local varieties. About the use of long, 'sesquipedalian' Latin words to describe species barely a quarter of an inch long and a fifteenth of an inch in diameter, Jeffreys could do nothing short of inventing a new coinage and this, of course, would have led to further confusion.[12] But he could do something about the language and tone of his expository passages and in these he seldom strays from the vernacular. On occasion he is poetic, mystical even; his aim was not just to encourage interest in conchology but to convey some sense of the beauty of shells and the mystique of the sea.

His usual device is literary – frequently classical – allusion but from time to time he indulges in some fine writing of his own. He was clearly affected by the vulnerable *tellina*, a long cockle-like mollusc that, because it does not burrow deep in the sand, was apt to be tossed about in storms and heavy seas. 'Helplessly stranded, amid seaweeds and foam, they lie in the rays of the setting sun, wet and glistening, ruby, gold, amber, and opal . . . and afterwards the sea puts on a sorrowful face, as if half conscious and repenting of the havoc he had lately made'.[13] But in general Jeffreys, who seemed able to draw on an inexhaustible store of literary and scientific sources, was more comfortable quoting others. To convey a sense of the ineffable appeal of molluscs and the sea, he quotes a passage from the work of a lamented friend, Edward Forbes, the renowned Scottish naturalist who died at the early age of thirty-nine: 'To sit down by the seaside at the commencement of ebb, and watch the shore gradually uncovered by the retiring water, is as if a great sheet of hieroglyphics . . . were being unfolded before us. Each line of the rock and strand has its peculiar characters inscribed upon it in living figures, and each figure is a mystery, which, though we may describe the appearance in precise and formal terms, has a meaning in its life and being beyond the wisdom of man to unravel'.[14]

The first volume of *British Conchology* was published in the year following Darwin's *Origin of Species*, leaving Jeffreys no choice but to take a position on evolution. He accepted Darwin's hypothesis that '*all* existing species have descended by modification from primeval forms' but he would not allow that such forms were very few or perhaps unique.[15] As a devout Christian, he was fully aware of the anti-Biblical implications of Darwinism, and of the challenge to religion of deep geological time, and he took every opportunity to soften the implications of both. In a lecture on the Pleicestocene glaciation – one of his few trespasses onto dry land – at the Llanelli Mechanics Institute in January 1863 he remarked, pointedly, that in the eyes of the maker a thousand years are but yesterday, and as a watch in the night.[16]

Like many other leading naturalists of the day, Jeffreys held the view that although species may have evolved through time the boundaries between them were finite and immutable. In short, there had been no increase in the diversity of life.[17] After examining extensive collections of marine shells found in the Coralline Crag, a fossil-rich Tertiary limestone in East Anglia, he concluded that out of 286 species no fewer than 167 are precisely similar with those that live in British seas. French naturalists on the other hand, led by d'Orbigny, contended that there was no specific identity between Tertiary and recent mollusca. They took the view that all Tertiary species became extinct and today are represented only by analogous forms. Jeffreys, however, thought it impossible for even the most critical species-maker to distinguish Tertiary from modern forms. In spite of his admiration for French conchologists, he suggested that they had allowed 'peculiar views', based on a preconception about the successive creation of species, to impair their judgement. 'The plan of the Creator as far as we can comprehend it', he insisted, 'has not been that of progressive development'. The absence of contemporary species in the fossil record he ascribed to the hit-and-miss nature of preservation and the wholesale erosion of sedimentary strata once they had been raised above the level of the sea.[18]

Jeffreys also subscribed to the comforting, age-old notion of a designed earth but, paradoxically, he did not accord humans a special place in it. Far from being the 'lords of the creation', they were but a link in the great chain of being – part, as we might now phrase it, of one great ecosystem. 'The countless and complicated links of the chainwork in which all nature is involved are so closely and wonderfully connected together, that not one of them can be broken or displaced without interfering with the economy of the whole'. This connection with our fellow creatures, in 'one common bond of sympathy' should have taught us a lesson in humility. 'All our physical, and perhaps even our mental faculties', he continued, 'are shared with us by other animals, far indeed inferior to us in organization, but equally enjoying the prescient and beneficent care of Him through whom we all live and move and have our being'.[19]

On less metaphysical grounds, Jeffreys makes a case for molluscs as the most useful of all the fossils to geologists and palaeontologists. More than other fossilized creatures, they tend to maintain their original structure so that fossil forms can easily be compared with living ones. He quotes Gideon Mantell, the Sussex surgeon and palaeontologist, for whom ammonites were 'medals of creation', as useful to geologists and palaeontologists as ancient coins to historians. As a field for study, too, Jeffreys contended that conchology could hardly be improved upon. It inculcates, 'in the most agreeable form', sound reasoning, the continual exercise of memory, a love of order, habits of observation and, above all, the necessity for truth. 'No pursuit of any other kind', he concluded, 'can excel it'. Conchology also had about it a quality of innocence that could disarm even intransigent officials. When travelling through Lombardy in 1850 he and his courier, on a mid-day halt at Rivigo to feed their horses, passed through an unattended customs barrier into Austrian territory in a search for shells. On their return they found an Austrian official at the barrier who demanded their passports. These they had left with their carriage, and passports then were indispensable for travelling through northern Italy. Explanations were to no avail until the courier produced from his coat a collecting box full of live snails. His remark of 'Eco, Signore, i nostri passporti!' was all that was needed to force an understanding smile from the customs officer and the raising of the barrier.

To draw readers into what he described as the brotherhood or freemasonry of conchologists, in the final volume of *British Conchology* Jeffreys offers, with his usual thoroughness, hints for collecting.[20] Land molluscs are found in woods, hedges, gardens and meadows, on rocks (especially chalk and limestone), old walls, dry grassy plains, trunks of trees, among fallen leaves, moss, herbage of every kind, the sides of lakes and ponds and under logs and stones. The best times for finding them were during rainy or moist weather in summer and autumn. Some species could be trapped by laying pieces of decayed wood or stones with an uneven base at the edges of ponds. He cites a French conchologist Jean de Charpentier who, when hunting for a particular Alpine mollusc, took with him a boy who squirted water from a large syringe into crevices where it was known to hide. Water brought the snail out of hiding and ultimately into Charpentier's collecting box. More plebeian methods were to sweep long grass with a butterfly net and ponds with a landing net. The serious collecting of marine molluscs required a boat and a dredge but molluscs living in the intertidal zone could be found by examining rocks and pools and, for the more zealous collectors, the stomachs of dead fish.

To raise the profile of the mollusc, Jeffreys realised that he had to convince nonspecialist readers of its utility as well as its scientific importance. He began, naturally, with food. Not only do molluscs support shoals of edible fish, such as cod, ling, haddock and halibut, but, as appetizers, they satisfy all palates. The lowly cockle, whelk, periwinkle and mussel were the staples of Billingsgate market and the mining and manufacturing districts of England while the oyster – the 'king of the Mollusks' – has been the food of emperors. In the first century B.C., Varro, the Roman writer on agriculture, described in detail methods of cultivating oysters and, through cross breeding, of improving the breeds. Jeffreys noted that in France, too, the cultivation of oyster beds ranked as a science, 'huitreculture', whereas in Britain, the land of the cockle and the whelk, 'we can, but (alas) do not, manage these things so well'. On the French taste for snails, however, he is less enthusiastic even allowing for France's shorter coastline, and therefore a choice of fish and marine molluscs more abbreviated than Britain's. Despite his admiration for French conchologists and French culture, he cannot suppress a note of disapproval: 'Even land-snails are pressed into the service of the French, and enter rather largely into their cookery'. Displayed in the windows of restaurants like kidneys and whitebait in the shop windows of London eating houses, they might have looked appetizing but Jeffreys was not tempted. It was a case, he remarked, of 'Chacun a son Gout'.

Molluscs were also a valued source of ornament. The inner coats of mother-of-pearl in the 'ormer' or ear shell from the Channel Islands were used to make buttons, studs and inlays. Many tons of them were gathered annually and shipped to the Birmingham market. Romans used shells to decorate dwellings and fountains, setting and inlaying them in mortar, while eighteenth century English gentlemen used them to decorate their grottos. The most prized

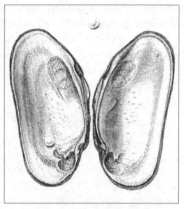

Unio Margaritifer and pearl.
Vol. 1, British Conchology.

ornament, however, was the gift of the pearl-yielding oyster. The Romans ransacked British seas and estuaries for the *Unio Margaritifer*, the chief source of pearls until superseded by the pearl fisheries of the Pacific. So sought after were the northern pearls that late in the eighteenth century Linnaeus took out a patent for their artificial production in the rivers of Sweden. The experiments were not successful but Jeffreys, conscious of the appeal of the product, used a drawing of a *Unio Margaritifer and pearl* as the frontispiece for the first volume of *British Conchology*.

Of the other uses of molluscs, Jeffreys had space for a selection only. Crushed snails were much esteemed as a remedy for pulmonary complaints while snail broth, though hardly a soup of choice, was said to be serviceable as a laxative. Mussels eaten raw were thought to be a remedy for sore eyes and the shell, before the invention or availability of hardened steel, served as a razor to shave with. Mussel shells also made excellent cream skimmers and the shell of the almond-whelk served Shetland and northern fishermen as a lamp. They filled the inside with fish oil, placed a wick or cotton tow into the canal at the extremity of the mouth, and suspended it from a wall or ceiling with a piece of string tied in a triangle around shell. It was as elegant, Jeffreys asserted, as any antique lamp. The valves of a freshwater mussel, *Unio Pictorum*, contained pigments used by the great 17th century Italian and Flemish masters. Molluscs and shellfish were also used as fertilizer. Live mussels were gathered and spread over fields in Lancashire just as lobsters, washed up in windrows after storms, were spread over Maritime fields in eastern Canada. In Guernsey, ormer shells strung together and suspended from a stick, made an effective scarecrow. In Iceland, where mussels were not eaten, lime made from their calcined shells was said to have been stronger than mortar made from limestone. In Bideford mussels were used to hold together the stones of a bridge stripped of their binding mortar by a rapid tide. The spaces between the stones were filled with mussels and the byssus, the gluey filaments that they use to attach themselves to rocks, held the stones together and prevented the bridge from being carried away.[21]

On the debit side of the mollusc/man balance Jeffreys made only one entry: the *Teredo* worm.[22] Until steel hulls replaced wooden ones, wood-boring Teredines, which inhabit all but the coldest seas, were the scourge of ships and wharves. The only effective prophylactic, which was of great significance to Swansea, was a skin-tight sheet of copper wrapped around the hull. For Jeffreys, as for many naturalists, Teredines were an obsessive interest. In the third volume of *British Conchology* he assigned more than fifty pages to the one entry, and as the illustration for the frontispiece he chose a drawing of a section of hull perforated by worms. For naturalists, the fascination for the *Teredo* worm lay in its seeming innocuousness balanced against the immense damage it could inflict on wharves and ships. How could a worm with an extremely tender shell, in fact no more than a mere film in the young *Teredo*, bore into solid oak? The paradox, though unspoken, is instinct in Jeffreys' definition: 'Body worm-shaped and almost gelatinous, more or less enclosed in a testaceous [shell-like] sheath, which is usually flexuous: *mantle* very thin and cylindrical, enveloping the whole body, open only for the passage of the foot at the anterior end, and for the orifices of the tubes or siphons at the posterior end.'

Technically the *Teredo* is a mollusc but because of its flexibility it is invariably described as a worm. Its long and nearly gelatinous body is without rings or segments and it ranges in length from a pinhead in the larval stage to as much as a foot or eighteen inches when mature. Inhabiting both temperate and tropical seas, and burrowing only into hard vegetable substances, it was known and feared in all maritime countries and went by many names: 'shipworm' in Britain, 'taret' in France, 'zeeworm' and 'paalworm' in Holland, 'seewurm' in Germany, 'troemark' in Norway, 'bysa' and 'bruna' in Italy, 'broma' in Spain.

As well as being the terror of ships and wharves, the *Teredo* was foul-smelling. When not admiring its efficiency, naturalists referred to it variously as a villainous creature and a noxious mollusc, and assigned to it the same scavenger office allotted to the white ant on land. The *Teredo* worked its way with the grain and, if they could not be avoided, through as well as around knots leaving the wood honeycombed and rusk-like. In warm seasons it could also destroy with remarkable speed. One spring a ferryboat serving a harbour on the north coast of Spain sank after an accident. Four months later fishermen, hoping to make use of the materials, raised the boat but the planks and beams were so worm-eaten that they were unusable. In tropical stations sailors reported that in places where paint had rubbed off below the water-line ship worms could quickly reduce a plank to the thickness of little more than an eggshell.

Like other naturalists, Jeffreys readily admitted to his obsession with the delicately-made mollusc. He examined carefully a 'multitude' of live and dead specimens yet he still felt as if he knew little about the 'wonderful' creature. His admiration was teleological. However dire its effects on wooden hulls, wharves and pilings, Jeffreys regarded the *Teredo* as an example of perfect adaptation – of, in effect, the design and purpose he perceived in nature. It lived only within hard vegetable substances, of which Jeffreys provides an exhaustive list. It is a measure of his fasci-nation: the hull of a ship, a harbour-pile, a shipping-stage, a float-ing tree or the roots of one growing on the banks of an estuarine river, a piece of balk timber, a fisherman's cork, a cocoa-nut, a bamboo rod, a walking-stick, a beacon or buoy, a mast, rudder, oar, plank, cask, hencoop, or other ligneous waif or stray of the ocean. These, he continues, the *Teredo* 'perforates, like a rabbit or mole in the earth, for the purpose of making its burrow and protecting its soft and sluggish frame. It is never free, nor living anywhere except in its wooden gallery: and it may be cited as a perfect teleological example – an exact adaptation of means to the end or object, viz. its existence'.

Another measure of Jeffreys' fascination was his familiarity with not only writings on the *Teredo* but on allusions to it in classical and other literature. The earliest reference to the worm, a claim that he felt no need to qualify, is in the *Knights* of Aristophanes. The chorus repeats a conversation said to have taken place between several triremes – galleys with three rows of oars on each side. The eldest trireme declared to her companions that, sooner than be engaged in a rumoured expedition, she would remain where she was, grow old and be consumed by Teredines. Jeffreys points out, however, that because it was the custom of the Greeks and Romans to lay up their vessels high and dry on the beach until needed for service, Aristophanes might have been referring to a wood-boring grub or beetle rather than a shipworm. Ovid's *Teredo*, cited in his first epistle from Pontus, in all probability, Jeffreys suggests, was of the genus *Teredo Navalis*. Jeffreys had examined specimens of the *Navalis* taken from a Russian vessel sunk at the entrance to Sebastopol during the Crimean war. For a medieval reference to the *Teredo*, he quotes a few lines of verse from the *Black Book of Carmarthen*, written in the thirteenth century. Yscolan, a monk and scholar, describes an imagined penance he endured for an unspecified ecclesiastical offence:

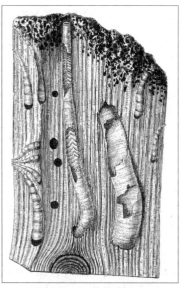

Teredo Norvegica.
Vol. 3, British Conchology.

A full year I was placed
At Bangor, on the pole of a weir.
Consider thou my sufferings from sea-worms.

The first treatises on the *Teredo* were written by Dutch naturalists and historians; wooden dykes and the Dutch merchant fleet were particularly at risk from the *zeeworm*. In 1733 alone eight separate works appeared. Pre-eminent among them was a history by Godfrey Sellius, a distinguished lawyer from Utrecht, a Fellow of London's Royal Society and a writer clearly after Jeffreys' heart. His 366-page *Historia Naturalis Teredinis* (1733), a masterpiece of learned research according to Jeffreys, was written entirely in Latin and, not the least of its attractions for Jeffreys, it was replete with classical allusions. The subject, and here Jeffreys could have been speaking of himself, appears to have fascinated Sellius 'much in the same way as a capricious mistress does her lover who now deprecates the cruelty of his fair tormentor, and then extols to the skies her beauty and gentleness'.

For Sellius the *Teredo* was at once a wicked beast, the worst plague that angry nature could inflict on man yet, in terms of its dwelling and its way of life, a masterpiece of symmetry, economy, ingenuity, social harmony and wonderful perfection in every particular. Sellius persuades us, Jeffreys noted, that its dwelling is a model for the architect and its mode of life, in its avoidance of controversy and litigation, the rule for the Christian. In its burrowing operations the *Teredo* is careful not to infringe on the territory of its neighbours and if a trespass is imminent the aggressor secretes a cup-shaped dome or plug, of a thinner texture than the rest of its sheath, and then walls itself into its burrow. Unable to eat its way through to the wood, it then dies of starvation, preferring death to invasion and injury to his fellows. Moved by the self-sacrifice, Sellius described it as a sacred duty performed with reverential care.

Sellius also addressed the problem of how the fragile *Teredo* bores into wood. The tender shell, a mere film, could hardly be the instrument of penetration and even if it were hard the tube, being broader at the bottom than the top, could not serve as an auger-like instrument. His conclusion, with which Jeffreys agreed, was that the *Teredo* perforates by suction aided by continual maceration and softening of the wood by water introduced into the tube by siphons. Jeffreys concluded that the foot, a muscular disk constantly supplied with moisture by the glandular tissues of the body, was the sole instrument of penetration, slowly detaching or tearing away the fibres of wood. For proof of the strength of a molluscular foot, Jeffreys invites the reader to try touching and removing a limpet from its native rock. No submerged wood was safe from attack by Teredines because the fry, furnished with a pair of close-fitting oval valves, eyes, and a large foot swims freely and rapidly and is capable of travelling long distances before settling on a fixed habitation. The *Teredo* attacks sound wood only but, as Jeffreys hinted darkly in an 1860 lecture, it might be capable of extending its range. An allied genus had been found to attack, at a depth of sixty to seventy fathoms, the recently laid telegraph cable between England and Gibraltar. The worm made its way through a thick wrapper of cordage into the gutta percha which covered the wire. The solution was to bind cable with solid steel wire.

In Sellius's day, supposed remedies were legion. He counted hundreds of ointments and preparations of an oily nature and Sellius himself proposed one, similar to creosote, that would penetrate the pores in the wood and harden the timber. He thought the best preventative was a coat of varnish thick enough and durable enough to keep out the fry. In *British Conchology* Jeffreys provided examples of prophylactics, other than oils and ointments, that were tried in Sellius's day. For ships there were double planking and/or an inner layer of calf-skins, cow-hair, pounded glass, ashes, glue, chalk, moss, or charcoal; and for wooden piles, large iron nails driven in close together. In the *Philosophical Transactions* for 1666, the year of the Great Fire, an anonymous Londoner suggested that a layer of pitch drawn out of sea coals might 'scare away these noisome insects'. Sellius himself, having considered all the proposed remedies and despaired of all of them, concluded that all that remained was constant prayer in the hope of intercession by the Almighty.

Failing divine intervention, the answer to the *Teredo*'s attacks clearly lay in preventing the fry, which was only the size of a pinhead, from attaching itself to the wood and beginning its burrow. Once attached it insinuates itself between the fibres of the wood and works its way slowly inward where it becomes snugly lodged and immovable. What was needed was a thin, impenetrable coating painted or fastened onto the hull. Phoenicians and Egyptians, and after them Greeks and Romans, used a mixture of pitch and wax to protect their merchant vessels and men-of-war. Tar seemed to answer the purpose but it was too easily rubbed off or removed by contact with wharves, the hulls of neighbouring vessels, and harbour bottoms. The eventual remedy was a paper-thin sheet of metal fastened tightly around the hull. The first experiments, conducted by the Royal Navy, were with lead, but lead tears easily, and is heavy, and for pursuit speed was essential. Copper, which was substituted for lead in the 1760s, was lighter and more durable, and as well as fending off Teredines it repelled weeds and barnacles allowing hulls, which were no longer spongey and barnacle encrusted, to glide more easily through the water.

By the 1780s, to the delight of Swansea's coppermasters, nearly all Royal Navy vessels were 'coppered', and where the Royal Navy led others followed. By 1785 most French, Spanish and Dutch naval vessels were wrapped in copper supplied by Swansea copperworks. Although tougher than lead, copper also tears fairly easily and in the 1830s it was replaced by yellow metal, a copper-zinc alloy cheaper and stronger than copper, patented by G. F. Muntz of Birmingham who conducted his research at the Upper Bank works in Swansea. But although copper and yellow metal were effective shields they could not be applied universally. Both were costly and neither could withstand the wear and tear on the hulls of vessels forced to take the ground in tidal harbours where there were no wet or floating docks.[23]

Coppering, too, was a remedy for vessels only. Wharves and piers remained unprotected and the damage to them was grave. At the Oxford meeting of the BAAS, 1860, Jeffreys recommended the forming of a committee, of which he was duly appointed chairman, to examine ways of preventing the damage to harbours.[24] The French and Dutch Governments had both appointed special commissions but in Britain where, as Jeffreys pointed out, there was not a single naturalist in parliament, the government had taken no action. As chairman of the British Association committee, he visited Holland where experiments on an extensive scale had already been conducted under the Academy of Sciences at Amsterdam. At the same time he wrote to the Admiralty requesting permission to conduct experiments in the naval dockyard at Plymouth where Teredines were known to be ravaging the Government wharves. He had to wait a month for a reply and when it came it was a flat refusal, with no accompanying explanation.

Most of the experiments on wharves and pilings, where coppering was not an option, involved poisons. All had failed. The *Teredo* attacks only in tidal harbours, never in floating harbours or wet docks to which the tide has only occasional access, and in tidal harbours poisons were either flushed out or they became too diluted to be effective. Jeffreys cites the French naturalist Quatrefages' futile efforts to kill the *Teredo* larvae, in the harbour of San Sebastian, by dissolving large quantities of corrosive sublimate or acetate of lead. Scupper nailing, that covered the timbers with a blanket of broad-headed iron nails, was also ineffective; the pinheaded larvae could negotiate the smallest interstices and mature Teredines could work their way through rust. Creosote, too, failed to deter and tar was too easily removed by wave action. What was needed, in Jeffreys' opinion, was a liquid solution that on drying and hardening would cover the wharf timbers with an impenetrable glassy surface. The ancient Egyptians protected their inscriptions on stone with a vitrifiable solution. Wood, as Jeffreys recognized, could not perhaps be treated in the same way but he thought it possible that a liquid mixture capable of penetrating and adhering to the fibrous surface might be invented.

At the 1860 Oxford BAAS meeting he admitted to being encouraged by experiments then being made to protect from weathering the stones of the Houses of Parliament by coating parts of the walls with silicate of lime and a mixture of pitch and wax; the latter had first been used by the Phoenicians and Egyptians on their merchant vessels and men of war. Although the efficacy of silicate of lime had yet to be proven, William Hutton of Hartlepool proposed impregnating wood with a solution of it, but as this required mechanical power, the costs were thought to be prohibitive. At the Oxford meeting Jeffreys also referred to an invention patented by Messrs Peacock and Buchan of a composition said to form, by a chemical combination with sea water, an unctuous or slimy pellicle that discouraged the attentions of barnacles and weeds. Peacock and Buchan's composition had yet to be tested on the *Teredo* but Jeffreys questioned whether even an unctuous and slimy pellicle would keep the determined worm at bay.

Until his admission to the Bar and his move to London, Jeffreys' research had been confined to the foreshore and to immediate offshore waters, where he dredged from rowboats and other small craft during weekends and holidays. Occasionally, material might be thrown up by storms or brought ashore by fishermen, whom he had persuaded not to discard chance captures on leadlines or longlines, or in trawls and oyster and clam dredges. But trawl nets were limited to depths of about twenty fathoms and long lines to about forty, and the specimens they produced, as Edward Forbes remarked, served only 'to whet curiosity, without affording the information we thirsted for'.[25] Fishermen, too, were an unreliable resource. All products of the sea that were not fish they dismissed as 'trash' and it was very difficult to induce them to bring anything ashore that they could not sell. In places where rare species were regarded as unlucky, nothing but saleable fish would reach the shore. Even when interesting material did reach the shore, neither the location, depth, nor temperature of the water could be determined accurately. For naturalists, the only solution was to collect their own material.

At the Birmingham Meeting of the British Association in 1839 a committee headed by Edward Forbes had been charged with promoting 'researches with the dredge'. Each summer the members of the committee worked off various parts of the coast of Britain, gradually compiling an inventory of fauna up to the 100-fathom line, the practical limit for work with small boats. By 1855, Jeffreys was convinced that the conchology of coastal Britain was 'nearly exhausted' and, not wishing to spend his long vacation dredging in known waters, he set out for the Mediterranean.[26] He left London on 1 August 1855 and travelled to Genoa via Paris, Lyons, Chambery and Turin. The largest items in his baggage, which confounded the Paris customs officials, were two iron dredges, replete with bags and nets, and six graduated brass-wire sieves. There being no category for conchology, and no snails with which to charm the puzzled officials, they were classified, unimaginatively, as machines. His destination was Sardinia but a

cholera outbreak in Genoa, his port of embarkation, and a man-
datory five-day quarantine for all sea-borne passengers prompted
a change in plan. Unable to leave Genoa, he hired a small boat
and dredged up to the forty fathom line on the coast between
Genoa and nearby Portofina. He was, he believed, the first
naturalist ever to have dredged in this part of the Mediterranean.

His quarantine over he sailed not for Sardinia, as planned, but
for Spezia, a small coastal town about sixty miles away. He took a
room at a small inn, which he set up as a laboratory, rented a
small boat and some boatmen, and one hundred fathoms of rope.
He dredged on alternate days having to stay ashore to sift and sort
material, with help from the boatmen, from the previous day's
dredging. On dredging days his practice was to dredge from
seven until noon and then ask the men to land him on some part
of the coast where he could bathe off the rocks. The boatmen
continued to dredge according to his directions but after bathing
he walked or, more accurately, waded back to town, 'con-
chologizing all the way'. Mediterranean tides are so feeble that
there is no foreshore, or intertidal zone, to speak of, so to collect
molluscs and other material, he had to wade in shallow water.
The shells and live molluscs he stored in his room whose shutters,
because he needed light in order to work, he had to leave open.
He washed the shells in chloride of lime, but with sunlight and
heat from the street pouring through the unguarded windows the
room was not as 'odoriferous' as he would have wished. Decay-
ing animal matter attracted 'a large and strange sort of fly' that
bred abundantly in the drawers of his extempore storage cabinet:
the hotel's wardrobe. His saviour, aside from a tolerant hotelier,
was a small red ant that emerged from 'some secret hiding place'
and cleaned the shells. Jeffreys' reward for a remarkably industrious long vacation were 13,000 specimens of marine testacea,
several thousand land and freshwater shells, and innumerable
sponges and zoophytes.

The most interesting discovery of the summer was that about
thirty of the Mediterranean shells were as familiar to him as if he
had dredged off the British coast. The findings contradicted the
widely held notion that molluscs occupied particular latitudinal
zones. The presence of northern shells in an almost enclosed
subtropical sea or, if the equation is reversed, Mediterranean

shells in a northern sea, raised the question of how they got there. Jeffreys found what he thought might be the answer in Charles Lyell's recently published *Principles of Geology.* In the early Tertiary period, according to Lyell and others, a broad channel joined the Bay of Biscay and the Gulf of Lyon, along the line of the present-day Midi Canal, allowing Atlantic and Mediterranean waters to merge. To explain the dispersal of molluscs between such different climatic zones, Jeffreys pointed to the fallacy of applying to marine creatures the same principles of distribution that apply to animals on land. Only waters near the shore are affected by the local climate. In deeper waters, beyond the reach of the sun, latitude has little effect upon temperature. At depth, temperatures remain equable over great ranges of latitude allowing some species considerable freedom of movement.

In one of his last reports before his untimely death in 1854, Edward Forbes declared that much of the sea around the Shetland Islands could not fail to reward the explorer: 'A series of dredgings between the Zetland and Faroe Isles, where the greatest depth is under 700 fathoms, would throw more light on the natural history of the North Atlantic and on marine geology generally, than any investigation that has yet been undertaken'. Unlike most of the British Isles, the Shetlands lay very close to deep water where conditions had changed little since pre-glacial times. Forbes believed that in the deep waters off the islands naturalists might find the rootstock of current European marine fauna and be able to explore links between the fauna of Norway and Britain.

Jeffreys was drawn to the Shetlands less, one suspects, by the possibility of solving questions of origin and dispersion than, as an impassioned collector, by the possibility of finding rare molluscs in the unexplored waters. He visited them first in 1841 and again in 1848 when he discovered a number of molluscs known previously only in fossilized form in the Coralline Crag. When his brother-in-law W. H. Nevill offered him the use of his yacht in 1860 (Jeffreys would later buy the vessel) he embarked on a series of lengthy summer expeditions: to the Shetlands in 1861, 1862, 1863, 1864, 1867, and 1868; to the Channel Islands in 1865, and the west coast of Scotland in 1866. These were financed in part by small grants from the British Association and by whatever his fellow researchers could afford, but most of the expenses Jeffreys bore himself. C. Wyville Thompson, comfortably placed as Professor of Natural History at Queen's, Belfast, could only admire Jeffreys' band of intrepid, independent researchers. In *Depths of the Sea,* his classic account of deep-sea exploration, he acknowledged not just the value of their regular reports to the British Association but the physical costs of getting them: 'compiled at an extraordinary expense of labour, discomfort and privation . . . through many years'.

Jeffreys' first Shetland bases were in the Out Skerries and on the west coast near Hillswick but for most of his cruises he chose Balta Sound, Uist, from which the deep water east, northwest and northeast of the islands could be reached if the weather was favourable. Balta Sound was the home of Dr Lawrence Edmonston, a physician and well-known naturalist and archaeologist of the Shetlands. On his Shetland expeditions, Jeffreys' most frequent companions were Alfred Merle Norman, Edward Waller and Charles William Peach. Norman and Waller were both gentlemen researchers: Waller a landowner from County Tyrone, and Christ-church-educated Norman a clergyman and chaplain to the Earl of Durham. Peach was an anomaly, the son of a saddler and harness-maker and, later, inn owner and farmer near Northampton. In his early twenties he was a riding officer in the coastguard at Weybourn, Norfolk, where he became a passionate student and collector of marine invertebrates.

Later, he moved to Cornwall where he managed to support a family of nine children and carry on his research, making important connections between living and extinct species. He presented his findings to the British Association meeting at Plymouth in 1841, but as a working man in the company of gentleman scientists he was not allowed to comment on their significance.[27] In 1848 he moved to Peterhead and in a letter to the geologist Henry de la Beche he pronounced palaeontology, in the ancient preCambrian formations, to be 'a dead letter here'. On the Shetland cruises Peach was the expert on sponges and sessile fauna. According to Waller he was also colourful: ' [he] has a general knowledge of most departments and is very strong in *Lepralia* and its more aspiring allies . . . Examines all stones and shells most anxiously . . . You know he is very chatty and attentive to the ladies and has his microscope to show off his wonders'. Throughout his life Peach nursed the hope that his accomplishments in geology and marine zoology would rescue him from the hazardous and poorly paid coastguard service. But they never did.

Jeffreys' Shetland cruises are documented in his published work, notably in the regular reports that he submitted to the British Association, but also in a remarkable correspondence between Jeffreys, Alfred Merle Norman and Joshua Alder. The letters, as the correspondents acknowledged, were diaries or journals of record in which they recorded details of weather, of species brought up by the dredges, and the character of the Shetlanders. Copies were sometimes made and Norman's letters to Joshua Alder were forwarded to a mutual friend and conchologist and then returned to Norman. The letters tend to be catalogues of frustration.

Inevitably, when dredging in the north Atlantic from a vessel not built for the purpose, weather was a preoccupation. North Atlantic weather is notoriously unpredictable and, more often than not, bad. 'Oh for fine weather!' wrote Norman in June 1863, 'If we could but get it we might yet do well and get good things to reward us for the heavy out lay. It is very tantalizing. Here we are with every possible appliance ready, close (only about 30 miles or 3-4 hours run) to the finest dredging grounds in the British Islands, yet the weather is such that we might almost as well be in England – and far better for our purses'.[28] And in June 1864, 'We are trying to make the best of a second winter . . . snow and sleet and for a time on Monday morning the Islands as far as we could see were white'.[29] And a day or so later, 'Today at 7am the wind got up from the dreadful quarter (NE) and continued to blow strong for hours'.[30] During that month Jeffreys' boat, the *Osprey*, caught between a strong headwind and powerful cross-seas north-east of Balta Sound, had narrowly escaped overturning.

In spite of the difficulties the crew were able to dredge enough samples to keep the scientists and their assistants occupied. From time to time Jeffreys and a helper stayed ashore to sort, identify and preserve the samples. Jeffreys, however, was the orchestrator of the work: 'I have sent the cutter out again for a long cruise with a couple of extra hands and some good beef and provisions as a treat. She left a little after 1 this morning. Phillips [captain of the

Osprey] and McNab [in charge of dredging] work the sieves, and nothing seems to escape them. They were well supplied with bags and jampots, besides some enamelled basins I got on purpose in London . . . and the water is changed 3 times a day. . . . This plan gives me time to examine the animals and some of the sand. I should not like being out many days together, and the men are anxious to 'do some good' as they call it, that I do not feel uneasy at being absent. McNab is a regular trump and so is Phillips'.

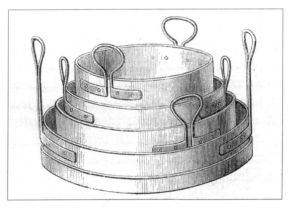

Nest of dredging sieves designed by Jeffreys.

The sailors raised the dredge with a winch, two winding and a third coiling the rope, and emptied it either by tipping and pouring from the mouth or by unlacing the bottom of the bag. The receptacle was either a frame or platform with a ledge around it, or simply a piece of tarpaulin laid on the deck. Any shells or molluscs on top of the heap were carefully removed and placed in jars or tubs of seawater. The rest of the heap was then sifted through a nest of copper or brass-wire sieves, designed by Jeffreys, set into a tub of seawater. The sieves, which were of increasingly finer mesh, were fitted one within the other. The top sieve was half filled with some of the contents of the dredge, and the set was gently moved up and down in water so that the rougher stones and gravel and larger organisms were retained in the upper sieve. The finer materials and mud passed through, the latter settling on the bottom of the tub. Any organisms trapped in the sieves were removed gently with a pair of brass or bone forceps and placed in jars of seawater, or bottles of weak spirit of wine. Accompanying each specimen was information on the circumstances of the dredging: date, location, depth, and nature of the ground.

In May and June 1863 the group attempted to combat the 'smiling and treacherous weather', as Jeffreys described it, and the limitations of a sailing vessel, by chartering a steam yacht from a company in Yorkshire. They hoped to be able to work with some regularity on what Jeffreys called the 'Margarita ground' in the open Atlantic about 35-40 miles north of Uist where a number of rare species had been discovered. Jeffreys, Norman, Waller, Captain Phillips and an artist named Bell, enlisted 'to take views', and joined the ship at Aberdeen. But not even a steam yacht was proof against the worst of the Shetland weather and during the first two weeks gales and rough seas allowed only four hours of successful dredging. At the beginning of June, when the weather eased, they were able to make several excursions to the Margarita ground where they dredged to 100 fathoms. But just as the weather was settling they received an order to return to Aberdeen. Although the steamer had been chartered for six weeks the company needed it back after five, and they felt they had no choice but to return. They had found some rare species but not enough for a specimen each for the naturalists.

Even when conditions were favourable for dredging, the way was seldom smooth. Although Jeffreys sympathised with a way of life that in a bad month might allow only a few days' fishing, he found the fishermen unreliable and frequently dishonest. 'The fishermen', he complained, 'cheated Waller last week and we have given up this part of our work. They played tricks by dividing the scoops and this gave us excellent opportunity for stopping . . . Only four have brought us any fish lice for you and these are few and apparently the same as you had before'. He was just as distressed with the general population. He disliked their rigid observance of the Sabbath – 'The Islanders are as much shocked as the Scotch at any desecration of the Sabbath' – which seemed to have no effect upon levels of honesty.[31]

'I am thoroughly disgusted with the Skerries people' he wrote in a letter to Alder, 'Humphrey tried to fleece the poor sailors, and

gave us before leaving his 'little account' with a most sancti-
monious face. Fancy his charging 5s for every day he went for a
cruise – i.e. counting the evening going out and the early morning
returning as two separate days, for doing nothing but *pretending*
to take us to good ground and eating our grub. He never touched
a rope'. He had no better luck with the new lighthouse keeper,
Laughton: 'I gave his wife two pounds for her services and her
daughter 5s for washing a few clothes – besides some stores and
whisky for her husband. She, as well as all the other people,
expressed herself thankful for the remuneration, but to my
astonishment I received last Saturday by post a letter from the
fellow saying that his wife was not satisfied and sending me an a
'account'. . . . The items in this precious 'account' are enough to
provoke a saint much less a disappointed dredger . . . I shall
never go to the Out Skerries again'. Worst of all, perhaps, was the
offence to his *amour propre*. A lecture he gave at the Free Church
in Lerwick on the marine fauna of the Shetlands, in which he
quoted Cicero, Dryden and Sir Francis Bacon, met with a cool
response. It was a case, he remarked unreasonably, of 'throwing
pearls'.[32]

In spite of difficult weather, problems with charters, and the
acquisitiveness of impoverished natives, on balance the Shetland
expeditions were successful. The dredges had been able to work
to depths of 170 fathoms and only the extremely poor weather of
1868 had prevented them from going deeper. Over the six years
of the expeditions, 156 species had been added to the list of
British fauna. The most important in Jeffreys' eyes were seven
species of living molluscs that he believed were known before
only from the Coralline Crag strata in Suffolk. He regarded them
as evidence of 'a prior state of things', that is as support for the
argument that species may have evolved through time but were
separate or discrete creations. By the summer of 1868, however,
Jeffreys concluded that the Shetland work had reached the point
of diminishing returns. In his last letter to Norman from Shetland
he wrote that despite frustrations taxing enough to make a saint
swear 'I shall regret exceedingly leaving this place forever'.[33] It
was, however, time to explore deeper waters. All dredging in the
Shetlands, as in Europe in general, had been on the continental
shelf, the drowned edge of the continent where the sea is rela-

tively shallow. Exploration in deeper waters had been discouraged, ironically, by an observation made by Edward Forbes when dredging in the Aegean in 1841/42. He declared that as a result of huge pressures, the scarcity or absence of light, cold temperatures, and the absence of suspended food particles, the azoic or lifeless zone began at about 300 fathoms.[34] This may have been more or less true of the part of the Aegean basin in which he was working but so reasonable was the argument and so unassailable Forbes' reputation that, despite evidence to the contrary, the assumption became a doctrine that was applied to all the oceans.

By 1860, however, it was evident that the assumed lifelessness of the deep seas was patently not true. Small tube-shaped samples of the bottom obtained during soundings for the laying of the transatlantic telegraph cable suggested that over large areas minute shell-covered creatures, *foraminifera,* lived at great depths. Telling, too, were the starfish, 'convulsively embracing' a sounding line, payed out too liberally, that had lain on the ocean floor at a depth of more than 1200 fathoms. As early as 1818 Sir John Ross, exploring in Baffin Bay, brought up in his 'deep sea clamm', an ingenious sounding machine of his own invention, several pounds of fine greenish mud that contained worms living at depths of a thousand fathoms.[35] These and other findings led his nephew and fellow Arctic explorer Sir James Clark Ross to declare emphatically that 'contrary to the general belief of naturalists, I have no doubt that from however great a depth we may be enabled to bring up the mud and stones of the bed of the ocean we shall find them teeming with animal life; the extreme pressure at the greatest depth does not appear to affect these creatures'. The perception grew that, far from being lifeless deserts, the deep-sea basins were a new field for zoological discovery – for naturalists, a true *terra incognita.*

In 1867, two exploratory cruises confirmed what was now widely supposed. In the United States Count Louis F. de Pourtales, an officer with the U.S. Coastal Survey, conducted a series of deep-sea dredgings across the Gulf Stream between Cuba and the Florida Keys. He found evidence of abundant deep-sea life below 300 fathoms. A year earlier Professor Michael Sars and his son George Ossian Sars of Sweden had dredged, with similar results, as deep as 450 fathoms near the Lofoten Islands off the northwest coast of Norway. C. Wyville Thompson travelled to Norway to examine the Sars' specimens and was so impressed that he persuaded fellow marine zoologist W. B. Carpenter, with whom he had worked off the coast of Ireland, that they should do some deep-sea exploration of their own. Carpenter, an eminent biologist as well as a marine zoologist, was both a vice president of the Royal Society and registrar of London University. To settle the deep-sea question in the North Atlantic, Thompson suggested to Carpenter that, by working through the Council of the Royal Society, they might persuade the Admiralty to provide a vessel fitted with dredging gear and the required scientific equipment.

In their approach to the president and council of the Society they emphasized that no individual or group of individuals could afford to carry out investigations on the scale required. Professor Sars had use of a Swedish government vessel and a trained crew.[36] Thompson and Carpenter had learned that a number of Royal Navy gun-boats and cruisers were then operating in northern and northwestern waters and they wondered if one of these might be placed at their disposal. They also inferred that because speed was not a requirement they were looking for a workhorse, equipped with a donkey engine for pulling up the dredge, not a thoroughbred. The proposed dredging area lay between the Shetlands and the Faroe Islands, and from there as far northwest toward Iceland as time and weather allowed. Convinced of the importance of the research, the Lords Commissioners of the Admiralty placed the *Lightning*, a small gun vessel, at the disposal of the Society. They also took the naturalists at their word. The *Lightning* was no thoroughbred. Thompson described it as 'a cranky little vessel, which had the somewhat doubtful title to respect of being perhaps the very oldest paddle-steamer in her Majesty's navy'.

In deplorable weather that persisted for most of the six weeks of the cruise, the crew of the leaky and barely seaworthy *Lightning* managed only ten days of dredging and of these only four were at depths of more than 500 fathoms. Yet in spite of the few opportunities for dredging, the cruise had demonstrated that not only microscopic foraminifera but higher forms of marine life (sponges, rhizopods, echinoderms, crustaceans and molluscs) many of which were not previously known, could live on the deep-sea floor.[37] The azoic hypothesis had been conclusively disproved. On the practical level, the cruise had also demonstrated that with the aid of a donkey engine and an experienced captain there were virtually no limits to the depths that could be dredged.

Encouraged by the results of the *Lightning* expedition, the Council of the Royal Society resolved at their January meeting 1869 that deep-sea explorations should be continued and conducted over a wider area. All depended, however, on continued Admiralty support. A month later the Committee on Marine Researches, of which Carpenter and Gwyn Jeffreys were members, presented to Council a report that could be used as the basis for a fresh submission to the Admiralty. The authors asserted that in spite of atrocious weather and want of a custom-made vessel, the cruise of the *Lightning* had demonstrated beyond doubt that the ocean below 500 fathoms offered a vast field for research in the physical, biological and geological sciences. The form of the ocean floor, the amount of light available at great depths, the temperature of the water, its chemical composition, and the nature of organic life were largely unknowns. While the Royal Society could supply equipment and scientific personnel, a suitable vessel and crew were far beyond its means.

Convinced by the argument, the Admiralty acquiesced and undertook to provide Her Majesty's surveying-vessel *Porcupine*, a 382-ton converted gunboat, for the 1869 and 1870 sailing seasons.[38] The *Porcupine* had been fitted up for the surveying service off the north and east coasts of Britain and, unlike the *Lightning*, it was thoroughly seaworthy. From long experience in the coastal survey, Captain Calver and his officers and men were well used to handling scientific equipment and, hardly less important in north Atlantic waters, inured to rough seas, uncertain weather and interminable delays. Most of the crew were Shetlanders. They spent the summer under Captain Calver's command but in winter, when the vessel was laid up and the officers busy writing reports at their Sunderland headquarters, they returned home.

To organize and conduct the 1869 and 1870 explorations the Royal Society appointed a three-man scientific committee: Dr W. B. Carpenter, Gwyn Jeffreys and Professor C. Wyville Thompson. Jeffreys had retired from the Bar in 1866 and apart from duties as legal and financial adviser to the Linnaean and Geological Societies he was free to collect and conduct research. As the *Porcupine* would cover more ground in greater detail and over a longer period (mid May to mid September) than the *Lightning*, they decided that each member of the working committee should have an assistant trained in the use of microscopes and chemical apparatus, and that the chartroom of the vessel be fitted up as a temporary laboratory. Because Carpenter and Thompson had university duties that prevented them from devoting the entire summer to research, the three naturalists settled on three separate cruises. The first, between 18 May and 13 July, would be conducted by Jeffreys with W. Lant Carpenter, chemist and eldest son of W. B. Carpenter, as his scientific assistant. Captain Calver would be responsible for the operation of the dredge but the handling of the dredged materials would be the responsibility of assistants chosen by Jeffreys: Mr. B. S. Dodd and Mr. Laughrin of Polperro. Laughrin, an old coastguard man and an associate of the Linnaean Society, would organize the handling and sifting of the material and Dodd would pick out, clean, and store the specimens. Both men worked on all three cruises.

The survey area for the first cruise extended for 450 miles along the Atlantic coasts of Ireland and Scotland, from Cape Clear to Rockall, including the deep channel between the British continental shelf and the Rockall Bank. West of Galway the Atlantic deepens rapidly from 150 to 1500 fathoms. The *Porcupine* dredged first in 110 fathoms about 40 miles off Valentia and, after coaling at Galway, steamed south again into very coarse weather and dredged in Dingle Bay at 30-40 fathoms. As on the *Osprey* when dredging in relatively shallow water off the Shetlands, the *Porcupine* had two dredges out, one in the bow and the other in the stern. The following week, however, when sounding and dredging between Valentia and Galway at depths ranging from 88-808 fathoms, she dredged only from the stern. The 808 fathom dredge was, Jefferys believed, a new record. The 1110 fathoms of rope paid out by Captain Calver took 55 minutes to haul back in, roughly five minutes for every 100 fathoms of rope. The reward was two hundredweight of soft, sticky mud that resembled 'China clay'.

After coaling at Killibegs in Co. Donegal the *Porcupine* steamed

Stern derrick of the Porcupine *showing the dredge. The accumulator
and the method of stowing the ropes. The accumulator indicated
the amount of strain when the vessel was pitching.*

west toward Rockall, 200 miles from the nearest land, coals
packed on the decks as well as in the bunkers in anticipation of a
two-week cruise. In the ocean deep between the edge of the
continental shelf and the Rockall Bank, the *Porcupine* dredged
for seven days at depths of more than 1200 fathoms. The greatest
depth reached was 1476 fathoms and even at this level the dredge

brought up several living molluscs in the fine, clayey mud. Before each dredge Captain Calver, who even at the greatest depths could feel the arrest of the weight upon the ocean floor, sounded the bottom. To haul the dredge the *Porcupine* had been fitted with a double-cylinder 12 horsepower donkey engine equipped with surging drums of different sizes: a large drum for bringing up light weights very rapidly and smaller drums for the slower, heavy work. The engine, which was set up amidships so that the dredge and sounding lines could be led to drums placed either fore or aft, proved to be a model of reliability.

From strong derricks rigged over the bow and stern it brought in the sounding line and the dredge rope, no matter what the weight on the latter, at a uniform rate of one foot per second. The bow derrick was the stronger and, when dredging at depth, the one usually dredged from. To overcome the buoying effect of the great length of dredge line paid out, the dredge was a massive 225 pounds of wrought iron. To it was attached a bag of coarse canvas 4.5 feet wide but only six inches deep at the throat. Surrounding it was a bag of strong twine netting. To prevent the dredge from sinking into the bottom mud like an anchor, and to ensure that the scrapers and the mouth of the dredge addressed the bottom at an angle that scraped rather than dug into the bottom, Captain Calver attached heavy iron weights to the rope at a distance of 300-400 fathoms from the dredge. By dredging from the weights rather than the ship, the dredge met the bottom at a more acute angle.[39]

The first *Porcupine* voyage had so far exceeded expectations in terms of the depth of dredging and the existence of animal life, that it forced changes in the direction of the second cruise led by Professor Wyville Thompson. The first cruise suggested that there was no depth at which animal life could not exist. Captain Calver of the *Porcupine* was so confident of his ability to dredge at depths even greater than those reached so far that he applied to the Hydrographer for permission to dredge to 2500 fathoms, 250 miles west of Ushant. If life were found at these depths it could safely be assumed that animal life had no bathymetrical limit. The Hydrographer granted the request and on 17 July the *Porcupine* steamed out of Belfast. The weather was remarkably fine and on 22 July at 47 N and 12 W soundings were taken at a depth of 2435 fathoms. Late that afternoon Captain Calver lowered a dredge. The *Porcupine*'s dredge rope was 3000 fathoms long, nearly 3.5 statute miles, and of this 2000 fathoms were 'hawser-laid' of the best Russian hemp 2.5 inches in circumference. The 1000 fathoms next to the dredge had a circumference of two inches. Russian hemp is not as strong as wire or manilla rope but it was more flexible and less likely to break if the rope were 'kinked'. From start to finish, the dredging operation took seven to eight hours. The ooze contained fresh examples of invertebrate life; the soft parts were perfectly fresh and showed every sign of having been alive when they entered the dredge.

The following year, 1870, the *Porcupine* made two cruises, one in the Atlantic conducted by Gwyn Jeffreys and the other in the Mediterranean conducted by Dr Carpenter. The Jeffreys cruise examined the seabed between Falmouth and the Strait of Gibraltar in a line that took the vessel along the west coasts of Spain and Portugal. The dredges were shallower than in the previous year but no less interesting. In one haul at 994 fathoms off the coast of Portugal no fewer than 186 species of shells were brought up, of which 71 were previously undescribed, while 24 were known only as fossils.

Although Jeffreys professed to 'detest the sea for its own sake', putting up with its discomforts only 'for the sake of science or natural history', he could never resist an expedition.[40] When plans for an Admiralty expedition to Baffin Bay and the Arctic became known, in 1874/75, Jeffreys volunteered to go along as a scientific observer. Carpenter wrote to the president of the Royal Society, suggesting that the Admiralty be requested to place a naturalist aboard the supply ship that would accompany the Arctic vessels as far as Disco Island in Baffin Bay. There would be little time for scientific observation on the outward voyage, but on the slower return there would be opportunities for systematic sounding and dredging in seas about which very little was known. In the letter Carpenter informed the president that Gwyn Jeffreys had offered his services. Apart from accommodation his only requirements were a donkey engine and dredge, some scientific equipment, and a paid assistant. In its application to the Admiralty, which was duly granted, the Society offered to pay the assistant and provide the scientific equipment.[41]

The store ship, the *Valorous*, was a large paddle-wheel steamer of 1247 tons which, when in service, accommodated a crew of 248 officers, men and marines, and six guns. For the Arctic voyage the guns had been removed to make room for extra cabins. It had also been fitted with a donkey engine, a dredge, sounding equipment and, as Jeffreys put it, 'a goodly supply of ropes'. Laden with coal and provisions and accompanied by the *Alert* and the *Discovery*, the Arctic vessels, the *Valorous* left Spithead on 29 May. It touched at Cork to post letters for the squadron and to take on more coal, and there parted company with the Arctic vessels until the *rendezvous* in Greenland. With heavy weather and persistent northwest winds that sometimes reduced speed to a few knots, virtually no scientific work was possible on the outward voyage. Between two and three hundred miles east of Cape Farewell, the southern tip of Greenland, they caught in a towing net some floating masses of pulpy greenish matter which at first looked like sponge but was later identified as an undescribed diatom and named *Synedra Jeffreysi*. At Godhavn on the west coast of Greenland where the *Valorous* transferred coal and provisions to the Arctic ships, they were able to dredge from one of the ship's cutters at depths up to 80 fathoms.

The results were interesting, because Jeffreys was able to observe in their native habitat Arctic mollusca which at home he had been able to study only as fossils, in post tertiary and glacial deposits. On land he found *Vitrina pellucida* among moss and various water plants at the sides of small streams formed by melting ice. But these land finds came at the price of persistent wet and foggy weather, a bleak, treeless landscape and, when the sun did shine, molestation by mosquitoes and blackflies.

At Godhavn, Jeffreys saw his first 'esquimaux', a colony of about one hundred strong, some living in two-room sod and board huts and others in low sod dwellings that were entered on hands and knees via long tunnels. Like all Arctic settlements, it 'swarmed' with dogs.[42] From Godhavn the *Valorous* sailed north to the Danish settlement of Rittenbank in Waigat Strait and from there to Kulbrud, where the crew dug lignite coal from the Miocene strata that made up the cliffs. Jeffreys was able to do some dredging near the cliffs and, as at Godhavn, he found no diminution of life. They then sailed north through the strait at the

The Valorous *parting from the* Alert *and the* Discovery.

upper end of Disco Island into Baffin Bay where they did their
first dredging at 175 fathoms. His assistant Herbert Carpenter did
the sifting, using a nested sets of five sieves in large tubs, and
Jeffreys did the sorting and classifying using, as supplements to
more professional apparatus, soup plates, jam pots and glass
bottles. Their work area was a small enclosure, made from sail
and ropes, on the foredeck. They did more dredging on their way
south down the east coast of Davis Strait but on 27 July, when
edging their way through fog into the natural harbour at Holstein-
borg to take on ballast, they ran onto a sunken reef of rocks not
marked on the charts.

The ship was eventually freed by the rising tide and made
safely for Holsteinborg where divers examined the hull and were
able to fix iron plates over the holed sections. During the week-
long delay, some of the officers went trout fishing ashore and on
neighbouring islands and brought back specimens of molluscs
and crabs. They left Holsteinborg on 8 August and did not touch
land again until they reached Plymouth. On their way south they

sounded and dredged at more than a thousand fathoms in the Davis Strait but on the 12 August they were obliged, ominously, to keep the pumps going day and night. On 14 August they sounded and dredged at 1450 fathoms at the entrance to the Davis Strait and on the 19 August at the same depth in the North Atlantic. The last sounding and dredging, producing a 'good load of ooze' but not much else, was on 23 August at 1785 fathoms.

The following day an Atlantic gale struck and the injured vessel had to be battened down and the pumps worked continuously. On 29 August, with only eleven out of twenty stations in the Admiralty programme examined, the *Valorous* docked at Plymouth. Jeffreys was clearly disappointed and in his report to the Royal Society he asserted that a little advance planning by the Admiralty might have forestalled the need for taking on ballast at Holstein-borg and thus prevented the grounding. The few dredges in Baffin Bay and the Davis Strait, however, had been worthwhile and the soundings taken in the North Atlantic almost connected with those taken by the *Porcupine* west of Ireland. They were meagre results for a three-month voyage, but they demonstrated that not even icebergs and frigid waters were proof against the vitality of submarine life.

Despite ice, near shipwreck, and a perennial dislike of the sea, Jeffreys still had not finished with deep-sea exploration. He dredged in Norway with A. M. Norman in 1878 and in 1880, at the request of the French government, he and Norman joined a

The Alert *towing the* Discovery *through icebergs.*

111

French expedition (on *Le Travailleur*) to dredge in the deep waters off the Bay of Biscay. In his report on the *Valorous* expedition, he acknowledged that a lifetime of dredging amounted only to the scraping, 'in an imperfect manner' the surface of a few score of acres of ocean floor – an effort that offered 'a mere glimpse of that 'wonderland' which underlies the vast ocean'.[43] Yet however limited his understanding of the ocean floor, he was now the acknowledged British authority on molluscs and when Darwin needed to identify a particular freshwater bivalve mollusc he turned automatically to Jeffreys. Darwin had been asked to verify whether the species in question might have been dispersed by individual molluscs attaching themselves to the legs of water beetles. To identify the mollusc, Darwin sent it in a glass container to Ware Priory, Jeffreys' Hertfordshire home after his retirement from the Bar. Jeffreys, however, was in Italy at the time and on being informed of this Darwin wrote to Jeffreys' housekeeper to ask if she would return the container and shell. He assumed that she would pack it carefully but when he opened the parcel he found a mixture of glass shards and shell fragments.

In an article on Gwyn Jeffreys and Edward Forbes, Professor Eric Mills raises the question of the degree of Jeffreys' interest in marine life and the marine environment.[44] Was he truly interested in molluscs and their habitats or was he, as Professor Mills suggests, a compulsive collector who cloaked the narrowness of his interests in a mantle of marine scholarship? The evidence he cites are Jeffreys' letters from the Shetlands to Joshua Alder and Alfred Merle Norman. They are dominated by descriptions of the specimens found, the weather, and the unreliability and deviousness of the Shetlanders. In short, they are the reports of a hunter and gatherer. There are few references to habitat, or to the geographical distribution of molluscs, and no speculation about possible connections between British and Norwegian species, questions that had preoccupied Edward Forbes. The letters, however, were written as diaries of record but all are discursive and, had Jeffreys been so inclined, there would have been ample time and space for general observations and speculation.

Against the narrow interests of the letters must be weighed the broad scholarship of *British Conchology*, his interest in the Teredines, his defence of species boundaries in the Darwinian debate and his more than one hundred published papers and commentaries on molluscs and deep sea dredging.[45] He was not of course the kind of narrow collector to whom context did not matter, but it may be fair to say that his other interests flowed from his need to collect. Jeffreys made no secret of his dislike of the sea, and of his greater interest in the shells than the anatomy and physiology of molluscs, but if the reward was an 'exquisite Margarita' then even Shetland weather and seas were worth braving.[46] If Eric Mills is right, and Gwyn Jeffreys was at heart a collector and classifier then, to return to a Swansea context, it suggests that you may remove the boy from Dillwyn but you can never remove Dillwyn from the boy.

NOTES

1. RISW, Letters, John Gwyn Jeffreys to Lewis Weston Dillwyn, 1 September 1828.
2. John Gwyn Jeffreys, *British Conchology*, Vol. 1 (London , 1862), preface vi.
3. RISW, Letters, undated. See also David Dykes, *The University College of Swansea*, 35.
4. Quoted by Colin Matheson, 'John Gwyn Jeffreys, a Famous Glamorgan Naturalist', *Glamorgan Historian*, 8 (1972), 29-35.
5. *Alder-Norman Correspondence*, 1826-1911, 7 Vols. (London, British Museum, Natural History, 1963), #61. Joshua Alder to Alfred Merle Norman, 26 January 1862.
6. Ibid., #91. Joshua Alder to A. M. Norman, 12 April 1864.
7. Ibid., #117. Joshua Alder to A. M. Norman, 12 December 1865.
8. Ibid., #91. Joshua Alder to A. M. Norman, 12 April 1864.
9. Ibid., #61. Joshua Alder to A. M. Norman, 26 January 1862.
10. Ibid., #1045. A. M. Norman to Joshua Alder, 23 June 1862.
11. *Cambrian* (20 May 1864).
12. Jeffreys, *British Conchology*, 1, Intro. xxii-xxiii.
13. Jeffreys, *British Conchology*, 2, 381.
14. Jeffreys, *British Conchology*, 1, Intro. cxiii
15. Ibid., Intro. xxii, xc-xciii.
16. *Cambrian* (30 January 1863).
17. In a lecture on deep-sea exploration Jeffreys quoted the marine zoologist C. Wyville Thompson: 'In this, as in all cases in which it has been possible to bring the question, however remotely, to the test of observation, the character of the abyssal fauna refuses to give the least support to the theory which refers the evolution of species to extreme variation guided only by natural selection'. 'Deep-Sea Exploration', *Nature* 23 (1881), 1-20.
18. Jeffreys, *British Conchology*, 1, Intro. xc-xci.

19. Ibid., Intro. lxii-lxiii, lxx1-lxii.
20. Jeffreys, *British Conchology*, 5, 229-234.
21. Jeffreys, *British Conchology*, 2, 110-111.
22. Jeffreys, *British Conchology*, 3, 122-175.
23. For copper sheathing see Gareth Rees, 'Copper sheathing: an example of technological diffusion in the English merchant fleet', *Journal of Transport History*, 1 (1971-2), 85-94; and J. R. Harris, 'Copper and shipping in the eighteenth century', *Economic History Review*, 29, (1966), 550-68.
24. 'Mr Jeffreys on the Teredines', Abstract of a communication to the Oxford B.A.A.S. Meeting, 1860, *Annals Mag. Natural. History*, August (1860), 6-11.
25. Jeffreys, *British Conchology*, 3, Intro. x.
26. J Gwyn Jeffreys, On the Marine Testacea of the Piedmontese Coast, *Annals Mag. Natural History*, Series 2, 17: 155-188; repr. in *Gleanings in British Conchology* (London, 1858).
27. Simon J. Knell, *Culture of English Geology*, 6.
28. *Alder-Norman Correspondence*, #1054-55. Norman to Joshua Alder, 1 June 1863.
29. Ibid., #737. Jeffreys to Joshua Alder, 2 June 1864.
30. Ibid., Jeffreys to Joshua Alder, #739, June 1864.
31. Ibid., #734. Jeffreys to Joshua Alder, 24 May 1864.
32. Ibid., #726. Jeffreys to Joshua Alder, 20 July 1861.
33. Ibid., #788, Jeffreys to Alfred Merle Norman, 30 July 1868.
34. Jeffreys, *British Conchology*, 3, Intro, viii.
35. C. Wyville Thompson, *The Depths of the Sea* (London, 1873), 209-210.
36. Ibid., 'The Cruise of the *Lightning*', 49-81.
37. Margaret Deacon, *Scientists and the Sea 1650-1900* (London, 1971), 307-310.
38. For a report of the preliminary proceedings and of the expedition itself see *Proceedings of the Royal Society*, 121, 397-490, and C. Wyville Thompson, *Depths of the Sea*, 83-137. Expeditions in which Jeffreys participated were also reported in the *Cambrian*. See 24 December 1869.
39. C. Wyville Thompson, *Depths of the Sea*, 237-255.
40. *Alder-Norman Correspondence*, #804. Jeffreys to Alfred Merle Norman, 15 July 1870.
41. J. Gwyn Jeffreys, 'Preliminary Report of the Biological Results of a Cruise in H.M.S. *Valorous* to Davis Strait in 1875', *Proceedings of the Royal Society*, 173, 1876, 177-237.
42. 'News of the Arctic Expedition', *Illustrated London News* (11 September 1875), 186.
43. Ibid.
44. Eric L Mills, 'Edward Forbes, John Gwyn Jeffreys, and British dredging before the Challenger Expedition', *Socy. Biblphy. Nat. Hist.* 8, 4, (1978): 507-536.
45. For a complete list of Jeffreys' published works see 'The Contributions of Welshmen to Science', *Trans. Hon. Soc. Cymmrodorion* (1932-33), 106-111.
46. *Alder-Norman Correspondence*, #731. Jeffreys to Joshua Alder, 20 July 1864.

HENRY DE LA BECHE FRS
1796-1855

Geologist
Founding Director of the Geological Survey
of Great Britain

At a meeting in Swansea convened in April 1838 for 'Gentlemen interested in the erection of a building for an Institution and Museum' was the director of the nascent Geological Survey of Great Britain, the first ever national geological survey. Henry De la Beche attended the meeting probably at the request of Lewis Weston Dillwyn, the president of Swansea's Philosophical and Literary Institution, whom he had known for fifteen years. Both were fellows of the Royal Society and the Geological Society, and on Dillwyn's visits to Bristol he and De la Beche attended meetings of the city's Philosophical Society and, accompanied by the geologist William Daniel Conybeare, had taken occasional geological rambles. Both men, also, were friends of William Buckland, the Oxford geologist. In the early 1820s De la Beche and Conybeare had been heavily involved in planning a building for the Bristol Philosophical Society so it is likely that De la Beche would have attended the Swansea meeting even without encouragement from Dillwyn. He had been in Swansea for four months setting up his headquarters for the mapping of the mineral basin of south Wales, the next stage in the national Geological Survey.

Always conscious, too, of the political need to justify the Survey he seldom missed an opportunity to promote its economic benefits – of demonstrating, as he put it, how natural history could be turned to profitable account. The Swansea meeting of course was a gathering of the converted, and when invited to speak he had little need to preach. He emphasized the need for both a lecture hall and a museum; these were standard equipment for all philosophical societies and as a geologist he hoped that

Henry De la Beche.

lectures on palaeontology and mineralogy would encourage members to donate fossil and mineral specimens. These would be useful not only to the Survey geologists but also to miners and mining engineers who could compare them with similar specimens from other coal basins. At the meeting he was invited to join the organizing and planning committee and the following July he was elected an honorary member of the Institution. Swansea and the Royal Institution had landed a very large fish.[1]

When England and Wales had only two universities, and neither offering mainstream classes in geology, geologists were largely self taught. For those with means, influence and access to London, probably the best instruction available at the time were the lectures and discussions at the Geological Society of London.[2] Geology required no special equipment or apparatus and until the 1840s its literature was well within the grasp of the well-read person. For enthusiasts, the chief requirements were a reasonable degree of leisure, a sound pair of legs, and the means for at least a little travelling. De la Beche qualified on all counts. Like most of the early geologists, he was of the privileged or gentlemanly class.

He was born in Wimpole Street, London, in 1796, the son of Thomas Beach, a Brevet Major in the Norfolk Fencible Cavalry regiment and a man of some social pretension. Although descended from a long line of respectable land-owning Wiltshire Beaches, he insisted that his true forebears were Norman barons who by the fourteenth century had settled in Aldworth, Berkshire. He exchanged, by Royal Sign Manual, the native Beach for the exotic De la Beche.[3] Thomas De la Beche inherited from his father, who was also Thomas Beach, the 4,500-acre Halse Hall sugar estate in Clarendon, Jamaica. The father, a former Chief Justice of Jamaica, had acquired the estate through marriage. In 1800 Thomas De la Beche took his wife Elizabeth and their son Henry on a lengthy and, for him, fateful visit to the colony. He died from an unspecified fever in June of the following year and four months later Henry, the only son and now owner, in trust, of the estate, returned to England with his mother.

Schooling seems to have been erratic, the place determined by his mother's domicile after her remarriage. It began in Hammersmith in 1802 and from there shifted to Keynsham, near Bristol, in 1805, and to Ottery St Mary's, Devon, in 1808. At Keynsham he met and befriended the cleric and geologist William Daniel Conybeare, co-author in 1822 of *Outlines of the Geology of England and Wales*. In 1809/10 De la Beche enrolled at the Royal Military College, Great Marlow, where, like all young cadets, he learned to draw 'ground'. Drawing ground, or topography, was regarded as a necessary preliminary to laying out the defences of a site, forcing cadets who might not be instinctive warriors to examine, and not just look at, the lay of the land. The founder of the college, Major-General le Marchant, was an accomplished landscape painter.

Henry De la Beche had both a keen eye and a gifted hand, and at Great Marlow he acquired the habit of sketching that he practiced throughout his life. For a field geologist, as his friend Conybeare remarked in his obituary notice, it was a particularly useful accomplishment. '[At Great Marlow] he first exhibited those powers of the pencil and that facility of sketching the physical features of ground which so materially favoured his success in subsequent pursuits and obligations'.[4] Had it not been an obituary, Conybeare might have added that sketching was also a useful accomplishment for a young man who enjoyed baiting his peers. De la Beche's weapons were the caricature and the cartoon and he seldom hesitated to use them. Conybeare was also circumspect in the matter of De la Beche's military career, which proved to be short-lived, and his private life, which seems to have been eventful. De la Beche liked women and women quite clearly liked him.

He was handsome, successful and, in middle life, unattached. To these attractions he could add an aristocratic name and, so some fancied, French manners. In *Memories of Old Friends*, Caroline Fox left this intriguing vignette: 'Falmouth, April 7. – Sir Charles Lemon, John Enys, and Henry De la Beche came to luncheon. The last-named is a very entertaining person, his manners rather French, his conversation spirited and full of illustrative anecdote. He looks about forty – a handsome but careworn face, brown eyes and hair, and gold spectacles. He exhibited and explained the geological maps of Devon and Cornwall, which he is now perfecting for the Ordnance'.[5] In his European journal, written during an extended honeymoon in 1819/20, De la Beche confessed in light verse, accompanied by a sketch of a ringletted, Mediterranean beauty, to the fatal attraction:

> *I like the women too! Forgive my folly!*
> *From the rich peasant-cheek of ruddy bronze,*
> *And large black eyes that flash on you a volley*
> *Of rays that say a thousand things at once.*[6]

Conybeare's explanation for the brevity of De la Beche's military career, that may well have been his subject's invention, is simply a gloss: 'Notwithstanding the charms of society, to which he was by no means insensible', [the military] could not have satisfied such an 'active and inquiring mind' especially at a time, he continued, when Europe was on the threshold of a prolonged peace. Conybeare's inference is that De la Beche sacrificed a dashing, if peaceful, military career for a life of the mind. But the truth was otherwise, and more interesting. Shortly after his entry into the junior department of the college, the adjutant general warned of the rise of a 'dangerous spirit of Jacobinism'. An anonymous

118

pamphlet, described as 'rebellious', was followed by insubordinate behaviour that threatened 'consequences of the most alarming nature'. The author of the pamphlet remained unnamed, but De la Beche was one of the insubordinates whose conduct was judged to have fallen well short of 'the utmost deference and respect' due to civil professors and military officers. A few of the rebellious cadets escaped the ultimate official sanction but Cadet De la Beche was among those who, in October 1811, the Commander-in-Chief was 'pleased to direct . . . shall be immediately sent away from the College'.[7]

Expulsion from Great Marlow seems to have spelled the end of his formal schooling. According to a one-page curriculum vitae in a diary discovered in the 1970s, the year 1811 found him in Dawlish, and 1812 in Charmouth and Lyme Regis, the heart of the Lias fossil country on the south coast of England. At Lyme Regis he met the legendary Mary Anning, then only 12 or 13 years old who, with her mother, made a living by searching for fossils on the shore, in winter cliff falls, and in nearby quarries and selling them to collectors and gentleman geologists. Close to the beach at Lyme Regis they had, as one visitor described it, a 'tiny, old curiosity shop' with a window filled with 'the most remarkable petrifactions and fossil remains'. Mary, who became an extraordinarily well-informed supplier, is reputed to have been the subject of the sibilant 'She sells sea-shells on the sea-shore'. Her meeting with De la Beche was the beginning of a lifelong association, if not friendship.

To boost sales when Mary's income began to decline in the 1830s, De la Beche drew a cartoon, *Dura antiquior*, in which he reconstructed the fauna and flora of the Liassic period. The vegetation is tropical and lush and the monsters, several wearing disarming half-smiles, seem deceptively good-natured. It was made into a lithograph and sold to members of the Geological Society of London. De la Beche was one of the few geologists who regularly acknowledged the importance of her work and when she was dying he arranged, as president of the Geological Society, for her election as an honorary member. On her death in 1847 he wrote the obituary notice for the Society's *Proceedings*.

As a young man of means De la Beche, unlike Mary Anning and the other fossil gatherers, had no need to make a living. His majority gave him direct access to the income, about £3,000 annually, from his Jamaican estate and he was free to follow his interests. He collected fossils, studied local and regional geology and cultivated naturalists, among them William Daniel Conybeare and William Buckland. In 1817 he was elected a member of the Geological Society and in 1819, following the publication of a geological memoir on part of the south coast of England, of the Royal Society. His private income allowed him to marry and travel, the latter seen as essential to the education of a young geologist. He married Letitia Whyte in 1818 and in 1819/20 the couple, accompanied by Letitia's mother and several servants, toured the continent for twelve months. A daughter, Bessie, was born in Geneva in 1819.

During the tour, De la Beche kept detailed diaries in which he recorded meteorological and geological observations and drew sketches and cartoons of social life and customs. On their return the De la Beches settled in London but Henry, unable to resist the fossils in the Lias, made frequent visits to Dorset. In 1821 he wrote, with Conybeare, a detailed paper for the Geological Society on the icthyosaurus, a remarkable seventeen foot long fish-lizard discovered by Mary Anning. The previous year he and Conybeare had announced the discovery of a new fossil, the pleiosaurus ('a turtle threaded through the body of a snake', in Buckland's description), that they interpreted as a link between the icthyosaurus and the crocodile. In 1822 he completed the fieldwork for a map of southern Pembrokeshire in which he used methods of illustration that would be adopted by the Geological Survey. The following year, during a thirteen-month visit to Jamaica, he braved dense tropical vegetation to survey the bedrock and alluvial deposits of the eastern half of the island. On the Island he followed a disciplined regime, rising early, plunging into a tubful of cold water, and riding for several miles before breakfast. His account of the Island geology, 'Remarks on the geology of Jamaica', was read before the Geological Society and published later as a monograph. It was the first modern account of the geology of Jamaica.

On his return to London he also published (in 1824) 'Notes on the present condition of the negroes in Jamaica'. As a plantation owner of liberal tendencies he was uneasy about his role as slave-owner and absentee landlord. In December 1818 he noted in his diary that Maria Edgeworth's novel, *The Absentee*, about Irish landlords living in England, had made him think deeply about his own absence from Jamaica.[8] A letter to Conybeare from Jamaica, expressing his disquiet about slave-owning, triggered an anti-slavery diatribe. Jamaica, fulminated Conybeare, was a 'land of physical and moral pestilence' and he had no doubt that De la Beche would do his best to improve matters 'especially with regard to the education and good treatment of the slaves'. As De la Beche lived on the income from the plantation, his views on abolition were understandably mixed. Like St Augustine in his desire for celibacy, he wanted abolition – but not immediately: 'You know', he wrote to Conybeare, 'that I am a well-wisher to the slave population, but I wish their condition to be gradually bettered, not suddenly'. In the slavery debate a distinction was made between the traffic in slaves and the continued ownership of them. Where the slaves were not being physically abused, gradual emancipation was seen as a tenable position. Without intending to suggest that slaves in general were treated well, De la Beche contended that the two hundred on his plantation were better off materially than the peasants in some of the European countries he had visited. And, with his fondness for baiting authority, he added that he would like to produce in Parliament some of his Halse Hall people after 'some fine long-winded speech . . . about the condition of the negroes'.[9]

On the Halse Hall estate he did introduce reforms, substituting a bell and a bosun's whistle for whip-cracking as a means of summoning the slaves, and in the fields he resolved, apparently with success, to 'gradually . . . abolish the whip altogether'. To provide some schooling and raise levels of 'moral conduct' among his slaves – 'they cannot be brought without vast trouble to think of marrying' – he engaged Wesleyan missionaries.[10] As a reward for good conduct he had two medals struck, one inscribed with a profile of H. T. De la Beche that later was replaced with a sketch of the Halse Hall estate. Good conduct medals of course were hardly the answer to the problem of slave unrest, and he knew that failing some accommodation between abolitionists and plantation owners, he stood 'a very good chance of losing [his] property'.

Despite uncertainty about the future of his plantation and his own misgivings about slaveholding and absentee landlordship, by 1830 De la Beche had settled into the comfortable life of a gentleman geologist. Between 1831 and 1835 he published three books, *Geological Manual, How to Observe*, and the ambitious *Researches in Theoretical Geology*, 1834, in which he examined the contribution that geology could make to sciences such as chemistry and astronomy. The book presented no new theoretical systems or constructs, but Charles Lyell thought it was 'infinitely the best work De la Beche had done', and Roderick Impie Murchison that it was 'one of the cleverest and best written works we have ever had.'[11] But not even the blessings of two of the most eminent geologists of the day could boost sales. It sold fewer than a thousand copies over a dozen years. Much more successful were the instructional works *Geological Manual*, 1831, and *How to Observe*, 1835. The former proved so popular that there were English, French, German and American editions. Robert Jameson, Professor of Natural Philosophy at Edinburgh, also assigned it to his classes. For the preface to the determinedly non-theoretical *How to Observe,* De la Beche chose an uncompromising dictum by the poet Thomas Gray, for whom reverie and recollection in tranquility had no appeal: 'Half a word fixed upon, or near the spot, is worth a cart-load of recollection'.

Although not uninterested in theories and speculation about the origin and structure of the earth, which had dominated the early years of geology, De la Beche at heart was a working field geologist, an observer and 'hammerer' whose job it was to lay down a solid platform of fact. He wrote disapprovingly of earlier geologists who had been 'much more intent on making little worlds of their own, than examining the crust of that which they inhabit'. In other words, facts and reliable maps first, theory and speculation a very distant second. J. S. Flett, the historian of the Geological Survey, described him as 'a man of the type who likes to take a piece of complicated unmapped country and to follow its geological lines day by day, gradually unravelling the details of structure and filling it in bit by bit till he completes a scientific whole'.[12]

De la Beche's fears for the Halse Hall estate and his income were soon realised. The first Jamaican slaves were freed in the

1830s and the last in 1839. The plantation economy faltered and the sugar trade languished. Debts incurred by the estate at the time of his inheritance, which in prosperous times it had been able to carry, now became millstones and during De la Beche's lifetime it was never free of them. His income declined to the point that geology, which until then had been a consuming interest, now had to be looked upon as a means of support. In March 1832 he wrote to the Ordnance Survey proposing that he 'colour', or add geological information to, its new one-inch to the mile topographical maps of southern England. He explained that he had already begun work on a geological map of Devon but 'the failure of certain funds' had forced its abandonment. He offered, for a sum of three hundred pounds, to 'colour' each of the eight one-inch topographical maps of the county – a price, he emphasised 'that . . .will be much below the sum they will have cost me when completed'.[13] His timing could not have been better. Colonel Thomas F. Colby, the director of the Ordnance Survey, was keen to add archaeological and geological informa-tion to the topographical maps and during the previous year, Roderick Impey Murchison, voicing a sentiment held by most members of the Geological Society, had suggested that the Survey should add a geological wing to its operations.

Even without such strong support, De la Beche's offer was one that no budget-conscious government agency could ignore and he was duly appointed to the ad hoc position of geological surveyor within the Ordnance Survey. His fee was to be paid in instalments, at the completion of each of the eight maps, and any explanatory text would be published at his expense. Not even the maps would be officially published by the Survey, De la Beche having to arrange the publication and the price with the Survey's mapseller in London. They were tight-fisted arrangements and De la Beche would spend his stipend several times over before the completion of the project. But regarded as a claim on future employment it was a sound investment. For the foreseeable future, colouring Ordnance Survey maps would be his only source of income. Working alone, except for the help of 'an intelligent Cornish miner' who did the rough or commoner work in the latter stages of the survey, he spent the next four years in the lanes and fields of Devon and Cornwall examining outcrops and mapping boundaries, making note of any features that might be useful to both academic geologists and practical men: miners, farmers, and road, canal and railway builders, all of whom, as he phrased it, looked to science for 'useful applications'.

For the first two years his work for the Ordnance Survey went smoothly, without incident or surprises. But when working on little known rocks in the Greywacke or Transition zone below the Carboniferous in North Devon he found fossil plants in a layer of culm, or low grade anthracite. He sent a hamperful of the fossils and the host rock to William Londsdale, librarian and curator of the Geological Society, with instructions that they be sent to John Lindley, an eminent palaeobotanist and Professor of Botany at London University.[14] Lindley complained about the size of the sample but declared the fossils to be identical with the fossil plants of the Carboniferous Coal Measures.[15] As interesting discoveries, they were displayed at the December 1834 meeting of the Geological Society which De la Beche, unable to afford the journey to London, could not attend. A discovery that ordinarily would have interested or excited the members proved to be a bombshell. After the meeting George Bellas Greenough, president of the Society, wrote immediately to De la Beche: 'Your Bideford paper gave rise yesterday evening to a very animated discussion. Murchison led the attack and expressed astonishment that so experienced a Geologist should have fallen into so great a mistake – as to fancy that the specimens on the table had anything to do with transition rocks'.[16]

For several years Murchison had worked on the equivalent sedimentary rocks of Wales, below the Carboniferous series, which he assumed to be of the same age as the rocks in Devonshire. Murchison's rocks, which he would name Silurian, contained no coal and no obvious signs of plant life. Murchison placed great weight on fossil evidence as a means of dating and identifying strata, and without ever having investigated the rocks of the southwest he, supported by Charles Lyell, insisted that the fossil bearing rocks that De la Beche had identified as Transition or Greywacke must really be Coal Measures. In short, De la Beche had completely mistaken the character of the rocks he had studied. For an experienced field geologist who had spent months walking the lanes, fields and footpaths of Devon there could hardly have been a greater affront or a more serious accusation. As he would write in a subsequent report, 'every road and lane has been carefully examined, every quarry and broken piece of ground inspected, [and] the greater part of the rivulets walked up'.[17]

With his reputation to defend, De la Beche began marshalling his forces. He wrote a rejoinder to be read at the next meeting of the Geological Society, explaining to the president, Bellas Greenough, that were he able to afford it he would 'run up to town for the next Geol. Meeting and give my objectors that good humoured trimming which I think they deserve'. But the price of a coach ticket and the tariff (a hefty fifteen shillings) for each of the Society's dinners were beyond his current means. Unable to travel frequently to London he had been forced to resign his secretaryship at the Geological Society in 1831 'on account', as a tactfully worded minute recorded, 'of urgent occupations'.[18] With the stipend for the Devon survey not even covering his expenses and his income from Jamaica severely reduced he was, in his own phrase, short of the needful. 'The present state of the West Indian property', he remarked, 'has nearly smashed me' and he feared that he might have to give up geology and live as best he could on the estate.

To continue in geology, his survey work would have to be better paid and made permanent, and to convince the Board of Ordnance to provide both a salary and permanence he needed the support of the geological establishment. To Adam Sedgwick, Professor of Geology at Cambridge, he complained of critics, 'who confessedly never saw a square yard of the country', accusing him of 'a gross mistake as to the geological position of the beds'. As a working geologist who had 'toiled day after day, for months in the district, examining every hole and cranny in it', he considered Murchison's a priori judgement 'a pretty good go' of pitting 'preconceived opinions against facts . . . so plain that the merest infant in geology could make no mistake'. To illustrate the account of proceedings at the Geological Society meeting he drew a now-famous caricature, 'Preconceived Opinions versus Facts', that he sent to Sedgwick and Bellas Greenough knowing it would be circulated. On one side of the sketch is De la Beche, dressed in the topcoat of a working geologist, and on the other, in elegant tailcoats, are his 'armchair' critics. All are holding spectacles through which they peer at De la Beche's enlarged nose.

*De la Beche accusing his critics of placing preconceived opinions
before facts. His opponents are holding coloured Claude glasses.*

The inference, of course, is that their preconceptions are as
distorting as the effects of a coloured or tinted Claude glass. The
caption reads: De la Beche: 'This gentlemen is my Nose'. His
Critics: 'My dear Fellow! – your account of yourself generally may
be very well, but as we have classed you, before we saw you,
among men without noses, you cannot possibly have a nose'.
Murchison insisted that it was not the facts, or the importance of
field work, that were in dispute, but De la Beche's interpretation
of them and his rejection of the fossil evidence. But to De la
Beche, champion of the Baconian principles of experience and
observation this was a blatant example of a priori reasoning.

In his formal rejoinder to the Geological Society he persisted in
the role of the lone empirical field geologist confronting a battery
of formidable theorists. His letter was a reminder to the Society
that it had been founded in the expectation of countering the
grand cosmological theorizing that had fruitlessly dominated
much of early geology. 'Let us hope that the day is past when preconceived opinions are to be set up, as good arguments, against
facts; because if they are let that fact be clearly understood, and
let us be consistent, and no longer boast of our adherence to the
Baconian philosophy'. He concluded with a challenge. Let them
examine the district in question and either present their findings

to the Geological Society or publish them in an appropriate periodical. Either would allow De la Beche the right of reply.

Feigning surprise at De la Beche's reaction, Murchison wrote to him in private: 'I was surprised to find . . . that the comments I had made re. your notice of coal measure plants in the Greywacke should have produced *so lively* a feeling on your part. . . . Would you have so novel a position as that which your discovery puts forth, pass by unheeded? Was it possible that anyone who had been studying the Transition and Grauwacke rocks for some years should hear this *solecism* announced (for such it is) in *English*

A disconsolate De la Beche after an attack from fellows of the Geological Society. Reproduced from a letter to his daughter, Bessie.

geology without attempting a reply'.[19] The gloves were off and to forestall a heated confrontation and embarassing publicity for the Society, Bellas Greenough ruled that in the absence of new facts public exchanges should be curtailed. With such large reputations on the line, however, the most he could hope for was a lull before the next round.

For De la Beche the hiatus was a godsend that allowed him to seek, with his reputation still intact, backing for the continuation of the Survey in Cornwall. By May 1835 he had completed the mapping of Devon and applied to the Board of Ordnance to move into Cornwall. In his letter he carefully pointed out that by showing how geological data could be applied to ordnance maps 'the expense of engraving another map for the purpose . . . is wholly saved.'[20] His proposal was referred to Bellas Greenough and by him to a three-man advisory committee: William Buckland and Adam Sedgwick, respectively Professors of Geology at Oxford and Cambridge, and Charles Lyell. Although Lyell was in the Murchison camp, he was the most junior of the three. Marshalled by Buckland, they reported that De la Beche's mapping was 'the result of great labour combined with great skill' and that it was unequalled in Europe for its detailed accuracy. They recommended the establishment of a properly staffed geological branch within the Ordnance Survey with De la Beche as its salaried head.

During his inaugural address as President of the Geological Society, in 1835, Lyell reiterated the conclusions of the committee and congratulated the Survey for choosing De la Beche 'to discharge an office for which he is so eminently qualified'. Their backing had the complete support of Thomas Colby who was anxious to maintain the Survey's association with a geologist who gave a scholarly sheen to an enterprise his superiors were inclined to regard as a simple exercise in mechanical mapping.

De la Beche's future appeared to have been secured but Murchison, who had been temporarily stilled by Bellas Greenough's ruling, was simply lying in wait. In June and July 1835, mindful of Greenough's demand for new facts, he resumed his campaign. Accompanied by Adam Sedgwick, who had also worked on the older rocks of Wales, and armed with a set of De la Beche's newly finished maps, he descended upon Devon and immediately went on the attack. 'This portion of De la Beche's map wretchedly worked out – no angles of inclination given – & the strike not apparent'. And of another locality, 'half the Limestone omitted'. More serious, however, was a perceived error in identification. De la Beche had labeled as Greywacke a small coal-bearing area which Murchison judged to be Carboniferous. Without any fore-warning of which aspects of De la Beche's survey he found want-ing, Murchison disclosed the errors to the British Association meet-ing at Bristol in August 1838.

At the same time he presented a revised interpretation of the geology of Devon that, he declared, promised to clear up once and for all the anomaly of Coal Measures plants in the Grey-wacke. Whereas De la Beche had placed the fossil bearing culm or anthracite a third of the way down the Greywacke, Murchison placed it near the top. The inference was clear: De la Beche had misinterpreted the sequence of the strata – in effect turned them topsy-turvey – and that the fossils occurred in coal-bearing strata above the Greywacke or Transition rocks and just below the Carboniferous. De la Beche was nonplussed and could only withdraw: 'The heavy column was on me before I had a notion of any attack having been meditated. . . . I was taken most deucedly in the flank, my ammunition being in my magazines, and my guns dismantled, expecting nothing but peace, I made my retreat in the best manner I could'.[21]

Murchisons charges were so serious a questioning of De la Beche's competence that he even considered resigning. In a much-reproduced sketch in a letter to his daughter Bessie, he sits disconsolately before a window in his Cornish cottage. But his dejection was brief and within weeks he retaliated. He staunchly insisted that there was no unconformity between the coal-bearing strata and the older rock, and he objected to the 'slapdash' introduction of new systems by geologists who had not studied the Devon rocks as carefully as he had. The dispute was now public, the tone acrimonious and the metaphors military. 'We have enough powder and shot in our tumbrils to sink him', Murchison declared confidently to his supporters at the Geological Society. De la Beche's reputation and office were now at risk but it transpired that the Greywacke or Transition zone was not nearly as fossil-free as Murchison contended. A respected Devon geo-logist working in the zone found plant fossils at levels that

Murchison had declared lifeless or azoic. And, even more telling, the curator/librarian of the Geological Society pointed out that fossils being found in increasing numbers in the upper levels of the Transition zone were intermediate in character between those of the Carboniferous limestone and Murchison's Silurian system.

In other words, there was no break in the stratigraphic sequence. De la Beche had not misread the sequence of the rocks and the fossils he had found were not, as Murchison had contended, Carboniferous. The actual resolution, however, was neither quick nor clean but with concessions from the protagonists and the acceptance of a new series of rocks, the Devonian, immediately below the Carboniferous, the dispute was resolved and though feathers were ruffled reputations were not seriously damaged. Hurt feelings were also quickly patched up, Murchison in 1839 dedicating a shortened and revised version of his Silurian System to Sir Henry Thomas De la Beche.

As if to atone for its former parsimony, the Board of Ordnance awarded De la Beche an annual salary of five hundred pounds plus expenses of one thousand pounds. The expenses were subsequently withdrawn by the Treasury but a salary, as opposed to a stipend, meant that De la Beche's position was now more or less permanent and that the Board contemplated a geological survey on a national scale. De la Beche was never formally appointed but in his annual address to the Geological Society in 1836 Charles Lyell referred to him as the organizer and director of operations. Questions of costs or competence were never raised again and De la Beche, by increments, became the director of the Geological Survey of England and Wales.

Within days of receiving permission to move into Cornwall, and taking for granted the permanence of his position, he requested a building where he might store material collected during the course of the survey and display, for the edification of the public, economic rocks and minerals. A permanent display of rocks and minerals used in roads, buildings and metal-making would also, of course, be an excellent advertisement for the practical value of a national survey. Treasury approval was prompt and in 1835 a building in Craig's Court, Whitehall, adjoining Scotland Yard, was assigned to the Survey for offices and a museum. De la

Beche insisted that the immediate emphasis should be on collection and classification rather than display and it was not until 1841 that the Museum of Economic Geology opened its doors to the public. Attached to it was a laboratory, open to the public, where rocks could be assayed, soils analysed, and building stone tested for its weathering properties. The chemist, Richard Phillips, was also the curator. Richard Phillips was a founding member of the Geological Society, Britain's best-known and probably most able chemist and, like De la Beche, an honorary member of the Royal Institution of South Wales. 'In the analysis of mineral or inorganic substances', wrote Michael Faraday in a letter to De la Beche, 'there is no man I would trust sooner than him'.

With the completion of the Devon and Cornwall survey, in 1837, Thomas Colby, the director of the Ordnance Survey to whom De la Beche was still responsible, suggested that he proceed to Pembrokeshire. The topographical maps of the county were, but for corrections, ready for colouring and De la Beche was familiar with the geology. In 1823 he read to the Geological Society a paper, based on fieldwork conducted during the previous year, on the geology of Southern Pembrokeshire. He followed this by publishing, in 1826, a geological map on a scale of two miles to the inch. But in spite of the appeal of covering familiar ground, De la Beche demurred suggesting, for political reasons, that a location nearer the centre of the great coal basin of south Wales would be a more expedient starting point.

The economic advantages would be obvious to all and for the geologists the work would be challenging, 'the geology of that county [being] so backward'. A new survey would also provide protection for landowners who, in their eagerness to find coal, were prey to over-optimistic and, in some cases, unscrupulous mineshaft sinkers and surveyors. The latter objected to the Survey on grounds that it would make public information that previously could be obtained only through them. Writing from Chepstow, one of De la Beche's new assistants, David Hiram Williams, reported that he had found men sinking a shaft in the Old Red Sandstone strata that lay many hundreds of feet below the lowest coal seam. They had already sunk a shaft of almost 300 feet and had built a yard to receive the coal. 'The gent. who employs these rogues', wrote Williams, 'has already spent upwards of £2,000 and intends boring until he meets the coal'. An authentic survey showing the coal seams would, Williams insisted, put a stop to 'stupid' schemes and, in places where coal might profitably be mined, it could greatly increase the value of land.[22]

Colby, whose bias was toward economic geology, needed no convincing and in his application to government for funds he reiterated what were now well-rehearsed economic arguments for, as he phrased it, 'the continuance of the Survey over the Mineral District of South Wales'. Located on the southern edge of the coalfield and on the main road to London, Swansea was a natural centre from which to conduct the survey. By December 1837 De la Beche had moved his headquarters, prompting an entry in Lewis Weston Dillwyn's diary: Saturday 16 December 1837: 'My old friend De la Beche has arrived as superintendent of a National Mineralogical Survey and has taken Lilliput (a small house on the sea front) for a temporary residence'. Accompanying him was his daughter Bessie, who shared his peripatetic life. They made frequent visits to the Dillwyns, at Sketty Hall, where Bessie met Dillwyn's son, Lewis Llewellyn. Eyes, as De la Beche might have put it, must have met, if not flashed, and Bessie and 'Lewy' were engaged the following May and married in August. As the historian David Painting has pointed out, it was a singular union: bride and groom were the children of distinguished natural scientists and the grandchildren of a cavalier slave-owner on the one side and a pioneering Quaker abolitionist on the other. But to Bessie and the ardent Lewy, politics and social justice were of no concern.

The day in May 1838 when he walked down to Lilliput from Sketty Hall to propose to his 'dearest Bessie' was, he recorded later, 'the happiest day of my life'. To celebrate his marriage, Lewis Llewellyn Dillwyn, who had taken over the *Cambrian* Pottery in 1838, gave 'a most sumptuous dinner' to the workers. Bessie, born during De la Beche's brief marriage to Letitia Whyte, was the elder of two De la Beche daughters. De la Beche's other daughter, Rosie (Rosalie Torre), was born out of wedlock in 1834 while he was at work in Devon. Despite differences in age and legitimacy, Bessie and Rosie were friends. Rosie died in 1858 and was buried beside her father in Kensal Green, London.

Although the South Wales coalfield had never been systematically surveyed, its basic geology was well understood. On a journey through south and central Wales in 1819 De la Beche reconnoitred the coalfield. Crossing the Severn at the New Passage with a strong wind blowing against the ebb tide, he made light of a passage that was unpleasant and wet, but his '*compagnons de voyage* were much alarmed, being landsmen and not accustomed to the sea'.[23] South of Caerphilly he began to note the succession of the beds: Old Red Sandstone succeeded by Carboniferous limestone and the limestone, in turn, by the shales and sandstones of the Coal Measures. He found that in southern districts the strata dipped toward the north while farther north, at Merthyr, the sequence was repeated but with a southern dip. A short distance north of Merthyr, the Coal Measures gave way to Carboniferous limestone and, after about four miles, the limestone to Old Red Sandstone that continued all the way to Brecon. From this he concluded that the coalfield must be basin-shaped. He drew a cross section from Newport to Brecon of 'what appears to be the geology'.

De la Beche's section across the coalfield is the oldest known but the basin-like structure had been noted several years earlier. In his *Natural History of the Mineral Kingdom*, 1789, of which De la Beche may well have been unaware, John Williams noted the ways in which the coal seams rise to the surface on each side of the coalfield. He came to the same conclusion as De la Beche: 'Now this does not look like the coals dipping down to the centre of the earth'. Rather, he surmised, 'that when they have declined down so far, they become quite flat, and afterwards rise again upon the opposite side of the coalfield'.[24] Similar views were expressed in a paper presented to the Royal Society by Edward Martin in 1806. He, too, noted the basin-like structure and pointed to differences in the characteristics of the coal: coking coals in the north and east, 'binding' or bituminous coals in the south, and 'stone' or anthracitic coals in the west.

In his now-famous 1815 map of the geology of England and Wales, William Smith, in the south Wales portion of the map, identified three groups of rocks: limestones, coal measures, and sandstones, arranged in a basin-like formation. In south Glamorgan and Gower, Smith, who worked alone without institutional support, mistook Carboniferous limestone for Magnesian limestone and in the very south of Glamorgan he failed to identify the Lias. Backed by the Geological Society, from which Smith, an artisan, had been excluded, George Bellas Greenough in 1819 produced a more accurate map of England and Wales.

Whereas Smith's map was a work of pioneer investigation, Greenough's was a compilation based on the work of many observers and geologists and more up-to-date information. In south Wales Greenough correctly identified the Carboniferous limestone and in south Glamorgan he delineated several formations rather than the one Smith had supposed. Both maps, however, were drawn at a scale – six miles to the inch – that was too small to be of much use to practical men. In his prize-winning essay on the Mineral Basin of Glamorgan, submitted to the Cardiff Eisteddfod, 1835, 'Tubal Cain' appealed for a more detailed map at a much larger scale.[25] Apparently unaware of the approach of the Geological Survey, he thought it unlikely that such a work would be undertaken 'for ages yet to come'. With so many faults or 'leaps' in the ground a complete survey, he feared, 'would be an undertaking so expensive, and a task of so much difficulty, as to require the united labour of three or four capable men for, perhaps, twelve months'.

Although he appreciated the difficulties involved in a complete survey of the coalfield, 'Tubal Cain' underestimated both the time and the number of hands that would be required. De la Beche and Colby both recognized that in the interests of accuracy and comprehensiveness, the Survey in south Wales would have to move into a higher and more professional gear. Government did not demur. The treasury approved an estimated budget of £3,000 for the 1837/38 season, a ten-fold increase over the amount allotted for the Devon survey five years earlier. De la Beche applied for, and was granted, permission by the Board of Ordnance to appoint a handful of full-time assistants: De la Beche's 'little army of good observers', as Sedgewick would describe them. In support of the Survey, Buckland , who was Sir Robert Peel's unofficial scientific adviser, wrote: 'He (De la Beche) has collected about him a little staff of the most talented young men he has found in England, and has educated them in a way that renders them especially qualified to assist in carrying on the survey over the most important mining districts'.[26] As an unschooled geologist himself, De la Beche chose his associates less for their knowledge than for their aptitude and enthusiasm for the work. Like William Smith, he believed that geology was open to all. More important to a good field geologist than 'hard names' or books were a keen eye, a sound pair of legs, and the ability to apply a few basic principles.

Holding to his credo, for one of his first recruits to Wales De la Beche chose an Ordnance surveyor, Henry McLauchlan, whom he co-opted to do some geological mapping. McLauchlan, however, was no novice. He may not have had any geological training but he knew enough about geological structures for Bellas Greenough to consult him when preparing his geological map of England and Wales. As an all-round naturalist, McLauchlan's interests ranged from rocks to insects; he once asked De la Beche where he might purchase a copy of Dillwyn's monograph on the coleopterous insects of Swansea. Although there were no contours on the first Ordnance Survey maps, McLauchlan appreciated the relationship between geology and surface morphology. 'It is surprising how much an idea of the Geological formation of a country adds to the pleasure of our labours: and as we trace out the detail and find the contours agree with the line of bearing and dip, our pleasure increases'.

De la Beche's first dedicated assistant in Wales, and his first Welsh recruit, was the Swansea-born David Hiram Williams. De la Beche regarded him as 'a very clever hand and a regular good one', and Charles Lyell as 'the best of practical men'.[27] He was one of De la Beche's most successful appointments. As a mineral surveyor, and the son of a mineral surveyor, Williams was engaged to make vertical cross sections as supplements to the one inch maps. Williams proved, however, to have 'a good eye for fossils' and he spent much of his time moving between survey teams. Impressed by his competence and reliability, and touched by his loyalty, De la Beche recommended him to lead the Indian Geological Survey in whose service he died tragically of 'jungle fever' in 1848. De la Beche's second Welsh recruit, however, Josiah Rees, was a disappointment. Unable to reconcile himself to the 'total want of society' for which he could see no remedy while he continued in the Survey, he resigned in 1840 to study analytical chemistry in London. Exasperated with an assistant who could not bear working alone 'for a fortnight or so' in what was, after all, inhabited country – he was then in Wells, Somerset – De la Beche consigned him to the basket of Celtic self-destruction. 'It strikes me that Rees has missed his opportunity; surely if ever a young man kicked the ladder of advancement among mankind to the devil he has done it'.[28]

The palaeontologist for the Survey, John Phillips, also had Welsh connections, but he was not one of De la Beche's young recruits. Phillips was born in Wiltshire, the son of an excise officer from Blaen-y-Ddol, Carmarthenshire. Orphaned at an early age he was raised by his uncle, William Smith, the famed map-maker and brother to his mother Elizabeth. At forty John Phillips was one of the most experienced palaeontologists in the country, an FRS, prospective reader in geology at Oxford and winner, in 1845, of the coveted Wollaston medal. He had been engaged by the Survey to write an account of the fossils of Devon and Cornwall as an appendix to the geological maps.

At Swansea, De la Beche was able to convince his superiors of the advantages of having the fossil or palaeontological work done at the same time as the geological mapping. As they traced the boundaries of the strata, the assistants, superintended by Phillips, also gathered fossil evidence. The integrated approach meant that Survey geologists for the first time were no longer dependent on 'potterers' and fossil collectors. Add to this new professional approach the application of chemistry and physics to rock and mineral analysis, and what De la Beche described as the *Geologie des Dames* was on its way out. In south Wales, as Simon Knell has remarked, the ambience, or 'culture' of geology was transformed. Camaraderie replaced rivalry, and information-sharing and the sense of a shared mission the former world of secrecy.[29]

Of De la Beche's younger recruits, the most talented, and the one closest to him, was Andrew Crombie Ramsay, the son of a Glasgow chemical manufacturer. He had come to notice at the British Association meeting at Glasgow in 1840 where he exhibited a coloured geological model of the Isle of Arran, accompanied by a map, sections and rock samples. As a youth, Ramsay spent his holidays on the island. The model, at a scale of two inches to the mile, so impressed Murchison that he proposed taking Ramsay to Russia the following year. But while Ramsay was in London, en route for Russia, Murchison changed his mind about taking him and arranged for Ramsay to work with the Geological Survey in Wales. Denied 'bearded Muscovites [and] horrible escapes from bears and wolves', Ramsay had to settle, happily as it turned out, for Welsh miners, farmers and sheep. Ramsay was De la Beche's protégée, his 'geological son' as he was fond of referring to him, who was elected President of the Geological Society in 1862 and appointed Director-General of the Geological Survey in 1871.[30]

From Swansea, De la Beche's little army of loyal surveyors fanned outward. In the uncomplicated central and eastern parts of the coalfield progress was relatively rapid. West of the Neath valley, however, where there were many faults and leaps in the ground, mapping was more difficult and most difficult of all in the intensely folded rocks of Pembrokeshire, which is now recognized as one of the most difficult tracts in Britain. In the west-central section of the coalfield, however, De la Beche and the Survey had an enormous stroke of luck. From Swansea, the Canadian-born manager of the Forest copper works, William Edmond Logan, in the best tradition of self-motivated amateurs, had mapped the coal measures between Neath and Cydweli. De la Beche immediately co-opted him as a 'colourer' of the one-inch maps and while he remained in Swansea Logan was an unpaid but vital associate of the Survey.

In his desire to prove the economic worth of the Survey, De la Beche complained from the time of his arrival in Swansea of the limitations of mapping on a small scale. A one inch scale might have been adequate for Devon and Cornwall, but to be truly useful geological maps of a large mineral basin ought, in the interests of detail and accuracy, to be at a larger scale. With no room to manoeuvre, he submitted to the one-inch stricture, but 'with much regret'. Yet he continued to complain to Colby, writing from Swansea in April 1839: 'The one-inch scale is much too small to chronicle much valuable matter connected with the coal of the South Welsh basin – for instance yesterday I could only insert two out of five beds . . . with a six-inch scale we might easily accomplish work upon which the practical miner could act . . . From want of such a map large sums of money are thrown away and an immense amount of mineral wealth has been neglected'. And again from Cardiff in 1840 with reference to a proposed survey of the Derbyshire coalfield: 'I have no hesitation in stating that [a scale] of six inches to a mile appears to me particularly well calculated to answer to the end proposed. First because it is not too large to prevent a general view of the subject from being taken . . . and secondly because it is of sufficient size to contain all the [data] from which working plans for separate mines can readily be constructed'.[31] Much of the opposition to the six-inch scale came from surveyors who objected to placing in public hands information which generally was available only through them.

To counter the limitations of a small scale, De la Beche adopted Logan's practice of supplementing his one-inch maps with large scale horizontal and vertical sections. In addition to hammers, levels, chains for measuring distance, and barometers for altitude – the standard equipment for field geologists – De la Beche asked Colby for a theodolite or two so that he could draw accurate horizontal sections at a scale of six inches to the mile. On the Ordnance Survey maps there were no contour lines, only surveyed trigonometrical points. Hill shading and hachures indicated slopes. A surveyed line showing correct relative heights would demonstrate relationships between relief and underground structure and, in a mineral basin, enable miners and engineers to determine the true vertical distance between coal beds. By measuring the dip of the beds, and making due allowance for faults, wasteful shaft-sinking and mining schemes might be avoided. De la Beche's vertical sections, showing the succession of strata, were at a scale of forty feet to the inch and depended on the evidence from deep wells, mining shafts, and reports from miners. The latter however, as his assistant Henry Sills reported, were liable to tell you anything.[32]

When moving from one headquarters to another the geologists travelled by coach, but in the field when doing actual survey work, on horseback or, if the weather was particularly wet, on foot. If on the move they stayed at inns, but if stationary for a week or two, then usually in lodgings. It was pleasant work for the most part. From Usk, where he examined Silurian rocks, John Phillips wrote to De la Beche: 'You have put me down in a comfortable Inn in pleasant country, with a pretty piece of business to perform. Therefore I thank you, not as the world does with words of air, but with a resolution to help you in your excellent purposes'. [33] In south Wales De la Beche made only occasional forays into the field, but when his assistants knew that he was about to leave his command post at Swansea for unfamiliar territory they would send him travellers' tips. On learning that he proposed to spend some time in Pembrokeshire, Henry McLauchlan struck a cautionary note: 'Find out and avoid the Fairs and the drover fellows that get up at 3 in the morning and fill the house with dirt and all sorts of confusion. Mount your horse the moment they appear and sleep at Fishguard'. For a temporary lodging he recommended the farmhouse at Clyn-saith-maen – 'the best farmhouse in Cwm Cerwyn to put your horse at. The man speaks English and knows the mountains well – but don't attempt to cross to the Bethel Chapel on horse back. I fell in a bog, horse and all'.[34]

Young, fit geologists combing the countryside and staying at inns and lodging houses were inevitably exposed to the fatal attraction. Particularly susceptible was the unmarried twenty-eight year old Andrew Crombie Ramsay, who used his popularity with local women to organize large informal collecting parties. When Ramsay wrote about his admiration for the daughter of a family he befriended in Carmarthenshire, De la Beche replied: 'Take care of the flashing intelligent eyes. When gallant clever young men have to encounter eyes of the love-inspiring and intelligent order, they have to encounter fearful odds against their peace and quiet'. Ramsay, who was De la Beche's equal in the repartee department, retorted: 'Touching the Department of *Flashing eyes,* I can only say that whatever impression they have made on my stony heart, it is not of the metamorphic order. The edges may be a little altered, but the core must remain true to the steely hammer. With 500 a year there is no saying what a man *might* be weak enough to do, but with 150 he must sing dumb'.[35] Under De la Beche's light touch, and the fellowship of the field parties, Ramsay blossomed. John Phillips, who was himself won over by the spirit of cooperation and companionship, noted in a letter to De la Beche, that Ramsay, was now beginning to 'live'.[36]

From the field the assistants sent regular reports in the form of letters to a leader they clearly regarded as a fond associate. They reveal much about the life of a field geologist. The largest collec-

tion of letters to survive (twenty in all) were written by the conscientious Hiram Williams who was never as easy in his relations
with De la Beche as McLauchlan, Ramsay or Phillips. One of the
most affecting concerned the loss of a map: 'I have had a sad loss
this morning; while out on duty I lost 7 portfolio squares of the
map of this part of the country. As soon as I had discovered my
loss I immediately returned to Carmarthen and had them cried by
the town crier, and I again returned enquiring at all the houses
along and back again to town without the slightest information
as to their recovery. I am afraid they have been found by some
country person who might fancy they are pictures as two of them
are coloured. Should such be the case I am fearful they will be
stuck upon the wall of some cottage. I am sorry, very sorry, to say
I am in great trouble about the loss of those sketches, I hope and
trust I shall have the good fortune to meet with them again'.[37] In
another letter he cited yet another instance of a mining company
being duped by an unscrupulous land agent.

The field geologists were frequently approached for their
opinions on proposed or operational mining ventures. 'You will
be glad to hear something about the disputed question of the
Risca Minerals under Sir B's property, which has been taken by
the Monmouthshire Co. and was considered by them and Sir B's
agent only 60 yds. Deep at Abercarn. If you remember I always
class their Pit just under the Troed-y-Rhiw vein, and that they
would have from 1,200 to 1,600 feet of sinking to the bottom
measures'. Finding nothing at 60 yards, and £30,000 poorer, the
company consulted an independent mineral surveyor who dole-
fully confirmed Williams's estimate.[38]

In circumstances where mineral rights attached to property, not
the state, surveyors were under continual pressure from landowners to confirm or indicate the presence of minerals. From
Carmarthenshire, in 1842, Ramsay reported: 'A fat old Gentleman,
a Mr Lloyd, has called on me three times (when I was always out)
to see if I could go to see some lead ore on his property. I have
been obliged to say I would fix a day soon. He insists with the
landlord here on the presence of *Black Jack* [a miner's term for
Blende, or ore of zinc] in company with the lead'.[39]

By the time of the Welsh survey De la Beche and Murchison
might have patched up their differences, but privately De la Beche

and his little army still smarted over the mauling he received in Devonshire. They were now in Murchison territory and amongst themselves they took every opportunity to retaliate. On 4 October 1841, John Phillips, whose own palaeontological work in Devon had been questioned, reported gleefully from Carmarthenshire that 'Murchison's map . . . is utterly at fault owing to some un-accountable error'; and on 16 October 1841, 'By the bye, we have reason to think that since Mr. Murchison's map (1837) there has been a volcanic eruption near Carmarthen. This at least is certain that a very bold Trap hill exists with abundance of felsp. [felspar] trap, where in Mr. Murchison's day it was lower Silurian! The place is near Pen y Mulfre, crossed by Mr. Murchison's section nearly; so you see l'eruption est bien constatee.'[40]

By 1844 the Survey geologists had finished most of their work in south Wales and De la Beche now spent most of his time in London at the national headquarters. But his official duties in Swansea and south Wales were not yet over. Newly knighted (in 1842), and as director of the Geological Survey and the Museum of Economic Geology, he was now a prominent and respected figure and, as such, a candidate for royal commissions. In 1844 Edwin Chadwick, asked to submit 'names that carry weight', appointed him along with Lyon Playfair, chemist to the Geological Survey since 1842, and four others to a commission to examine and report on the health of towns in England and Wales. De la Beche and Playfair were chosen to lend 'scientific force' to the Commission.[41] In his three-volume 1842 report, *Survey into the Sanitary Condition of the Labouring Classes in Britain*, Chadwick demonstrated incontrovertibly the connection between rates of mortality and foul air, contaminated water, poor drainage, urban cemeteries and overcrowding.

The mechanisms of diseases such as typhus, consumption and cholera may not have been understood but the conditions that harboured and encouraged them were. In the absence of medical antidotes, Chadwick's approach was environmental: to eliminate through massive public clean-ups the conditions in which disease flourished. He envisaged a network of drains and sewers into which household wastes could be flushed, and paved streets that could be easily cleaned. Water delivered at high pressure was the key. Curative medicine he dismissed as an irrelevance:

'The medical controversy as to causes of fever; as to whether it is caused by filth and vitiated atmosphere, or whether the state of the atmosphere is a predisposing cause to the reception of the fever, or the means of propagating that disease which has really some other, superior, independent or specific cause, does not appear to be one that for practical purposes need be considered, except that its effect is prejudicial in diverting attention from the practical means of prevention'.

His commissioners and witnesses, therefore, were practical rather than medical men: surveyors of sewers, Poor Law officials, architects and engineers. Among the latter were the men who had driven the tunnels and excavated the cuttings for the canals and railways. So critical were an understanding of topography and geology to planning drainage schemes and locating public reservoirs that Chadwick introduced the idea of 'geological areas', that is natural areas where the bedrock and surface topography allowed for an integrated water supply and drainage system, administered by a single sanitary authority. 'Drainage', he emphasised, 'is a matter of science, or its practical application and not of mere common sense or general knowledge'.

Thus De la Beche was appointed to the Commission. In a letter to De la Beche, October 1842, Chadwick admitted that at first he had no clear role for him: 'When I first called upon you I had some hazy perceptions of the service you might render the sanitary proceedings.' Later, however, he was gratified to discover 'how our thoughts jump together'.[42] In the preface to his general report, De la Beche affirmed the importance of geology: 'The character of the surface, more especially as regards dryness and damp and the nature and supply of springwater, is so intimately connected with the kind of rock occurring beneath'.

For the Health of Towns Survey, Chadwick and the Commissioners selected fifty of the largest towns in England and Wales. The objective was, through the study of particular towns, to assess (in reality to confirm) the general observations in Chadwick's 1842 report and to implement his proposed remedies. The Welsh towns selected were Swansea, Merthyr and Brecon, the latter as a rural counterpoint to its industrial cohorts.[43] As the commissioner most familiar with south Wales, De la Beche was the investigating officer for each. Although he had been appointed as a scientist, the work of a Health of Towns Commissioner was no antiseptic, intellectual exercise in the identification of drainage basins and the planning of water supply and drainage systems. Like the other commissioners, De la Beche had to inspect stinking courts and alleys and refuse and ordure-strewn streets. In Bristol at the start of the exercise, while examining with the chemist Lyon Playfair overflowing privies in a crowded court, he was obliged to retreat to the street and vomit.

In Swansea neither the increase in population nor – through the copper trade – in wealth, had prompted improvements in public health. In 1786 the town's aged but powerful portreeve had travelled by coach to London to oppose, on grounds that it opened the door to government intervention, a decision taken at a public meeting for a street-paving bill. For several years, Swansea became a byword for municipal neglect, a cartoon in the *Gentleman's Magazine* by Moses Harris showing a dilapidated well in a filthy street that had become a pen for rooting pigs. Intent, too, on becoming a fashionable resort, the town wanted no suggestion that it was anything other than an elysium of good health. Onshore winds drove copper smoke away from the hotels and fashionable houses, and the wretched slums and courts were some distance from the shore.

Unwilling to offend the public interest, the medical and scientific establishment acceded to what, in effect, was a conspiracy of silence. A statistical committee of the Philosophical and Literary Institution, responding to the enthusiasm for statistical studies initiated by insurance companies and the Board of Trade, demonstrated that it, too, had no appetite for the truth. It acknowledged that typhus occurred among the poorer classes, and conceded that this might have something to do with inadequate sewerage and filthy streets, but still managed to conclude that compared with other places 'epidemic diseases are of an innocuous character'. Doctors, too, were just as acquiescent, arguing that copper-smoke was a prophylactic, and salt water tides, which in fact caused sewers and drains to back up, an effective disinfectant.

In his role as Commissioner of Health, De la Beche, who had fought battles with opponents far more formidable than the town's merchants and physicians, descended like an avenging angel. Like all industrial towns Swansea's population had grown rapidly, from 6,000 in 1801 to 20,000 in 1840, with few if any additions in public services. He opened his report, as Chadwick would have liked, with observations on groundwater. The interleaving of porous with impervious rocks – of sands and gravels with clays – and the frequency of joints and discontinuities combined with copious rainfall made for an abundant supply of springs and groundwater. But conditions that favoured the storage and movement of groundwater offered the same advantages to pollutants. The pervious layers of sandstone and the loose detrital material that covered the bedrock allowed liquids from privies, cesspits and cemeteries to percolate and mingle with well water.

Only one house in seven was supplied with reservoir water from the Swansea Waterworks Company, the rest having to rely on wells, streams and water vendors. Of drainage and sewerage there was very little. 'Nothing', noted De la Beche, 'deserving the name of a drainage system can be said to exist'. Large numbers of water closets and privies had no drains and the contents were allowed to percolate into the adjacent soil. In the poorer quarters, many of the houses had no 'necessaries' and such necessaries as there were had no drains. Slops, soapsuds, dish-water, urine, ordure and ashes were thrown into the streets and gutters. Scavenging or street cleaning was utterly inadequate and, as Chadwick had pointed out in his earlier report, inefficient and expensive. There were only four carts and five men for a population of 20,000. The scavengers were poorly paid and although they professed to go into all parts of the town once a week, in practice months could go by without any public cleaning.

The myth of Swansea as a citadel of health crumbled before De la Beche's 1845 report. He showed that Swansea was no healthier than other industrial towns and somewhat less healthy than the countryside: mortality rates in Swansea were 23 per thousand compared with 15 per thousand in Gower. The rate for Swansea was lower than in some other towns but this, he pointed out, was a result of the masking of high rates of infant mortality by the large number of adults who came into town in search of work. Both typhus and consumption were widespread and the incidence of the latter was even higher in the smelting districts than elsewhere. In smoke-plagued Morriston, one in every three or four deaths was from consumption. For apologists for the smoke, even worse was to come. 'For deaths by epidemics generally, and including typhus, the rate of mortality at Swansea is high, closely followed by Cardiff; so that the supposed corrective influence of the copper smoke for these diseases is not apparent.' As a sop to the physicians, most of whom were fellow members of the Royal Institution, he conceded that their claims for the benign influence of copper-smoke 'could scarcely be doubted' but immediately withdrew the concession by asserting that such a conclusion 'is not very clearly seen from known data'.

Conditions at Merthyr had not improved since his 1819 visit when he found it 'a nasty town' of small, mean houses and roads black from coal dirt. As in Swansea the inter- stratified shales, sandstones and gravels of the coal measures were ideal for tapping springs and digging wells. If, De la Beche added, 'careful arrangements were made, the inhabitants might receive a good supply of water, one which would but little interfere with that required for the works'. Neither the topography nor the geo-logical structure presented difficulties for drainage but houses had been built and streets laid out without a thought to waste dis-posal. Instead of opening onto well-drained streets, houses faced stagnant, refuse-filled pools and ditches.

With no copper works, Merthyr, unlike Swansea, was not a 'smoky' town but with the exception of smoke it scored lower in almost every other category of nuisance. Streets, which were little more than gutters for the disposal of all household wastes, were 'complete networks of filth, emitting noxious exhalations'. Even by the standards of the mid-nineteenth century, the town was notable for the scarcity of privies; recent houses had been built without them and in some districts a single privy served fifty people. When a school with privies was built at adjacent Dowlais most of the children had to be taught how to use them. According to the chairman of Merthyr's Board of Guardians, no town in England and Wales was 'so much in want of proper regulations as to cleansing, lighting, paving and watering'.

By contrast with Merthyr, Brecon was almost a model town. The northern part of the town, which lay on the sandstones and marls of the Old Red Sandstone, may be considered naturally dry and even the alluvial flats of Llanfaes to the south, in which there is an admixture of sand and gravel may be considered dry under normal conditions. Parts of the town, however, suffered from inadequate drainage and sewerage and many of the poorer houses either had no privies or the privies were not connected to drains. But water supply, paving and street cleaning for parts of the town were the responsibility of a commission that, however ineffective it might have been, suggested that sanitation was a municipal responsibility. The inhabitants, too, were required to sweep the footpaths in front of their houses, and were penalized for throwing ash upon footways and allowing pigs to wander.

Although he returned to Swansea for the 1848 meeting, the Health of Towns investigation was De la Beche's last official connection with the town. He returned from time to time to visit the Dillwyns but the infrequency of his visits prompted a mock family petition despatched from Parkwern on 25 December 1846: 'We the undersigned having long and patiently expected that an inspection of this our fortress at Parkwern . . . would be vouch-safed by your honourable self and as yet having been disap-pointed in this our expectation, humbly request that you will allay our anxiety and reward our patience by an early or rather imme-diate visit'. Signed Bessie Dillwyn (Commander of the Garrison and others).[44]

In London his responsibilities mounted. Work on a new build-ing in Jermyn Street for the Survey offices and a Museum of Practical Geology began in 1847. In 1847/48 he was also elected president of the Geological Society. In 1849 a committee of the House of Lords admitted the need for a school of mines, nine years after the closure of a short-lived mining school in Cornwall and thirty-four years after John Henry Vivian's initial advocacy. Like Vivian, De la Beche had been greatly impressed by the mining academy at Freiburg. The new school would function in association with the Geological Survey and the Museum for Practical Geology and, as its prospective director, De la Beche advocated that part of its programme be evening lectures for workers in shops and factories.

When the new Museum and School of Mines opened in May 1851 Roderick Impey Murchison, who would succeed De la

Beche as director, described it as the first building in Britain to be devoted entirely to the advancement of science. With his gift for assembling talented associates, De la Beche brought together, as teachers, a group of brilliant scientists, most of whom were connected with the Survey. Among them were Edward Forbes, Professor of Palaeontology, John Percy, Professor of Metallurgy and a frequent visitor to Swansea, Andrew Crombie Ramsay, Professor of Geology, and Lyon Playfair, Professor of Chemistry. The much-loved Richard Phillips, who had been the Survey's chemist since 1839, died on the eve of the opening ceremony on 11 May 1851. In his presidential address to the Geological Society, W. T. Blandford proclaimed: 'Rarely in any country, and probably never in England, was a more gifted staff brought together for teaching purposes'.

In 1853 De la Beche's health began to fail and by 1855, partly paralyzed, he was confined to a wheelchair. In the last-known photograph taken of him he is at Sketty Hall accompanied by his daughters Bessie and Rosie. He is in his mid to late fifties, but looks older and, although seated, he is holding a cane. He died in April 1855, the same year as Lewis Weston Dillwyn, and a few months after he had been awarded the Wollaston Medal by the

De la Beche photographed at Sketty Hall with his grandchildren.

Geological Society. The *Cambrian* granted him only a brief death notice, acknowledging his family connections to the town and his work for the Geological Survey. As the bearer of unwelcome news, his role in the Health of Towns Commission was not mentioned. The town was more generous, naming two streets after him, one in the centre of town and the other in Sketty. At the RISW he is still an icon, an eminent self-taught scientist who, at a time when there were few universities, brought science to the public.

At the national level, as Tom Sharpe, geologist and co-editor of the De la Beche Papers at the National Museum of Wales has pointed out, he almost single-handedly established geology as a profession outside the universities.[45] More clearly than any of his contemporaries, he recognized the economic value of geology and the need to make science serve the needs of practical men; in geology, this meant making accurate surveys, maps and sections, and, no less important, creating and maintaining the government-supported structures and institutions that made these possible.

NOTES

1. *Cambrian* (21 April 1838).
2. J. S. Flett, *The First Hundred Years of the Geological Survey of Great Britain* (London, 1939), 16.
3. F. J. North, unfinished manuscript biography of Henry De la Beche, NMW, unpaged.
4. Paul J. McCartney, *Henry De la Beche: Observations of an Observer* (Cardiff, 1977), 2.
5. Caroline Fox, *Memories of Old Friends*, 1 (London, 1882), 5.
6. Paul J. McCartney, 'Henry De la Beche – a new kind of geologist', *Amgueddfa* 21 (1975), 13-28.
7. McCartney, *Observations of an Observer*, 4.
8. NMW, De la Beche Papers, Diary, 6 Dec 1818; North Ms.
9. NMW, De la Beche Papers, De la Beche to Conybeare, 8 January 1824.
10. North Ms.
11. Quoted in McCartney, 'Henry De la Beche, A new kind of Geologist . . .' 15.
12. Flett, *The First Hundred Years of the Geological Survey*, 27.
13. North Ms.
14. Martin J. S. Rudwick, *The Great Devonian Controversy* (Chicago, 1985), 94-6.
15. NMW, De la Beche Papers, 880. John Lindley to Wm Lonsdale.
16. NMW, De la Beche Papers, 621. Bellas Greenough to De la Beche, Dec 1834.

17. F. J. North, 'Further Chapters in the History of Geology of South Wales', *Trans. Cardiff Naturalists' Soc.*, 67 (1934) 31-103; ref 56.
18. Rudwick, *The Great Devonian Controversy*, 90.
19. NMW, De la Beche Papers, 1013. Murchison to De a Beche, date (watermark).
20. North, 'Further Chapters in the History of Geology of South Wales', 43.
21. Rudwick, *The Great Devonian Controversy*, 165-6.
22. NMW, North Ms. To enlist support for Geological Survey, a copy of Williams' letter was sent by Buckland to Prime Minister Robert Peel on 10 Nov. 1841. 'It is one of those endless cases of searching for coal where it is impossible to be found'. (Torrens 108).
23. Notebook, 1819. Quoted in F. J. North, 'From the Geological Map to the Geological Survey', *Trans. Cardiff Naturalists' Soc.* 65 (1932), 42-115, ref. 73.
24. Ibid., ref. 44.
25. Tubal Cain, *The Mineral Basin of Glamorgan and Surrounding Adjoining Districts* (Merthyr Tydfil, 1865).
26. NMW, North Ms.
27. Quoted in H. S. Torrens, 'William Edmond Logan's Geological Apprenticeship in Britain 1831-1842', *Geoscience Canada*, 26, 3 (1999), 97-110; ref. 108.
28. NMW, North Ms.
29. Simon J. Knell, *The Culture of English Geology, 1815-1851* (Aldershot, 2000) 286-7.
30. North, 'Further Chapters in the History of Geology in South Wales', 68.
31. Ibid., 31-103, ref. 92-3.
32. Ibid., 87.
33. Ibid., 77.
34. NMW, North Ms.
35. Ibid.
36. NMW, De la Beche Papers, Phillips to De la Beche 28 May, 1841.
37. North, 'Further Chapters in the History of Geology in South Wales, 68.
38. Ibid., 69-70.
39. Ibid., 70.
40. NMW, De la Beche Papers, 1382. Phillips to De la Beche, 16 October 1841.
41. Ibid., 235. Chadwick to De la Beche, 21 Sept. 1847.
42. Ibid., 232. Chadwick to De la Beche, 26 Oct. 1842.
43. For reports on sanitary conditions in Swansea, Merthyr and Brecon see *Report of the Royal Commission into the State of Large Towns and Populous Districts* (London, 1845).
44. NMW, De la Beche Papers, 459. Bessie Dillwyn to De la Beche, 15 Dec. 1845.
45. Tom Sharpe, 'Henry De la Beche and the Geological Survey in Swansea', *Gower Journal*, 36 (1985), 5-12; and T. Sharpe and P. J. McCartney, *The Papers of H. T. De la Beche (1796-1855)*, National Museum of Wales (Cardiff, 1998).

SIR WILLIAM EDMOND LOGAN FRS
1798-1875

Geologist
Founding Director of the Geological Survey of Canada
Canada's Most Acclaimed Scientist

ß

If Henry De la Beche was the most colourful and charismatic of the early members of the Royal Institution at Swansea then the most enigmatic was his friend and fellow geologist William Edmond Logan. Even in a world of part-time gentlemen scholars, Logan was an anomaly. The usual pattern, enacted time after time in the nineteenth century, was for a youthful enthusiasm to blossom into a compelling adult interest. Vivian, Dillwyn, Jeffreys and De la Beche were attracted to science from boyhood.

Logan, on the other hand, one of the century's great field geologists, came to geology seemingly by accident. At thirty-two he was an accountant in London with, all the evidence suggests, no consuming interest in geology. But five years after his arrival in Swansea, at age thirty-seven, he was elected to the Geological Society of London and, at age forty-two, appointed founding director of the Geological Survey of Canada. A knighthood followed in 1856 and almost a century and a half later, in 1999, came his apotheosis: a panel of expert and informed lay jurists declared him to be Canada's most important scientist ever – ahead of Sir Frederick Banting, Alexander Graham Bell, and Sir William Osler.

The nature of Logan's rise has intrigued historians from the time of his biography (by Sir Bernard Harrington in 1883) to the present.[1] All agree that his background offers no clues. He was born in Montreal in 1798, the son of William Logan a prosperous baker and property owner and the grandson of James Logan of Stirling, Scotland. With two sons and a daughter James Logan and his wife Margaret Edmund emigrated to Montreal where they established a bakery business and invested in land in both Upper

Sir William Edmond Logan.

and Lower Canada and in Maine. Both ventures prospered. William, the eldest son, entered the bakery business and in 1794 he married his cousin, Janet Edmond, also of Stirling. They had nine children, five sons and four daughters, of whom William Edmond Logan was the third child. William and his brother, Hart, attended Montreal's Royal Grammar School, run by the Scotsman Alexander Skakel, after which they were sent to Edinburgh's prestigious High School, the alma mater of Sir Walter Scott, in the heart of the Old Town. A year later, in 1815, they were followed by their parents and sisters, the former after an absence of thirty-one years. They bought what they described as an elegant house in New Town from Lord Napier and in 1820/21 retired to Clarkstone, a small estate in Stirlingshire.

William Logan, who was clearly gifted, finished third in a class of 130. In a letter to a friend and associate in Montreal, his father noted that 'Willie was frequently Dux of the Rector's Class, which is the highest, in which there are upwards of 200 boys, and at the last examination he obtained two prizes'. His brother Hart, he also noted, was 'within a few places of Willie in the same class'.[2]

The University beckoned – 'Willie goes to colege [sic] next week' – and in 1816/17 he registered nominally as a medical student.[3] He began with classes in logic, mathematics and chemistry, the latter introducing him to mineralogy. His instructor in chemistry was Professor Thomas Charles Hope, who was then a protagonist in one of the most highly charged debates in the history of geology. On one side were the Plutonists, followers of James Hutton, who held that heat and pressure produced not only the granites and basalts, but also affected the stratified sedimentary rocks laid down on the beds of seas and oceans. Hutton's adversary was the German geologist, and tutor of John Henry Vivian, Abraham Gottlob Werner, who opposed fire with water by positing an aqueous origin for all rocks except those of recent volcanic origin. Heat and fire in geological time he attributed to the spontaneous combustion of beds of coal laid down in the great primeval oceans.

Hutton's nineteenth-century standard-bearer, and a gifted interpreter of his ideas, was John Playfair, who occupied the chair of natural philosophy at Edinburgh. Werner's chief British exponent was Robert Jameson, Professor of Natural History at the University, who studied with Werner at Freiburg in 1800-02. Thomas Charles Hope, whose father was an associate of James Hutton's, was an ardent Plutonist. The debate was international but its furious centre was in Edinburgh, in the halls of the university and the Royal Society. The historian Sir Archibald Geike, himself a dedicated Huttonian, conveys something of its flavour in his book *Landscape and History* (1905): 'His [Werner's] enthusiasm . . . fired his disciples with the zeal of proselytes, and they spread themselves over Europe to preach everywhere the artificial system that they had learned in Saxony'. By a curious fate Edinburgh became one of the great headquarters of Wernerism. The friends and followers of Hutton found themselves attacked in their own city by zealots who, proud of their superior mineralogical acquirements, turned most of their cherished ideas upside down and assailed them in the uncouth jargon of Freiburg. 'For Sir Walter Scott's neutral Meg Dods (*Waverley*, 1814), on the other hand, both houses were plagued. Geologists were simply people who 'rin uphill and down dale, knapping their chucky-stanes to pieces wi' hammers, like sae mony road-makers run daft, to see how the warld was made'.[4]

In his immensely popular lectures on chemistry, Hope would have introduced Logan, and the other five hundred students in the class, to mineralogy and geology as a matter of course. And, as an ardent supporter of Hutton and Playfair, there can be no doubt that he would not also have introduced the terms of the Plutonist-Neptunist debate. Nine years earlier, during a particularly volcanic phase of the debate, L. A. Necker de Saussure, a student of Hope's and prospective Professor of Geology at Geneva, left this vignette: 'The battles between the Huttonians and the Wernerians have been so frequent this past winter that much ground has been conquered and many prisoners taken on both sides. The field of battle is ordinarily the rooms of the Royal Society, but it is not uncommon to have skirmishes at the table of Sir James Hall'. In his lectures Hope 'inveigh[ed] always with insolence . . . against heretics who follow the maxims of a false prophet'.[5] Yet there is no evidence that the debate or Hope's advocacy had any effect on Logan. He won first prize in his mathematics class but within a few days of the end of his first university year, 1817, he left for London to work at the mercantile and accounting firm of his uncle Hart Logan in Finsbury Square, London. Away from the counting house, in a house he shared with an Edinburgh M.D., he lived the life of a cultivated London bachelor. He studied science and mathematics, took drawing lessons and studied languages – French, Italian and Spanish. 'Willie', wrote his proud father, 'is with his uncle in London, indefatigable in the pursuit of knowledge'.[6]

Willie also befriended Abel Lewes Gower, an associate of a neighbouring accounting firm, who had Welsh connections and who would marry his sister Elizabeth. Gower had geological interests and in 1833 he would be elected a member of the Geological Society of London. At that time, Logan's interest in geology seems to have been restricted to fossils collected on or near his uncle's estate at Kentwell in Suffolk and, on a visit to Italy in 1829, to noting in a diary filled with notes on art and architecture, the types of rock (granite, marble, porphyry, travertine, etc) from which columns, pediments and other architectural features were made.[7] But in this there is nothing that suggests more than a passing or, at most, a nascent interest in geology. On a walking and coach tour of the West Highlands in 1828, accompanied by Lewes Gower and two of his brothers, he reacted with fashionable fright to the 'sublime' features in the landscape. He noted their 'awfulness' but ignored the geology. At Glencoe, where towering rocks overhung the road in the 'most striking and terrific attitudes', he wrote: 'It is not without a secret feeling of dread that one beholds the awful scenery'. At Ballahulish, which his party reached after a fine moonlit drive along the shore of Loch Leven, he remarked, without apparent regret, that the light was too poor to see the slate quarry for which the place was famous. Of Ben Nevis, Britain's highest peak and – for a geologist – a mouth-watering remnant of exposed, ancient rock, he remarked only that it was a barren rock with, here and there, a permanent snow cover.[8]

For Logan to become even a competent geologist an epiphany was needed. Its instrument was his uncle, Hart Logan. In 1827 the accounting firm of Usborne and Benson, neighbours of Hart Logan in Finsbury Square, bought the Forest copper works at Morriston near Swansea. In 1830 Hart Logan, who had family connections in Glamorgan, had been induced to invest ten thousand pounds (a huge sum in 1830) in the works which, as well as smelting copper ore, experimented with a process for drawing the remaining metal from slag or furnace wastes that filled the valley. The assayer at the works was his sister's child, William Logan Edmond. The following spring he despatched another nephew, the accountant William Edmond Logan, to organize the company's affairs. Accounting soon turned to management, and management to the crucial matter of maintaining supplies of copper ore and coal. As a rule, maintaining supplies of ore was not difficult even though most of it came from places as distant as Cuba and Chile. Swansea had its own fleet of ore barques and as it was by far the largest market for ore, it controlled the world price and, to a large extent, the supply.

Coal, paradoxically, was a different matter especially in the early days of the copper industry. It took two or three times as much coal as ore to produce a given quantity of copper and, although the sources were local and abundant, securing a regular supply at a fair price was often difficult. The mines were small, the roads poor and, unless tramways had been built, overland transport was so costly that only coal near the rivers, or navigation, was of any value. Even more serious, most of the mines were owned by local landowners who, knowing full well the value of coal to the coppermen, clung to their mineral rights and charged to the limit. Robert Morris, founder of the Forest works, offered this recipe for amassing a fortune: 'I would have all who have money to adventure in mining especially on their own estates'. At his first copper works he had been wrung dry by a particularly knavish landowner who, having manoeuvred Morris into a position where he could buy only from his mines, then charged extortionate prices to supply 'muck and dirty coal'. Offered the lease of a colliery, which would allow him to dig his own coal, Morris seized the opportunity and built a new works, the Forest, on the riverbank below the mine. The new works was a quarter of a mile from the old.

Logan could not have been long at the Forest works without becoming aware of the importance of reliable supplies of ore and especially of coal. In June 1832 the superintendent at the Graigola mine, four miles from the works, told him that it would be two months before he got to the Forest coal.[9] The getting of coal and ore, Logan remarked in a letter to his brother James in Montreal was his true introduction to geology: 'The study of ores of copper has gradually led me to that of mineralogy and geology, and of specimens in both I have become a bit of a collector . . . I attend to nothing else but the making of copper and [the] digging of coal from morning to night'. As soon as he had set up what he described as 'a proper and regular system of accounts', a labour that involved months of work from early morning until late at night, he wrote to his brother Henry in London asking him to send scientific books. He specified works on mechanics, chemistry, mineralogy and geology. He also asked for his old clothes: 'This will be a famous place to wear them out . . . [and] a sin and a shame to wear anything else'. A year later, in 1832, with his interest in geology clearly rising, he asked Henry to buy him a theodolite, an indispensable instrument for any form of precise topographical and geological mapping. No expense was to be spared. 'If a pound or two would make the theodolite much better', he wrote, 'I should be disposed to give it. I'll live on a milk diet, and save the money in a short time'.

From this point on geology absorbed him. Self deprecatingly, he liked to insist later that he was nothing but a simple miner and metallurgist going about his business and that self-interest 'forced' him into the study of geology. But the period of compulsion could only have been fleeting. On a two-month business trip to France and Spain in 1834, where he hoped to increase metal sales and, from the latter, acquire new supplies of ore, he took along the third volume of Lyell's *Principles of Geology*. Even more telling was his behaviour during what he described as a tiresome session with the company's lawyers in London. He complained to his brother Hart that 'if it were not for the consolation of a little geology a leap from London Bridge would be my only cure'. His consolation on that occasion was a visit to the Isle of Sheppey, a favourite haunt of fossil-seeking gentlemen geologists five hours by steam packet down the estuary of the Thames. On his first day he studied the London clay formations, and on the second he got up at 3am to take a boat for Sheerness on the island's north coast. He arrived at Sheerness at 7 a.m. and after a quick breakfast, spent the day looking for fossils alongside the artisan collectors who, as at Lyme Regis, sold their finds to visiting collectors and geologists. On Sheppey there were no mines or metals.

While jointly managing the Forest works, Logan chose to live in Swansea, walking, except in the worst weather, the three or four miles to Morriston. He took rooms on the seafront in fashionable Cambrian Place, probably in the house of Starling Benson who was a fellow manager at the Forest and the son of one of the owners. Benson's house was next to the handsome Assembly Rooms, the scene of dancing, card and billiard playing, and general merriment. Benson, a fellow bachelor, seems to have been a bon vivant but Logan appears to have been retiring and restrained; he disapproved of his uncle Hart's fondness for vintage wines and rich food. Yet he could deliver a comic song and there is one record of his appearance at a fancy dress ball at the Assembly Rooms in the costume of a Contrabandista, possibly a souvenir from a visit to Spain.

Although there is some doubt about Logan's exact domicile in Cambrian Place – he was not a ratepayer – there is none about his spiritual home in Swansea. A short distance from the Assembly Rooms were the quarters of the Philosophical and Literary Institution of which Logan was one of eleven founding members.

When the Institution acquired its royal insignia, in 1838, Logan was elected to the ten-man General Purpose Committee. He was also one of two honorary secretaries and he would be appointed curator of the geology museum. When rehoused in its elegant Palladian home, the Institution was even closer to Cambrian Place. Logan contributed toward the costs of ashlaring the front in Bath stone and the purchase of meteorological instruments. He and his brother Hart also bought two shares of ten pounds each.

In his spare time, Logan studied geology and began mapping the outcrops of the western half of the south Wales coalfield. For general information on south Wales he read *Outlines of the Geology of England and Wales* by William Conybeare and John Phillips and, to guide him in his mapping and field observations, De la Beche's *Geological Manual*. In the *Manual*, De la Beche stressed the importance of plotting on the best available maps and of making geological cross-sections which, for preference, should have similar horizontal and vertical scales. A more specific work on the coalfield he is known to have consulted was Edward Martin's *Description of the Mineral Basin of South Wales,* 1806, which contained a detailed stratigraphic log listing all the known coal seams within the Swansea section of the coal basin. Martin was a mineral engineer and land surveyor. Other available maps were William Smith's 1815 map of the geology of England and Wales at a scale of five miles to the inch and George Bellas Greenough's 1819 map at the slightly smaller scale of six miles to the inch. Greenough's map, sponsored by the Geological Society and resting on the observations of many geologists, was more accurate than Smith's solo pioneer effort but it was still extremely generalized.

Precisely when Logan began his systematic survey and mapping of the coal measures is not known but attending, as he put it, 'to the minutest details of every branch of the business' must have kept him occupied for more than a year. In 1832, however, he had already indicated, when requesting a theodolite from his brother Henry, that he had made up his mind to prepare a geological map of the Swansea area, more detailed and larger in scale than the maps of Smith and Greenough.[10] In 1837, when the work was well underway, he wrote to his brother James in Montreal: 'The locality to which I have especially directed my attention is this immediate neighbourhood, of which during the leisure hours, I am gradually getting up a geological survey and sections. If I ever return to Canada again I shall geologize there'. One-inch Ordnance Survey maps of the Swansea region, on which he could begin colouring the outcrops, had been available since 1830.

For information on the coal seams and the stratigraphy he used Edward Martin's log, supplemented by whatever he could learn from miners, mining engineers and mineral surveyors. Most of the miners, many of whom came from the rural counties west of Swansea, would have been Welsh-speaking and there is evidence that Logan, alone among the *arrivistes,* attempted to learn Welsh. Among his many contributions to the Royal Institution were a Welsh New Testament and a Welsh primer. How much progress he made is questionable; later, in Canada, he described one of the aboriginal languages as opaque, 'nearly as unintelligible', as Welsh.

Logan's social standing, his prominence in the RISW, and his field accomplishments guaranteed his election to the Geological Society of London, in January 1837. Two of his sponsors were Richard Janion Nevill, owner of a Llanelli copper works and father-in-law of the conchologist Gwyn Jeffreys, and John Taylor, a mining and economic geologist and Treasurer of the GSL. Logan, who was clearly delighted with his election, wrote to his brother James: 'I have become a bit of a geologist of late years, and am now entitled to write after my name FGS – being a Fellow of the Geological Society'. In the field he would have worn the Society uniform, a black or white top hat (white in Logan's case), a formal (but not dress) coat, and a knapsack or backpack. . . . He might have been looking for coal seams to guarantee supplies for the Forest works but as a gentleman geologist he would also have wanted to maintain some social distance from miners, quarrymen, surveyors and engineers: men whose livelihoods depended on working the rocks and minerals. His basic equipment would have included a hammer, a field notebook and the best and largest-scale topographic maps available. A hammer, which was used for knapping 'chucky stanes' and breaking through weathered and moss or lichen-covered surfaces, was, with the top hat, the badge of a geologist. Other important accessories were a magnetic compass for measuring the strike, or direction of the outcrops; a clinometer for measuring the tilt or angle of dip of the strata; a barometer for measuring elevation; a small bottle of acid for detecting limestone; and a low-power hand lens for examining and identifying minerals. If a theodolite, for measuring relative heights, and a chain, for measuring distances, were needed then an assistant had to be hired.

Logan's star was rising but for the moment his stage was local. When not mapping or minding the works he immersed himself in the affairs of the RISW. As curator of geology he built up the collection with specimens of rocks, minerals and rare metals (palladium, tellurium, rhodium, cadmium) from his own collection as well as with others sent by his brother James from Canada, and those requested of mariners returning from Chile, Peru, Mexico and parts of Europe. To these he added crystals and solidified metal and mineral substances found deposited in the crevices of flues and in the bottoms of the furnaces. He hoped that these might throw some light on the chemistry of mineralogy and the mechanisms of crystallization.

As one of two honorary secretaries of the RISW, Logan wrote the report for the second annual meeting. He used the section on geology as a platform for the disclosure of – for a man reputed to be reserved – a surprisingly impassioned credo. He considered geology to be of the utmost benefit to mankind. As a science, it was 'calculated to awaken the attention and excite the imagination, to astonish by the tremendous facts it discloses'. To a receptive geologist, he asserted, even 'the most dead and desolate rock is replete with life' while a mining district, offering a mass of invaluable information ready to hand, 'is the very empire of Geology'. He followed this with an appeal and a suggested *modus vivendi* for the Institution: 'If all the facts known to each humble miner in the country surrounding us were gathered into a mass, and properly digested, the condition of this part of the earth would be nearly as plain to us as if its surfaces were transparent. . . . What service then would [this] Institution perform for Geology, were it to arrest this evanescent knowledge, by taking pains to collect the facts within the cognizance of the common miners of the country, and to obtain and preserve copies of the various maps and sections that so commonly abound.

In a short time there would remain little doubt as to the out-crop, strike and dip of the mineral beds of the coalfield, the course and magnitude of its faults, the composition of the rocks, . . . temperature of its mines and springs – all those numerous researches which the British Association warmly recommends local societies to undertake. 'The Committee', he concluded 'strongly urges the adoption of some systematic plan for the collection of such information and to entreat members to use all their influence with coal proprietors, surveyors and others to enlighten the Institution on the various points alluded to'.

In the report he also gave notice of his forthcoming map of the coalfield. At the last meeting of the British Association he noted that William Daniel Conybeare, when presenting a paper and map of a large portion of the south Wales coalfield, had expressed the hope that among the members of the recently founded Institution at Swansea might be found someone who would prosecute the work to a completion. The Committee, he wrote somewhat drolly, was pleased to report that the request had to some extent been anticipated, and one of its members was then engaged in laying down on the Ordnance maps the outcrops and the strike and dip of the beds between the Vale of Neath and Cydweli.

Although engrossed in geology Logan, as he intimated in a letter to his brother Henry, had some interest in the process of smelting copper: 'I shall master every branch of the business and as it is of a scientific nature I am pretty sure I shall like it'. After four centuries of smelting, Welsh coppermen had elevated the practice of smelting to a fine art, drawing, through the so-called Welsh Process, virtually every ounce of metal from the ore. Refining the slag at the Forest works proved to be unprofitable. The one problem that Welsh coppermen had not been able to overcome was how to remove from the smoke the poisons that killed grasses and shrubs and the animals that fed on them. Logan arrived in Swansea when local farmers and landowners were preparing to launch a series of lawsuits in which they hoped to either indict the copper works or wrest damages from them. Because all the works were vulnerable to prosecution it was almost inevitable that Logan, William Edmond and Starling Benson, all of whom had scientific interests, should tackle the smoke problem. To it Logan owed, in a letter written by Henry De la Beche, his introduction to Michael Faraday whom he wished to consult on 'one or two chemical points'. 'He is a gentleman', wrote De la Beche, 'who has devoted himself much to science, and I can answer for it, that among other things, he is better acquainted with the great Welsh coal field than anyone else'.[11]

The Forest's efforts at smoke suppression, which were orchestrated by Nicholas Troughton, were applauded by the council of the RISW as a sterling example of the application of chemistry to the useful arts. Troughton's contrivance, described by the council as 'simple and efficacious', was a retort or muffle in which the ores and semi metals were heated. The smoke from these was kept separate from coal smoke and treated with water long enough to remove, by absorption, the sulphurous acid gas. The process, Troughton maintained, did not seriously interfere with the draught, a sine qua non of smelting. In conjunction with a London patent agent, Richard Phillips, the chemist and curator of the Museum of Economic Geology, issued a detailed report on Troughton's designs and their application at the Forest works. He concluded that they were 'new, useful, and decidedly successful'. But the *Mining Journal* was less enthusiastic questioning, as always, the applicability of any invention that departed from long-standing smelting practices. Troughton's condensers were never adopted by the industry. By the end of the experiment, however, Richard Phillips and Logan were friends. Phillips submitted a bill, but apologetically, because 'those blind Jades, the Fates, made me a *chemist* instead of a *gentleman* as they might easily, and in point of fact, ought to have done'. Later, in 1842, he implored Logan that even if he couldn't travel to London '*at any rate let me hear from you*'.

In September 1837, at the British Association meeting in Liverpool, Logan presented his geological map of the coal basin between the Vale of Neath and Carmarthen Bay and, with Adam Sedgwick in the chair, delivered a companion paper on patterns of faulting and their effects on the distribution of coal. Logan laid great emphasis on faulting and its effect on mining, a subject that had been anticipated by Tubal Cain in his essay on the mineral basin of Glamorgan written for the Cardiff Eisteddfod, 1835.[12] Cain pointed out that there were not so many faults or 'leaps' in the ground in any part of the basin as on the south side in the neighbourhood of Neath. In many places there were as many as three or four in the space of forty or fifty yards, wholly preventing any person when beginning a patch or opening a level from knowing what kind of mine he might have.

Logan remarked on the parallelism of the faults, their general N-S direction, and the tendency of the master faults to run across the coal basin to the mountain limestone and into the Old Red Sandstone. Frequent and severe faulting made for complicated and frustrating mining, never more so than when the faults, dipping at shallow angles, arranged or stacked the coal seams in overlapping layers or, as the miners described them, 'leaves'. He also stressed the importance of weighing carefully the information given by miners who, as practical men, tended to observe closely only those disturbances or discontinuities that affected them. Faulting, too, as the Welsh miners reported, could also affect the quality of the coal and decisions about directions in which to drive adits or sink shafts. On the upthrow side of a fault, the seams – probably, Logan surmised, as a function of internal heating – frequently contained less bitumen.

When De la Beche arrived in Swansea in December 1837, two months after the British Association meeting at Liverpool, he had nothing but praise for Logan's work. He described the map as 'beautifully executed [and] of an order so greatly superior to that usual with geologists . . . we shall adopt it for that part of the country to which it relates'. Eighteen months later, when accepting an honorary membership of the RISW for the absent Richard Phillips, De la Beche remarked that compliments heaped on him by the chairman's report properly belonged to Logan. Logan's geological labours in the district had been 'indefatigable . . . and proof of the great advantage the practical miner may derive from such investigations'. Andrew Crombie Ramsay, who would be appointed director-general of the Geological Survey in 1872, considered that Logan's map had been rendered 'in a style of such beautiful detail, that no map of any coalfield that had been done before, approached it in excellence'.

The horizontal and vertical sections, at scales of six inches to the mile and forty feet to the inch, that accompanied the map, also elicited superlatives from Ramsay. They were made, he added, with such 'excessive' detail that anyone interested in mining could judge with great accuracy not only the lie of the beds of coal but the precise nature of the strata that would have to be sunk through in order to reach them.[13] Logan's accuracy was also confirmed by John Phillips, the Survey's palaeontogist, in a letter to De la Beche: 'I am happy to confirm [re. mapping the boundary of the Carboniferous Limestone] Logan's accuracy, in one or two places remarkably'.[14] In a lecture at Montreal in 1856, the renowned railway engineer Sir Sandford Fleming reiterated the earlier judgements. Logan's map was 'unrivalled in its time and never surpassed since'. With not a line out of place, Fleming noted, Logan had left the Geological Survey little choice but to adopt his method of mapping details.

The years 1837 and 1838 were pivotal ones for Logan. His map and his membership of the Geological Society propelled him from a local onto a national stage. They were also years in which he was released, by the near simultaneous deaths of his uncle Hart Logan and his brother Henry in April 1838, from management of the copper works. Both left him their shares in the Forest Works, amounting to 21/48ths of the whole. Starling Benson held the remainder. Hart Logan also left his nephew £5,000 and Henry left £10,000. Within months of their deaths, Logan resigned his salaried position with the company. But any prospect he might have held of sitting back and drawing dividends quickly evaporated. Later that year the Gowers recalled a loan of £50,000, made to the company in 1835, only £30,000 of which could be repaid. To raise the remainder the works had to be mortgaged. The company survived the recall but it never recovered fully. Logan might have been distressed – he confesssed on a voyage to Canada in 1843 that Coleman Street, the address of the Gowers, had made him bilious – but unlike De la Beche, who was impoverished by the troubles on his Jamaican estate, Logan was never short of the 'needful'.

However unsettling his business negotiations with the Gowers, Logan could now concentrate on geology. He continued to build up the Royal Institution's collection of fossils and minerals and as curator of geology, honorary secretary, and a member of the steering committee, he was instrumental in forging a link between the RISW and the Museum of Economic Geology in London. He pointed out how applicable to Swansea and south Wales were De la Beche's remarks, in his report on Devon and Cornwall, on geology as a useful art. Mining and smelting were now the main-stays of the regional, not only the town's economy. In a letter to De la Beche, he wondered if the RI might serve as a provincial agent for the Museum of Economic Geology, supplying it with information on local mining and manufacturing and receiving, in return, such guidance in its general operations as the Museum might afford. De la Beche, who had been impressed by what he described as the 'abundance of talent' in the institution, replied that Logan's proposal of a capital/provincial partnership accorded entirely with the objectives for which the Museum of Economic Geology had been established.[15]

During his remaining years in Swansea, Logan served as an unpaid adviser, surveyor and mapmaker to the Geological Survey. To the Survey, Logan was a gift and De la Beche wanted more from him than coloured maps: 'Now my dear Logan, as I want to do you every justice, had you not better give me some account of the coal beds themselves which I can quote as yours, or at any rate let me have the information which I can give as from you'.[16] Relations between them were warm from the outset. Profession-ally, too, they were an ideal pairing; both were committed field geologists who with maps and sketches could limn the form and structure of a landscape. Logan's credo 'Give me your facts first, theories afterward', was also De la Beche's.[17] Although both were career-long members of the Geological Society they frowned on its espousal of grand, all-encompassing theories at the expense of careful, detailed studies. In April 1844 Logan sent to De la Beche a report on the carboniferous beds at Joggins, Nova Scotia, with the telling rider 'You can make a public document of it if you like by communicating it to the Geological Society. I am aware they would not print it. There is not enough poetry about it for their pages'.

In addition to his finely drawn maps and sections of the south Wales coalfield, Logan's other major contribution to geology during his Swansea years were his observations on the origins of coal. He presented these in a paper read to the Geological Society in February 1840 and published them subsequently in the Trans-actions and in the annual report of the RISW.[18] Grand cosmo-logical theories may not have interested him but the coal

measures were his field and, because the Carboniferous represented the limits of accurate geological knowledge, they were a
subject of intense study and debate. There was general agreement
that coal formed from accumulations of vegetable matter, but
geologists were divided over how the accumulations occurred.
Some believed that primeval forests were swept by floods from
their original sites into deep lakes or estuaries where they became
waterlogged, sank to the bottom and were then covered by
deposits of sand and clay. Others held that they owed their
existence to the luxuriant growth of plants in vast marshes or
bogs that either subsided or were overwhelmed with floodwaters.
Places that were once their habitation, Logan noted sombrely,
became their tomb.

Loopholes in the hypothesis that coal seams began as great
swirling rafts of forest trees were obvious: the great lateral extent
of many of the seams, their uniform thickness, and their freedom
from mechanical mixtures of sand and clay suggested a less
capricious origin. But the most telling fact of all, Logan asserted,
was that in south Wales they were always underlain by 'a sub-
jacent seam of clay' known variously as under-clay, under-stone,
dan-stone, *carreg gwaelod*, and bottom stone. There was not a
miner in Wales, he insisted, who, when presented with a specimen, would not recognize it at once. In the coal measures of
south Wales, some 12 to 13,000 feet thick, there were more than a
hundred seams of coal about half of which, with a thickness of a
foot or more, had been worked. In every case the seams were
underlain by clays. So thoroughly conjoined were coal and clay
that a south Welsh miner, he declared, would as soon live in a
house without a foundation as work a coal seam without underclay.

The most distinguishing feature of the clays, which varied in
width from six inches to ten feet but averaged about three feet,
was what he described as the peculiar character of their organic
remains. In every possible direction they were penetrated by a
confused and tangled collection of slender fibrous impressions,
all covered with a thin covering of carbonaceous matter. To them
paleontologists had given the name *Stigmaria Ficoides*. William
Buckland and the botanist and palaeontogist John Lindley
concluded that the *Stigmaria* were the fossilized remains of

Fossilized trees found at Cwm Llech.

aquatic plants, trailing in swamps or floating in still and shallow lakes, that became entangled and anchored in mud. The mixture of mud and fine roots formed the soil for the growth and accumulation of the pure vegetable mass which was in time converted into coal. But drifting masses of vegetation which became anchored, Logan argued, could not account for the unfailing combination of coal and fibrous underclays, and for the extent of the coal seams. Logan was led to the inescapable conclusion, shared by H. Steinhauer who had examined underclays in Leeds and elsewhere, that the fibrous materials were the roots of standing trees. A few decades earlier the Swiss geologist Jean-Andre Deluc had declared that coal was no more than the remains of plants that had died where we now find the coal, rather than floating rafts of vegetation that had become anchored. In other words, Northern Europe must once have been covered with lush, near-waterlogged tropical rainforest.

If *Stigmaria* were the roots of fossil trees then, Logan asserted, it was logical to assume that the trees had grown in the clays. If the geological equivalent of a smoking gun were needed, he found it at Nant Llech, Coelbren, in 1837. Dillwyn's diary for 3 April reads: 'Four large Sigillariae [tree ferns], rising vertically through strata of shale and sandstone, as if they had grown on the spot, were this day discovered by my friend, W. E. Logan Esq., in Cwm Llech, near the head of the Swansea valley'. The fossil trees were preserved upright, in the growth position, exposed in the sides of a narrow wooded cleft, their lower extremities, according to the report of the Philosophical and Literary Institution, buried in a bed of shale. There were indications of so many other trunks in the vicinity that, the report continued, 'it is not extravagant to imagine that, were the sides of the dell cleared away, a whole primeval forest of those gigantic Segillaria [*sic*], standing as they grew, would be exhibited to the wondering eyes of the beholder'.[19] The two standing trees were excavated by De la Beche who used illustrations of them in his book *Geological Observer*. The trees, known still as the 'Logan trees', stand in an enclosed garden in front of the RISW.

'Logan's trees' found at Cwm Llech.

After 1838/39 family and business affairs interrupted Logan's work for De la Beche, and their written exchanges tended to take the form of apologies from Logan and friendly beseeching from De la Beche, who was anxious to get on with the south Welsh survey. In July 1839 Logan wrote from London: 'I found I had an appointment to keep in London and could not conveniently spend any time in Swansea. But I hope I shall not be detained here long. I am very anxious to make progress in my sections'.[20] And in November 1839: 'I am sadly annoyed at being called up to London so often to the great interruption of my west end sections. [De la Beche and his assistants were surveying the east end] and I am not without a lurking fear that such repeated absences may operate to render some things not so perfect as I intended they should be'.[21]

In the summer of 1840 he had to leave at short notice for Canada where, Dillwyn remarked to De la Beche, 'some screw was found to be loose in his affairs', ie family business.[22] Before leaving, Logan wrote to De la Beche: 'If I should sink in the Atlantic I must trust to you for posthumous fame. I shall put you down in my will, which I have not made yet, for all my sections etc'.[23] And, 'In the meantime if you want any of my papers you are welcome to use whatever you can lay your hands on in my room in Cambrian Place, only do not lose anything'.[24] De la Beche was in a quandary as the excursion to Canada meant an inevitable delay in the completion of the Neath-Carmarthen maps and sections, to which Logan wanted to add details, and he did not want to present unfinished maps to the public. Yet his humour did not fail him: 'Much as I value your documents and want to get them, I don't want to obtain them on the posthumous terms you speak of. I trust you will long continue to work geologically above ground'.[25]

By the summer of 1841 Logan, his business in Quebec and Montreal concluded, was still in North America intent on finding evidence to prove that under-clays were universal and not just regional phenomena. Several prominent members of the Geological Society were still sceptical of the theory, among them Roderick Impey Murchison who referred to underclays as 'the pabulum of our coalfields'. Murchison had done extensive field-work in Europe and Russia so it was understandable that Logan, not wishing to trespass, should turn toward North America. From Montreal he travelled to New York and from there to Philadelphia and the Pennsylvania coalfields. To ensure that in North America he would not be mistaken for anything but a gentleman geologist he had packed his Geological Society insignia: his tall white hat. When it did not reach New York his distress, in a letter to his brother James in Montreal, was palpable: 'In spite of all my care I have already lost my hatbox with my hat in it. There was the devil's own confusion . . . in putting the baggage into the baggage wagon . . . I saw my hat box go in but though I watched every article as it came out of the wagon my unfortunate hat box was not among the number. I spent *three hours* looking for it but all in vain'.[26] [My italics]

Distress at losing his hat would, however, have been softened by a chance meeting in New York with Charles Lyell who was on a lecture tour. Logan wrote to his brother James, 'By accident I saw Mr Lyell in the street and on returning to the hotel found his family had rooms in it. I therefore determined to make his acquaintance upon the strength of an introduction I had to him some 12 or 13 years ago'. Lyell, however, was not there on the Saturday so he waited until the following Monday in order to catch him. 'I met him in the lobby this morning and on my mentioning to him my name I found he knew me perfectly well as Mr Logan of Swansea'. He supplied Logan with introductions to the leading American experts on coal and directed him to mines in Pennsylvania that he knew were particularly rich in *Stigmaria*. He also informed him that he intended to notice at some length his paper on underclays in the next edition of his book *Principles of Geology*.[27]

On his return from Pennsylvania Logan wrote again to James from New York. 'If all other modes of support fail me I feel assured that in the gigantic coalfields of America I should be able to derive a comfortable subsistence from coal viewing. The inhabitants and proprietors of the various coal fields are anxious for information on the subjects of coal deposits and look with eagerness to the opinions of practical miners with education from Britain'. The coal seams were so thick and, in contrast to south Wales, so little faulted, that it was as if Providence, he remarked, had determined to make Virginia, Pennsylvania and Ohio the workshops of the world. 'Imagine', he exclaimed, 'a coal seam 50 feet thick!' But in the Appalachian fields his real interest was not so much in the coal seams, however thick and unbroken, as in what lay beneath them. 'You may suppose that in my examination of those parts it did not displease me to find that my underclay plays as conspicuous a figure – it tells exactly the same story it does in South Wales. I am now pretty certain that the facts I have stated of that district are not merely local but universal, and I shall be confirmed of this opinion if it is not contradicted at Pictou'.[28]

Pictou, Nova Scotia, did not disappoint. At the Albion mines, he found what he was looking for. When about to sail from Halifax to Britain, he wrote to James in Montreal. 'I know what the ground contains for a mile deep in that [the Pictou] neighbourhood and in every case where I have seen a seam of coal it is accompanied by an underclay, filled with stigmaria ficoides. My [fact?] therefore I now consider established beyond controversy and I shall tell the Geological Society the same before the winter is over'.[29] At Pictou he met Thomas Chandler Haliburton, creator of Nova Scotia's legendary fictional character Sam Slick, who owned property on which there were plaster mines. But Haliburton was a humorist not a miner and Logan's questions on stratigraphy and plaster rock met an insuperable fault line.

After the Pictou visit he wrote again to Lyell, who was lecturing to American audiences of a thousand and more, to tell him of his finds. Lyell replied from Boston that he had received the letter 'with independent confirmation of your theory beyond your wildest expectations'.[30] Logan also told De la Beche of his discoveries at Manchunk on the Lehigh River and at Wilkesbarre on the Susquahanna: 'I now consider it a truth universally applicable, that immediately below every workable Coal Seam will be found a bed filled with the remains of Stigmariae ficoides. As in Wales these beds are almost always fireclays'. De la Beche's feelings on Logan's prolonged absence were decidedly mixed. He was anxious to get Logan home to finish his maps but as a friend and fellow natural scientist he also wanted him to demonstrate the universality of his underclay theory. In July he had written: 'When will we see you in England? And when to complete the geology of your portion of the South Welsh Coalfield? Month after month rolls on and I am told 'Logan will soon be here' but somehow Logan does not come'.[31] When Logan did return, De la Beche greeted him not as a long overdue associate and colleague but as a long-absent friend. From Pembrokeshire in November he expressed delight at the news of Logan's return and hoped that he would soon come to see him so that 'I should have the pleasure of shaking you again by the hand and talking over our old coal measure rambles'.

As a strong proponent of the theory of under-clays, De la Beche had defended it against powerful opposition at the British Association meeting at Newcastle in 1838: 'I told them that there could be *no doubt* that coal beds were [not?] *all drifted* vegetable matter. I was shuffled and banged about . . . most unmercifully by all the geologicals there' but he was pleased to report that most were now coming to.[32] Earlier that year, 1841, he had recommended Logan's paper on underclays for publication in the Society's Transactions. 'I ought not according to the rules to tell you so, but the paper was referred to me and I reported that it should be printed in our Transactions. . . . By the way you will laugh when I tell you that the whole kit of Geologicals after being in opposition to us are now coming around to the growth of coal in place. They stick fast in the underclays – capital that'.[33] As a precaution, he advised Logan to inform the Society of his discoveries in North America: 'Had you not better send a letter to the Geol. Society, London, about your American underclays, so that they may not rob you of your discovery there'. He also cautioned Logan about confiding in Lyell (Murchison's ally in the Devonian controversy) who had, or was about to (the handwriting is not clear) present the underclay theory at the Geological Society: 'but whether or not he quotes *you* for the knowledge of it I cannot tell'.[34] Like all writers of popular works of synthesis, Lyell relied heavily on the research of others, and to his detractors he was known as 'the pump'.

The finger of plagiarism, or of unacknowledged appropriation, was also pointed at Logan, and probably just as unfairly. In May 1842 Harvey Buchanan Holl, then of the Pennsylvania Survey wrote to De la Beche accusing Logan of falsely claiming to be the first to notice *Stigmaria* in the underclays. Logan may not have cited Holl's candidate for the honour, a Mr. Masurnath who, according to Holl, had mentioned the fact some 6-8 years earlier, but he had been careful to point out that his aim was to establish the universality of the conjunction of coal seams and underclays, not the primacy of his observation.[35] Holl, who appears to have been nursing a grudge, in the same letter also accused Logan of not acknowledging his sources in a paper to the Geological Society: 'That gentleman' [Logan] had forgotten to state the sources of much of his information, especially when referring to the ridges and axes of the Great Western Coal basin. Some of the information had been provided by members of the Corps and some abstracted from published reports. But Logan, Holl accused, 'with great care suppresses any allusion to these documents'.

While in Pennsylvania Logan was encouraged by members of the state Survey to present himself as a candidate for the position of founding director of the Geological Survey of Canada. In July 1841 the Natural History Society of Montreal and the Historical Society of Quebec petitioned the first united parliament of Upper and Lower Canada for a sum not exceeding 1500 pounds, to embark on a geological survey of the country. With no base, or topographical maps to work with, and in rough forested and mosquito and black-fly infested country, Logan knew that survey-ing in Canada would hardly be the same as surveying in south Wales. But he wanted the position and he was confident that it could be his. In a letter to his brother James from New York in September he wrote: 'I am not afraid of competition with anyone I know of. De la Beche once told me that I am the best geological mapper in Britain'.[36] As an associate of Logan's and director of the British Survey, De la Beche would be his most influential referee. 'No testimonial', wrote Logan, 'would be so weighty as one from yourself', and he reminded him, a little ungraciously, that he was owed something by the Survey. 'I hope I do not presume too much in saying that the Ordnance owes me a good word. . . . Buckland said to me he would give me a character if I referred to him'. And, to reassure De la Beche that he would finish his maps he added: 'In respect to the coalfield of South Wales it is my intention to work at it at the rate of a hundred horsepower steam engine'.[37]

A week later he sent another entreaty: 'If there is to be a survey of that province [Canada] it would not be a bad thing perhaps to have it supposed that the director of it was approved by the head of the Survey of this Country'.[38] This was followed by another reassuring reference to the south Wales maps: 'I have been working like a negro (sometimes as near to it in colour to one as coal could make me) morning noon & night at my sections & maps'.[39] But Logan had no need to call in professional debts. De la Beche was only too willing to lend support and assured Logan that he need never fear for a good word from him: 'only tell me how the matter is to be managed and it shall be done'.[40] Logan must also have intimated that he had been encouraged by Lyell, whom De la Beche still clearly distrusted after the Devonian dispute: 'I don't see how being humbugged by Lyell can do you any good – quite the contrary. His influence is not worth a pinch of snuff'.[41]

De la Beche's letter to Sir Charles Bagot, governor general of Canada, was long and astute; it cited Logan's abilities as a field geologist and map maker and his generous contributions to the British Geological Survey. His work on south Wales was not only of 'an order so greatly superior to that usual with geologists' but it had been 'most handsomely placed at our disposal'. He trumped this with the utility card: 'And I would further observe that Mr Logan is highly qualified as a miner and metallurgist to point out the applications of geology to the useful purposes of life, an object of the highest importance in a country like Canada, the mineral wealth of which is so little known'. Charles Bagot also received, via the Colonial Office, glowing testimonials from Adam Sedgewick at Cambridge, and Sir Roderick Impey Murchison who was then president of the Geological Society. Buckland, who had also been approached, wrote to the Bishop of Oxford, the brother of Sir Charles Bagot, describing Logan not only as an outstanding geologist and an agreeable companion but 'also a man of modest and gentlemanly demeanour and of high principle'.

His letter, relayed via Sir Charles Bagot and the Natural History Society of Montreal, reached the press. It had, Logan wrote to De la Beche 'a wonderful effect in Canada'. As a result, 'I am afraid I must look as wise as an owl & practice humbug a little to keep up my character of Sir Oracle'.[42] Lyell, too, writing from Boston on learning of Logan's discovery of *Stigmaria*, gave him his blessing: 'I wish you success in your Canada plans, and I think them very fortunate if they obtain your services'.[43] It was generous of Lyell as he, too, was not uninterested in the Canadian position but it was the gift of a Tory government and Lyell was a Whig. In 1842 he wrote to James Hall of the New York Survey: 'I have no reason to suppose it would be offered to me, nor if it were am I sure I should best promote the good cause by undertaking it in preference to projected operations. It will be time enough to think of this when I am invited'.[44]

With Lyell a non-starter in the competition, Logan was an automatic choice and he was duly appointed on 14 April 1842. When Lewis Weston Dillwyn announced his appointment at the seventh annual general meeting of the RISW the members responded with hurrahs and loud cheers. Logan was one of their own, if not strictly speaking a Swansea boy then certainly a Swansea product. On his return to Wales, he completed the work on his south Wales maps and sections, and sailed for Canada in the spring of 1843.[45] His equipment included a rifle bought from a Birmingham manufacturer, some canvas tents, and his tall, white gentleman geologist's hat.[46]

As much as Logan coveted the directorship of the Canadian Survey, he was uneasy about the emphasis placed on mineral resources, and feared that Canada in its desire to know the possibilities would, like the American states, insist on annual reports. He regarded these as hasty, 'unsatisfactory documents, for the most part undigested records of real progress' that could be 'detrimental to the true progress of science'.[47] At heart he was a scholar, an academic geologist and the discovery of minerals was incidental, not central to his aims. In his desire to perpetuate the Survey once it was underway, he, like De la Beche in Devon and Cornwall, subsidized it. From his annual budget of £1,500 he was supposed to provide his own salary of £500, his assistant's salary of £150, maintain an office, museum and a laboratory and pay a chemist. By the end of the second year the Survey owed him £800. Historians of geology argue over the relative weighting of Logan's interests but there can be no question that science weighed more heavily than practical utility.

To please the public and politicians he was fond of characterising himself as a simple miner and metallurgist, in much the same way as a distinguished agronomist might describe himself as a farmer. But this, as the Canadian historian Nancy Christie argues, was a disarming conceit designed to convince government that he was looking for minerals, when his real intentions were scientific. His aim was to examine the geology of what is now eastern Canada and establish links between its rock formations and those of Britain and Europe. De la Beche, to whom Logan had confided his fear of being restricted to the search for economic minerals, offered this unequivocal advice: 'You must consider us [at the BGS] as a kind of colleagues, all working for the same end, and that the cause of truth'.[48] To provide himself with some freedom of action Logan, according to Christie, never once drew his director's salary.

Although his first executive action was to conduct a survey of the Silurian formations in the St Lawrence Lowlands, which were of great interest to British geologists, Logan could not, and did not ignore the metallic minerals. In 1845 he initiated a search for copper, nickel and iron in the metal-rich Precambrian rocks of the Canadian Shield, and when asked by the Government to prepare a display of economic minerals for the 1851 Exhibition of the Industries of all Nations in London, Logan produced one that outclassed its rivals. Honours now rained upon him. In 1851 he was elected to a fellowship of the Royal Society, the first Canadian scientist to be so honoured. Also elected that year were the zoologist and Darwinist Thomas Henry Huxley and Robert Fitzroy, commander of the Beagle, a pioneer of weather forecasting, and an ardent Creationist. Among Logan's proposers were Henry De la Beche, Charles Lyell, Edward Forbes, and Charles Darwin. A knighthood followed in 1856, the year in which the Geological Society of London also awarded him its prized Wollaston medal for his *in situ* coal theory. In 1863, with co-authors Murray, Hunt and Billings, he published the *Geology of Canada* and followed this in 1865 with an atlas of coloured geological maps. For his many contributions to geology the Royal Society in 1867 awarded him its Royal Gold Medal. On receiving a copy of the *Geology of Canada*, an aging Michael Faraday wrote a wistful and touching tribute, regretting that he had not spent more time 'in the fields, the valleys and the mountains' and assuring Logan that he heard of him 'continually from the men I most value'.

However fêted he might have been in Europe, in Canada, at least in the early days of the Survey, he had to learn to rough it in the bush. Outside the settled areas all movement was by foot or by canoe and because there were no topographic maps Logan and his assistants had to devise their own. Distances were determined by pacing, directions by compass, and heights by barometer. His letters to De la Beche, although a catalogue of discomforts, are really exultations. April 1844:'I worked like a slave all summer on the gulph of St Lawrence, living the life of a savage, inhabiting an open tent, sleeping on the beach in a blanket and sack, with my feet to the fire, seldom taking my clothes off, eating salt pork, & ship's biscuit, & occasionally tormented by mosquitoes. I sailed the whole of the coast, I surveyed & counted my paces for three months from morning to night'.[49] Later in the season salt pork had been replaced by wild meat – partridges, bear, porcupines, and otters – and mosquitoes had given way to blackflies. 'Worse than all the other devils in hell' they, like lice, worked their way through and under clothing onto the skin.

As protection from aerial bombardment from mosquitoes and blackflies outside the tent, he kept his head in a bag that had a gauze window in front. Occasionally, however, he had to climb a tree to make a sighting or measure an angle with a sextant, a procedure that was virtual martyrdom by insect bites – hundreds of them biting at will, each drawing blood, while he steadied his hand and body to determine a bearing within half a degree.[50] On other occasions he had to bleed an Indian helper suffering from inflammation of the lungs and shoot a bear, presumably with the rifle he had ordered from Birmingham.

Mistaking discomfort for discontent, De la Beche in March 1845 asked Logan if he would consider founding the Geological Survey of India at a salary considerably higher than his Canadian one. Logan thanked De la Beche for the compliment but replied that he was committed to the Canadian Survey. On De la Beche's recommendation, the position was offered to David Hiram Williams, De la Beche's loyal assistant on the south Wales Survey. As Hiram Williams' tragic fate demonstrated, the mosquitoes and blackflies of Canada may have been discomfiting, but they were not deadly. Hiram Williams died in India of 'jungle fever', presumed to be malaria, in 1848, aged 36. He was a geologist in the De la Beche/ Logan mould and on discovering underclays beneath Indian coal seams he wrote triumphantly to De la Beche: 'Oh by Jupiter you will be delighted to hear that these Coals have underclays with impressions like Stigmaria. The large branches from which these impressions shoot look more like Calamites – but there is no mistake about the underclays. I have discovered two beds so like our English fireclays that I am having some bricks made so as to have this point tested beyond doubt'.[51]

Throughout his Canadian service, Logan maintained close contact with Britain and the Geological Survey through letters and frequent visits. Whenever in London he would be invited as a matter of course to dine with Gwyn and Anne Jeffreys at their home in Devonshire Place. Logan and Gwyn Jeffreys had been friends since their Swansea days. In 1870 Jeffreys was also invited to visit Logan. 'I shall deem it strange that we who used to dig together in the bone caverns of Gowerland should be shell-grubbing together on my paternal acres in Canada'. Jeffreys visited Harvard and Woods Hole, Massachusetts, in the autumn of 1871 and then travelled inland to the Chicago Academy of Sciences to examine, on an invitation from Professor Alexander Agassiz, molluscs collected during an expedition in the Gulf of Florida.[52] He arrived in Montreal in October having asked Logan to reserve him the *best* cabin on the Allen Line. His voyage from England had been rough and disagreeable. He stayed at Logan's town-house, the former home of his brother James, and visited a farm outside Montreal where for his guests Logan sang the 'Land of Cockayne', his party piece. Jeffreys returned to his 'dulce domum' on 17th Oct. 1871 after a quick but still rough passage. He took with him an otter skin, a gift from Logan for his wife Ann, and a selection of duplicate molluscs from the U.S. Florida survey that he might compare with those recovered from his own dredges on the *Porcupine* in 1869 and 1870. On landing, he learned that the entire main collection at the Chicago Academy of Sciences been destroyed in the Great Fire of Chicago, 8/9 October 1871.[53]

Logan now seventy-two and in the second year of his retirement began to spend more time in Britain. His brother James had died in 1865. Neither Logan nor his four brothers had married. In March 1870 he spent two months with his widowed sister Elizabeth Gower at Castell Malgwyn, a fine country house at Llechryd, Pembrokeshire. It was a prelude to his permanent return to Wales. He spent the winter of 1872/73 in Britain and in August

Castell Malgwyn, Llechryd, the home of Logan's sister, Elizabeth Gower.

1874, his health failing, he settled permanently at Castell Malgwyn. In February 1875 he became seriously ill and died the following June. He is buried beside his brother Hart and his brother-in-law Abel Lewes Gower in the churchyard at Cilgerran, a few miles from Llechryd.

Logan's return to Wales and his burial there has raised questions about his attachment to Canada. As a colonial geologist who had spent much of his adult life in Britain, London was his intellectual home and it, or Britain, might well have been his emotional one. As Nancy Christie has pointed out he, like most members of the Canadian Survey, had opposed the confederation of the provinces on grounds that an awakening national spirit and a new westward orientation would weaken scientific and cultural ties with Britain and the British Geological Survey. The eve of Confederation (July 1867) found Logan in London attending to his most recent work on Devonian and Silurian fossils, not to economic geology and the welfare of the new Dominion. Yet whatever the

178

Logan's grave, Cilgerran.

degree of his attachment to Canada, this irony remains: the man who limned the very foundations of the country lies buried in a rural churchyard in a remote corner of Wales. William Logan was an enigma to the end.

NOTES

1. Sir Bernard Harrington, *Sir William Logan* (Montreal, 1883).
2. McGill Univ., Logan Papers, William Logan Sr. to John Catanach, 8 Dec. 1815.
3. Ibid, 28 October 1816.
4. Sir Archibald Geikie, *Landscape and History and other essays* (London, 1905), 166.
5. Quoted in G. C. Winder, 'Logan and South Wales', *Proceedings Geol. Assoc. Canada* , 16 (1965), 103-121.
6. McGill Univ., Logan Papers, William Logan Sr. to John Catanach, 28 Oct. 1816.
7. H. S. Torrens, 'William Edmond Logan's Geological Apprenticeship in Great Britain 1831-1842', *Geoscience Canada*, 26, 3 (September 1999), 97-109.
8. Harrington, ibid. 1883.
9. McGill Univ., Logan Papers, William Logan to Henry Logan, 13 June 1842.
10. NMW, F. J. North, De la Beche Ms.
11. McGill Univ., Logan Papers, 0120, 5 January, 1839.
12. Tubal Cain, The Mineral Basin of Glamorgan and Adjoining Districts (Merthyr Tydfil, 1835).
13. Quoted in Winder, 'Logan and South Wales', 111.
14. NMW, De la Beche Papers, 1387. John Phillips to Henry De la Beche, 2 Nov. 1841.
15. RISW, Minute Book, 4 May and 18 May, 1839.
16. NMW, North, De la Beche Ms.
17. McGill Univ., Logan Papers, 'Anecdotes of the Life of William Logan', Ms. (probably Murray)
18. W. E. Logan, 'On the Characters of the Beds of Clay immediately below the Coal Seams of South Wales', RISW, 5th Annual Report, 47-51.
19. Swansea Philosophical and Literary Institution, Annual Report, 1838.
20. NMW, De la Deche Papers, 871. Logan to De la Beche, 11 July 1839.
21. Ibid., 872., Logan to De la Beche, 27 Nov. 1839.
22. NMW, North, De la Beche Ms.
23 .NMW, De la Beche Papers, 873. Logan to De la Beche, 11 August 1840.
24. NMW, North, De la Beche Ms.
25. NMW, De la Beche Papers, De la Beche to Logan, 3 August 1840.
26. McGill Univ., Logan Papers, William Logan to James Logan, 14 August 1841.
27. McGill Univ., Logan Papers, William Logan to James Logan, 16 August 1841.

28. Ibid., William Logan to James Logan, 6 Sept. 1841.

29. Ibid., William Logan to James Logan, 2 October 1841.

30. Ibid. Charles Lyell to William Logan, 15 October, 1841. Two thousand more were unable to get tickets.

31. NMW, De la Beche Papers, Henry De la Beche to William Logan, 25 July 1841.

32. McGill Univ., Logan Papers, Henry De la Beche to William Logan, 30 Nov. 1841.

33. Ibid., Henry De la Beche to William Logan, 25 July 1841.

34. Ibid., Henry De la Beche to William Logan, 30 Nov. 1841.

35. NMW, De la Beche Papers, 695. H. Buchanan Holl to Henry De la Beche, 29 May 1842. De la Beche had described Holl, who had worked with him in the southwest of England, as 'a good chemist, natural historian and geologist'.

36. McGill Univ., Logan Papers, William Logan to James Logan, 6 Sept. 1841.

37. NMW, De la Beche Papers, 876. William Logan to Henry De la Beche, 3 December 1841.

38. Ibid., 877. William Logan to Henry De la Beche, 11 December 1841.

39. Ibid., 878. William Logan to Henry De la Beche, 3 Feb. 1842.

40. McGill Univ., Logan papers, Henry De la Beche to William Logan, 8 October 1841.

41. Ibid., Henry De la Beche to William Logan, 8 October 1841.

42. NMW, De la Beche Papers, 880. William Logan to Henry De la Beche, 4 August 1842.

43. McGill Univ., Logan Papers, Charles Lyell to William Logan, 15 Oct. 1841.

44. Quoted in John M Clarke, *James Hall of Albany, Geologist and Palaeontologist, 1811-1898* (New York, 1978) 18.

45. Logan's name appeared as joint author on three of the maps issued by the Ordnance Survey in 1845.

46. When Andrew Crombie Ramsay visited Logan in Canada in 1857 the latter was still wearing a white hat. The hat was tall and furry and after a day in the field, when they had scrambled through 'many a thicket', it became even furrier. Horace B. Woodward, *History of the Geological Society of London* (London, 1907), 42.

47. NMW, De la Beche Papers, North Ms.

48. Ibid., North Ms.

49. NMW, Logan Papers, 883. William Logan to Henry De la Beche, 20 April, 1844.

50. Ibid., 884, William Logan to Henry De la Beche, 11 November 1844.

51. Ibid., North Ms.

52. *Nature* (26 Oct. 1871), 512; *Cambrian* (24 Dec. 1869).

53. McGill Univ., Logan Papers, Gwyn Jeffreys to William Logan, 19 Oct. 1871.

THOMAS WILLIAMS MD FRS
1818-1865

Physician
Polymath and Pioneer Microbiologist

In his biographical essay on Lewis Weston Dillwyn, Thomas Williams returns again and again to Dillwyn's assiduity, to the unflagging attention to detail that allowed him to spend entire days classifying insects and shells and compiling indexes and bibliographies. Dillwyn's ability to eschew hypothesis and speculation and amass what were in effect impregnable fortresses of fact astounded him. It was the attraction of opposites.

Of all the scientists associated with the RISW in its early years Thomas Williams was the most mercurial and, as a young man, the one who promised most. He was born in Llandyfriog, a son of the manse, but his own inclinations were medical rather than ecclesiastical. After school he apprenticed to a physician or surgeon and at nineteen, in 1837, he enrolled as a medical student at Guy's Hospital, London. Guy's then, graced by luminaries such as Richard Bright, Thomas Addison and Thomas Hodgkin, was in its Golden Period. Bright, who instructed Thomas Williams, was the outstanding figure, the leading medical consultant in London and Queen Victoria's personal physician. On his death the *Lancet* lamented the loss of one of the medical profession's 'most original, observant and philosophic minds'.[1]

At Guy's Thomas Williams was a star who caught the eye of every instructor and student. His stage was Guy's Physical Society, one of the first of the London medical societies or, as the Lancet characterized them, 'medical parliaments' where papers on medicine were presented and debated. For a supremely confident young man who tapped an artesian well of words, it was a perfect setting. This was how he appeared to a fellow student: 'He was a most remarkable man, striking in appearance and manner;

Dr. Thomas Williams.

indeed, he came under the denomination of genius. It was grand to see him at the Physical Society standing up with long, flowing, black hair making a speech on some abstruse question, having an air of inspiration as the eloquent phrases flowed from him. But it was not all talk: he was eminently scientific'.[2] Richard Bright added his cautious voice to the chorus of approval, predicting a brilliant, Swedenborgian future for Williams provided he could rein in a temperament that always threatened to veer out of control. He wrote this astute retrospective:

> *Many of his fellow students who listened to his glowing discursive orations at the Physical Society – anything but dry matter-of-fact or physical as they were, and especially*

distaining to be tied down to the subject matter of debate – thought that imagination held sway over all his other faculties. Perhaps it did. Certainly this seductive, often deluding, faculty did then, and in after time, give colour if not substance to his utterances; but it also opened to him vistas of original inquiry not hinted at by his teachers. It led him on, too precipitately perhaps sometimes, to foresee conclusions and laws of Nature long before they could be reached by the slow, plodding, methodical groping of induction. And herein we see a striking instance of the admirable mind-regulating virtue of Medicine as a study. But for Medicine and other branches of natural history to serve as a counterpoise, and to supply an inexhaustible pasture for his greed for knowledge, Imagination would surely have soared away with Dr. Williams into unfathomable metaphysical space. He might have been a Swedenborg. Like his countryman Glendower, he might have abandoned Actuality to 'call spirits from the vasty deep'; or have floundered beyond redemption into some other dreary abyss of unreality. But Medicine had shown him how Nature, boundless in material for observation, and therefore boundless in suggestiveness, could employ, without satiating, imagination brilliant and impetuous as his own.[3]

The length and comprehensiveness of Richard Bright's assessment is a testament to the impact Thomas Williams, a youth from Cardiganshire, made on Guy's and on the most eminent physician in England. Bright recognized, however, that Thomas Williams's greatest strength, the power of his imagination, might also be his nemesis. He allowed that it could open vistas of original inquiry closed to his more earth-bound colleagues, but he also saw that in combination with a Glendower-like recklessness it could be his undoing – the 'mind-regulating' virtues of medicine notwithstanding.

After qualifying, Williams worked as a demonstrator in anatomy at Guy's and as curator of its microscopic department. He was one of the first medical researchers to appreciate the potential of the achromatic microscope that, unlike earlier microscopes, magnified without breaking up the white light into the several colours of the spectrum. Under the new microscope small objects were no longer surrounded by rings of colour. For Williams the instrument was a *sine qua non* of scientific research, a 'potent wand' that would revolutionize approaches to both research and clinical teaching: 'Faith in the verity of microscopic facts', he pronounced, 'is a fundamental article in the scientific creed of every living philosopher. The sphere of naked vision is exhausted: another is opened by the microscope'. His dedication to the microscope and his grasp of the cell theory of German physiologist Theodor Schwann, made him a pioneer of microbiology. For the *Microscopical Journal* in 1841 he wrote an article on the structure of stomata (leaf pores) and their function in respiration and followed this, in 1843, with a report on the pathology of cells for the *Guy's Hospital Reports*. The Guy's *Reports*, first published in 1836 were, by the 1840s, being acquired by libraries in Europe and America. In 1843, for a dissertation 'On the Structure and Functions of the Lungs', Thomas Williams also won the prestigious triennial prize of the Royal College of Surgeons.

As a brilliant young researcher, Thomas Williams's course seemed set for a consultancy at a teaching hospital but Guy's, possibly constrained by Richard Bright's reservations, offered no more than a tutorship. Disappointed, Williams then joined Grainger's of Webb St., generally regarded as the best private medical school in London. Writing of the Webb Street School in 1830, the *Lancet* offered this assessment: 'It was founded ten years ago by the late Edward Grainger, a man of splendid intellect, imagination, and industry. He raised the school to an eminence never before attained by any person unaided by an extensive hospital or by patronage'.[4] Edward Grainger, and his brother Richard, who succeeded him after his early death in 1824, had been able to persuade first rate physicians and scientists to lecture at the school, among them the chemist Richard Phillips.

At Grainger's, Thomas Williams continued to research and write and at the request of the *Lancet* he edited a series of lectures on the ear by Dr. Pilcher, the leading ear specialist of the day. As an accomplished anatomist, he was also asked to dissect the body of Richard Carlile, the radical Fleet Street bookseller who had donated his body to the school. In 1843, however, Richard Grainger, seduced by the offer of a professorship of anatomy at St Thomas's,

Wind Street, Swansea.

closed the school. Thomas Williams, whose health was uncertain, decided to return to Wales. He opened an office in Wind Street, Swansea, and later was appointed physician to the Swansea Infirmary.

Once settled in Swansea he gravitated inevitably to the Royal Institution where he arrived trailing clouds of London glory. In June 1844 he delivered, before a crowded and expectant audience in the lecture theatre, the first of two lectures on organic chemistry. Enthralled by Dr. Williams's 'master-like fluency', 'elocutionary power', and 'extensive knowledge of the facts', the *Cambrian* reporter ran through his catalogue of superlatives. 'We can declare without the slightest exaggeration that a finer display of eloquence and scientific learning was never made within the walls of our Institution'. Williams's second lecture was also an 'extemporaneous discourse', lasting about two hours, that, like the first, was delivered without benefit of a note before President Lewis Weston Dillwyn and a full assembly. In every respect, noted the *Cambrian* reporter, it 'equaled, if it did not surpass in merit, its distinguished predecessor'.[5]

In his time off from his practice and duties at the hospital Thomas Williams continued to research, lecture and write. Over the next decade he wrote more than a dozen articles, chiefly on methods of respiration in humans and animals, for leading medical and scientific journals.[6] His research was wide-ranging and, judging from the quality of the journals, respectably deep. It covered subjects such as the bronchial organs of shellfish, general mechanisms of aquatic breathing, respiration in invertebrate animals, lung disorders in humans, and the chemistry, physiology and pathology of blood. He also pursued comparative anatomy, dissecting sponges, jellyfish, barnacles, shrimp, oysters, scallops and cockles and examining their parts under a microscope. He combed the shore for littoral fauna and to collect creatures that lived beyond the intertidal zone he dredged from small boats.

Some of his ideas, which pointed to the increasing complexity of life forms over time, even bore on the theory of evolution: 'It is now a fundamental principle in the science of embryology that the ovum of the mammiferous animal during the process of development exhibits phases of structure which, although transient in duration, present the most remarkable correspondence with types of structure which belong persistently to animals inferior in the scale. It is therefore admitted to be necessary, in order to the attainment of the greatest perfection in the detail of organic structure, that nature should first realise the simplest formative idea, and subsequently make advance along the typical gradations of the extended scale which so remotely separates the most simple from the most complex and perfect of living forms'.[7] An 1845 lecture by Thomas Williams on the ideas on evolution in Robert Chambers' *Vestiges of the Natural History of Creation* might have been attended by Alfred Russel Wallace.[8]

In the 1850s Thomas Williams gathered his rewards. As a 'zealous cultivator of natural science, particularly of physiology and zoology', he was elected, in 1855, to a fellowship of the Linnean Society, crowning this in 1858 with election to the Royal Society at a time when entry was jealously guarded.[9] Abroad, his reputation was unassailable but at home, by 1850, it had begun to disintegrate. Shortly after his arrival in Swansea the duality that Richard Bright had noted between the brilliant intuitive scientist and the impetuous Glendower-like showman became evident. When writing for reputable journals, or lecturing to scientific bodies, he was subject to obvious restraints but in Swansea he could call up spirits from the vasty deep with a measure of impunity. To popularize science in the town, and to promote the work of the RISW he wrote, in 1844, a short book based loosely on his lectures on organic chemistry. He dedicated it to Lewis Weston Dillwyn. It is a remarkable document with a title of record-breaking length: *A Sketch of the Relations which Subsist between the Three Kingdoms of Nature: the Mineral, Vegetable and Animal: with a view to a brief exposition of the present state and future presentations of Organic Chemistry in relation to Agriculture, Physiology and Dietetics: with observations on the Hygiene of Swansea.*

The subjects range from reason and instinct, the principles of chemical combination, soils and manures, nutrition, teetotalism, the occupation of colliers, copper smoke, to climate and health, all within the compass of seventy dense pages. Williams admits in the preface that the work was 'hastily undertaken' and, with no access to large libraries, 'extemporaneously composed' from whatever was stored in his mind. In spite of its *ad hoc* nature the biologist R. Elwyn Hughes, commenting on the first twenty pages, considers it an unjustifiably neglected work. There are reasoned statements on evolution and the unity of nature, and a lucid presentation of contemporary thoughts on nutritional science. The final twenty pages, however, in which copper-smoke is presented as a benefit to health, might be interpreted as signs of a mind that was beginning to unravel.

The subjects of his lectures at the RISW were just as eclectic as those introduced in *A Sketch of the Relations*. In January 1846 he lectured on the natural history of the Hottentot and Bushman races of South Africa, enlivening his presentation with a Hottentot chieftain, a 'little sable stranger' brought from the southwest coast of Africa, opposite the guano island of Ichabo, by Captain Mitchell of the *Tom Cringle*.[10] In October of the same year he spoke, without notes, on the science of the weather and followed this in December with a two-and-a-half hour lecture on the 'Terraqeous Globe'. He was a great draw and at every Williams lecture the theatre was filled – 'literally crammed', as the *Cambrian* reported, for his lecture on the 'Terraqeous Globe'. The lecture theatre at the RISW had become his stage and on it he performed as electrifyingly and, as Richard Bright would have averred, as recklessly as he had at the Guy's Physical Society. There had to be a reckoning.

It came in 1848, three months after the British Association meeting in Swansea. In late November he delivered two lectures on the laws regulating the distribution of animals. The *Cambrian,* which had given his early lectures generous coverage, provided only short notices. On the first lecture it reported simply that the subject was interesting and extensive, that the lecture theatre was crowded, and the audience complimentary. On the second lecture it repeated the observation on the scope of the subject adding that it demonstrated an intimate knowledge of several important branches of knowledge and was well suited to popular treatment. As to the brevity of the notice, it added that it was following a policy adopted for the current lecture season at the RI of reporting fully only lectures of particular importance.

As if to endorse the *Cambrian's* position, Thomas Williams announced in advance of the lectures that they were 'the free-will offering of a gentleman anxious for the diffusion of useful knowledge'.[11] Williams, however, was angry that even a 'free-will offering' should have been treated so lightly and at the end of the following week's session he and another affronted local lecturer, the dentist Spence Bate, who shared Williams's taste for global themes, attacked the *Cambrian.*[12] 'The scientific instruction this evening', the newspaper reported, 'was varied by a more exciting entertainment. Several gentlemen who considered themselves aggrieved by the mode in which their free-will offerings had been dwelt upon by us gave vent to their feelings'.[13] The most vociferous of them was Thomas Williams whose language, so the editor reported, was of the Sarah Gamp and Betsy Prigg school and, as such, more appropriate to 'the pugnacious arena known as the Westminster pit . . . than the quiet theatre of the Royal Institution of South Wales'.[14]

In a published letter in support of the editor, W. Samuel, who wrote reviews for the *Cambrian* and the *Welshman,* referred to Dr. Williams' 'volley of venom' and 'mighty but mysterious tirade'. On the morning following the first lecture he had been summoned by Dr. Williams and asked to write a notice. Dr. Williams announced that he would write the notice for the second lecture himself. Samuel replied that his lecture would receive the same attention as previous lectures that season and it was unlikely that, as an admittedly extemporaneous discourse, it would warrant more extended treatment. A more serious reservation, he added, was that some of the positions 'he had so positively laid down in his discourse had seemed unsound'. He cited an observation made by Williams on the transmission of heat through transparent bodies. Several times during the lecture he had stated emphatically that ice transmitted all of the calorific heat that might be directed at it. It was widely acknowledged, however, that even under the most favourable circumstances ice transmits no more than six percent. Samuel also noted that in the lecture he referred several times to the mathematical theories of Mr Hopkins of Cambridge. Williams had intimated that he was familiar with a paper by Hopkins in the *Transactions* of the British Association but Samuel, knowing that to understand the paper required some knowledge of differential and integral calculus, taxed Williams with the question of how much calculus he knew. Cornered, Williams was forced to admit that he did not know any and that his knowledge of the paper was confined to a popular review of it. Even his knowledge of geography was faulty. He placed the island of Van Diemen's Land on the northern rather than the southern coast of Australia, a forgivable error had it not been essential to a theory he was propounding.[15]

In the following issue of the *Cambrian*, Samuels continued his attack, incensed that Dr. Williams should have attempted to advance his own cause to the 'detriment of the reputation of quieter, if not sounder men'. During the intervening week, he had been informed by a graduate of the University of London, concerned for the reputation of his alma mater, that Thomas Williams had matriculated from that institution via '*a side door*'. Taking advantage of an indulgence offered to certain medical students, Williams was able to matriculate without taking the matriculation examination. Had he been properly examined, averred Samuel, he might have 'cut his recent capers: he would have been better taught'.[16] For the more 'pantomimic' parts of Williams' performance, Samuel penned the following verse:

> *Lo Williams stands*
> *Tuning his voice and balancing his hands;*
> *How fluent nonsense trickles from his tongue!*
> *How sweet the periods neither said nor sung.*[17]

John Lewis, a reporter for the *Cambrian*, had also been accosted by Thomas Williams. Before the first lecture Williams approached Lewis in Wind Street and expressed a wish to have his lectures reported *in extenso*. Lewis replied that a long report in a regional newspaper might tax the patience of the readers. Lewis did not attend Dr. Williams's first lecture but he was familiar with his style. He reported, after talking to witnesses, that Dr. Williams had 'so far forgot himself as to indulge in a sweeping tirade, in his usual extra-ornate style'. He railed not only against the *Cambrian* but against individuals who had accused him of plagiarism, affectation and falsehood, accusing them in turn of traducing, by extension, the reputation of the RISW.[18] Lewis expressed astonishment that someone of Williams' standing would resort to such 'claptrap' in public and in a subsequent letter answered Williams' charges that the *Cambrian* had solicited a '*full report*' of the lecture.[19] Because of Samuel's contretemps with Thomas Williams, John Lewis had been asked to write a review of the second lecture. Having listened to only part of it, he asked Dr. Williams if he would allow him to look at his notes or at least provide him with a few extracts. Williams had previously informed Lewis that the lecture had been written out. Williams, however, refused. Determined to give readers some idea of the kind of 'phraseology in which he [Dr. Williams] delights to contemplate', Lewis quoted what he described as an 'elegant extract' from Dr. Williams's own work. It was from a recorded attack on the council of the RISW: 'May the mist of the copper smoke become, for one happy moment, translucent, that the sun's illuminating rays may pay one solitary visit to those obscure recesses of those benighted and ill-ventilated chambers in which the conclaves of the Councillors of our own Royal Institution are held, and may they be directed to a more just and faithful discharge of their duties'. The foregoing, Lewis added, is a fair specimen; let the doctor peruse his own moonshine and take the hint'.[20]

Unabashed by the public opprobrium, a few months later, in March 1849, Thomas Williams was again in the public eye. His target on this occasion was mesmerism or hypnotism. Franz Anton Mesmer was a Viennese physician who had developed techniques for inducing hypnotic sleep that relieved patients of physical pain and promised to alleviate mental disorders. Introduced to Britain in the 1830s, mesmerism excited great interest both inside and outside medicine. Dickens, Alfred Russel Wallace, Michael Faraday and William Robert Grove were keenly interested. Grove, who attended several sessions, acknowledged that a book on mesmerism by Chauncey Hare Townshend was 'sensible' and 'philosophical' and that the practice warranted further research.[21] Within medicine, mesmerism's chief advocate in Britain was Dr John Elliotson, a professor at University College, London, whose experiments and demonstrations eventually offended so many of his colleagues that he was compelled to resign his appointment. Results were difficult to quantify, patients' reactions were unpredictable, and there were accusations of feigned or fraudulent behaviour. Grove and a number of physicians, chief among them John Forbes, founder and editor of the *British and Foreign Medical Review*, urged doctors to evaluate mesmerism, not ignore it, pointing to the clear benefits of hypnotic sleep and anaesthesia. Opium and alcohol might take the edge off pain but it was dangerous to operate on people who had consumed enough of either to become unconscious.

In London, and in mainstream medicine in general, John Elliotson's resignation and the discovery in the 1840s of the anaesthetizing properties of ether and chloroform virtually eliminated interest in mesmerism. But outside London interest was not only sustained but gained momentum, and in the mid and late 1840s it took the country by storm. Its practitioners were travelling lecturers with mesmeric skills who demonstrated their powers in lecture halls throughout the country. Some were simply showmen but others were interested in exploring the nature of sensation and pain, and the influence of mind over body. Over a two-week period in December/January 1849 two well-known practitioners, W. H. Jackson and William Davey, demonstrated, on subjects drawn from the audience, the art of mesmerism at the Swansea Theatre.[22] The following March, in response to the demonstrations and burgeoning public interest, Thomas Williams, who had not attended any of the sessions, embarked on a public denunciation of the practice. In what was described as a 'long anticipated' lecture in a theatre (at the RISW) that was 'not only full but crammed' he delivered a three-hour discourse. In the audience was a group of young men, apparently proteges of Dr. Williams, for whom that particular session of lectures had been intended. Using drawings and diagrams, he described the human nervous system and followed this with a history of practitioners who 'pretended to this science', i.e. mesmerism.

He denounced Mesmer and John Elliotson as deceivers of the public without, as a frustrated reporter for the *Cambrian* reported, ever explaining what they purported to do. At the close of his address Mr. Curtis of Gower Street offered, to loud cheering from the audience, to mesmerize in Thomas Williams's presence, daring him to deny the reality of hypnotic sleep. Through a spokesman in the audience, and again to loud cheering, W. H. Jackson challenged Thomas Williams to a public debate. To both of these challenges, the *Cambrian* reported, Dr. Williams made an evasive reply. A member of the audience, Mr Rayner, begged Dr. Williams to accept at least one of them so that doubts about the validity of hypnotism could be laid to rest. But to Rayner's chagrin, Dr. Williams again refused.[23]

The following June, supporters of mesmerism responded to the denunciations with a series of lectures and demonstrations delivered and conducted by Dr. Owens, upon whom Thomas Williams had 'branded a foul stain', at the Swansea Theatre. During the first, Dr. Owens expressed regret that the absent Dr. Williams preferred his 'snug retreat' to a public forum and registered his objection to Williams' 'reckless assertions', and his denunciation of John Elliotson and his patients as 'deluders of the public'. He quoted a letter from a bemused Elliotson who observed that never in his life had he known a person such as Dr. Williams. Dr. Owens regretted the interruption of one of his sessions by a coterie of noisy youngsters who, so the *Cambrian* reported, seemed desirous 'to take upon themselves the defence of a certain M.D.' Dr. Owens, however, 'very properly refused to bandy words with them', but in the following lecture he denounced Dr. Williams for daring to taint young minds with his 'vain and malignant accusations'. 'Morally', he concluded, 'he cannot be excused'. To establish the authenticity of the hypnotic state he called upon two irreproachable townspeople: the Reverend Mr G. P. Evans as a subject and, as a witness, W. H. Michael, a surgeon and prospective Medical Officer of Health for Swansea. Michael had agreed to extract the tooth of a hypnotised girl. The Reverend Evans, who was convinced that hypnotism could alleviate suffering and pain, had come forward in a bid to counter Thomas Williams's denunciations.[24]

In spite of these lapses locally, Thomas Williams maintained and even enlarged his national reputation. At the British Association meeting at Ipswich in 1851 he presented a report on the habits, anatomy and classification of British Annelidae (segmented worms) that he had been appointed to prepare at the Swansea meeting in 1848. The report, illustrated with two hundred original drawings, elicited such strong expressions of admiration that proposals were made for its publication in the *Transactions* of the Association and that a recommendation be made to the Royal Society to publish the drawings. He followed this report with a paper on the reproductive organs of the Annelids requested in 1857 by the editor of the *Philosophical Transactions*. Thomas Williams' work on the natural history and anatomy of Annelidae was the first citation in his bid for election to the Royal Society. The other citations included his research on respiration and his general competence as a comparative anatomist and physiologist. On his election certificate there were signatures from twenty-two proposers, among them Henry de la Beche, Gwyn Jeffreys, William Robert Grove, the biologist Edward Forbes, the microscopist Dr Edwin Lankester, and the Physician to Guy's Hospital, B. G. Babbington. At home, in the theatre of the RISW, Thomas Williams might have been a purveyor of 'claptrap' and 'fluent nonsense', but abroad he was a celebrity.

In 1854, four years before his election to the Royal Society, he was invited by the General Board of Health in London to prepare a report of the effects of copper smoke upon health. The Board of Health had been been approached for information by the Council of Health in Hamburg and, having none, it invited Dr. Williams to prepare a report. As an acknowledged expert on respiration and the lungs, and physician to an infirmary in a town that produced, by Thomas Williams' estimate, 'one half of the copper smoke of the world', he was an obvious choice.

He completed the report, of more than a hundred dense pages, within months of the request.[25] Readers of his earlier work *A Sketch of the Relations . . .* might have known what to expect. In the final chapter of that book he dealt with the issue of public health in Swansea. A confident, award-winning London-trained physician might have been expected to view critically the obvious dangers to public health in Swansea but the lion on the debating platform was a lamb in the face of wealth and authority. He noted, for example, that the town's sewers backed up when the tides were high but instead of calling for a remedy he declared salt-water a natural solvent, thereby converting a hazard into a blessing.

In the same vein, he conceded that a mixture of muriatic acid gas and chlorine emitted by the chimneys of a Landore factory might constrict the throat when inhaled in concentrated doses but when mixed with air it 'simply stimulates the bronchial passages, and promotes expectoration'. To test the effects of copper smoke coming directly from the furnaces he stood before an open furnace at the Hafod works and inhaled. He coughed and sneezed uncontrollably, felt his chest tighten, and feared he might suffocate. He also lost his voice, but after a final bout of vigorous coughing and spitting had cleared his bronchial passages he recovered both his voice and his equanimity. He declared copper smoke to be no more harmful than muriatic acid gas. He acknowledged that boys employed at the works suffered initially from coughing fits and a temporary loss of voice but averred that they sustained no lasting respiratory injuries.[26]

The 1854 report, although more detailed, brought no comfort to enemies of the smoke and advocates of public health. He opened with a panegyric to the copper trade, outlining the un-questioned benefits in terms of relatively high wages and relatively good housing it brought to the town. In general the copper-masters, several of whom had gone to great lengths to suppress the smoke, were enlightened men and, more than this, enlight-ened Englishmen. In lectures at the RISW and in a *Sketch of the Relations* . . . he compiled racial and ethnic league tables. English and Germans were at the top, Celts somewhere in mid-table.[27] In south Wales the Celts were the 'minor agents' and 'cautious capitalists' while the coppermasters, most of whom were English, were 'ruling minds' endowed with 'the greater, stronger and more highly-schooled mind of the Saxon'. A throroughgoing deter-minist, he would declare in a lecture at the RISW in the winter of 1858/59 that in England the elements – a stimulating climate and the right admixture of races – had combined to produce the finest known type of man. 'The highest classes of Englishmen', he concluded, 'are the finest in the world. Noble in body, in mind, and in moral aspiration'.[28]

In his report, he dealt separately with copper workers and the general population. His first subjects were the men 'before the furnace' who worked twelve-hour shifts enveloped in dust and sulphur and arsenic-laden fumes – conditions that might lead the unwary to conclude that diseases of the lungs were the bane of coppermen. He conceded – as most experienced coppermen contended – that furnacemen spat more or less copiously every morning but he was not convinced that this indicated exceptionally high rates of asthma and chronic bronchitis. The incidence of these might have been higher than among ordinary labourers, but in 'a very inconsiderable proportion'. Beyond the furnaces, coppermen breathed air as free as cottagers on their hillsides. Even men who had spent twenty or thirty years before the furnace were 'generally as hale, florid and corpulent as their neighbours'. Henry de la Beche's observation, made in his Health of Towns Report, that the inhabitants of the copper districts were peculiarly susceptible to consumption he rejected on grounds that it was based on 'statistical statements'. He preferred to rely on his own judgement and the observations of fellow doctors which pointed to the conclusion that consumption was far less common in the smoke districts than in relatively smoke-free Swansea.[29] In Morriston, however, in the heart of the smoke district, 'statistical statements' indicated that one in every three or four deaths was from consumption.

One of the specific requests of the General Board of Health was an assessment of the effects of 'arsenical inhalations' upon coppermen and people living in the copper districts. Though fatal in large doses, arsenic in small amounts can serve as a medicine and general tonic. Citing the fresh complexions and general good health of the 'arsenic eaters' of Austria, Thomas Williams declared that at no time had a copperman or any inhabitant of the copper towns suffered in any degree whatever from inhaling arsenic fumes. On the contrary there was evidence, as in Austria, of preventive effects; people in the copper districts were notably free of skin diseases, for which arsenic was a known remedy.

Thomas Williams' enthusiasm for arsenic caught the attention of Dr Alex Williams, a professor of chemistry, who in two short paragraphs invalidated Thomas Williams' chemical analyses. He pointed out that Williams' water-solvent methods of measurement could detect only soluble forms of arsenic. In grass or smoke, Alex Williams observed, there might be significant and very poisonous amounts of insoluble arsenic.[30] In his column-long reply, Thomas Williams protested that, compression being the true symbol of mastery, he had chosen not to burden his readers with the detail or *arcana* of analytic chemistry. Within the space allowed by his report, he could present results but not processes, conclusions but not premises, and accused his adversary of labouring too exclusively on theoretical premises.

As to the effects of smoke on the general population, Thomas Williams was just as forgiving. Far from endangering health, copper smoke was a positive good. Like most physicians of the day, he subscribed to the idea that infectious diseases such as typhus, cholera and yellow fever were germinated by the rotting of vegetable and animal substances. Gases or miasma given off during the processes of decay created an 'epidemic atmosphere' that endangered human health. Wind-borne, the miasma were thought to travel as 'poison waves' that infected populations wherever they came to ground. Ideal conditions for the germination of miasma were, so the theory went, poorly drained, swampy and preferably humid places where vegetation growth was dense. The least suitable conditions for their germination were deserts and icecaps.

Swansea had no ice-cap and, climatically speaking, no desert but surrounding the works and the copper towns were vast stretches of cinders and slag through which water percolated as easily as through sand and gravel. In a technical sense the lower valley of the Tawe was a desert that harboured no miasma: 'dewless, wood-less, [and] grassless, this smoky desert is also poisonless'.[31] To make the point he invited the reader to paint the contrary scene: 'Clothe Kilvey Hill with a rich umbrageous forest: convert the treeless, shrubless waste of Llansamlet into a damp, foliaceous jungle; let the evergreen wave over the stony declivities beneath the castle of Morriston; restore the valley to its primeval morass, and how changed will be the climate! The expanse of leafy surface would augment the annual rainfall. . . . The low places along the river banks would be changed into exhalent pools of rank vegetation. The stagnant waters would become slimy, and the fevers would decimate a hapless population'.

Even if Swansea were to be invaded by waves of miasma generated elsewhere, in copper smoke it had, Thomas Williams argued, a built-in prophylactic. The pall of copper smoke that hung more or less permanently over the lower valley was a *cordon sanitaire* that protected the inhabitants from infectious disease. 'Does [the smoke] not, if anything, purify the air? . . . Has it not banished ague from the country? Is not the sphere of its distribution a demarcation defensive against the invasion of cholera? Is it not a most uncommon event to meet with a true case of typhus fever among the inhabitants of the smoke district?'[32] He offered a mechanism only in case of epidemic influenza: 'Is not copper-smoke a coat of mail against epidemic influenza, by decomposing the ozone of the air?' Swansea's problem was not too much smoke but too little. 'If it were possible to maintain a *permanent* infusion of copper smoke in the atmosphere of a given locality, the author records his deliberate belief that the population of such a locality would be *permanently* exempt from all those epidemic diseases, whose causative germs, whatever they be in essence, travel and multiply, from place to place, in the atmosphere'.[33] In response to a review of the report that failed to point up any of its obfuscations, one *Cambrian* reader concluded that on the subject of copper smoke Dr. Williams was 'in the land of dreams'.[34] According to the distinguished metallurgist Dr. John Percy, he suffered from 'a strange delusion'.

Thomas Williams's obsequiousness in the face of both municipal and corporate authority meant that an acknowledged expert on respiration failed to support the anti-smoke campaign conducted by promoters of the movement to improve public health. At a public meeting in 1860 convened to address an injunction against a patent fuel company that produced volumes of acrid smoke within the town, he presented a motion – couched within an address that lasted lasted three quarters of an hour – that the injuction was highly detrimental to the commercial interests of the port. In the same address he reiterated the sentiment found in his report on the copper smoke: that he had never encountered a single ailment that could be attributed to smoke of any kind.[35]

In the late 1860s his national reputation also began to suffer. In a lecture on the anatomy of the earthworm, read at the 1864 annual meeting of the British Association, John Lubbock was severely critical of a paper on earthworms written by Thomas Williams for the *Philosophical Transactions* of the Royal Society. Seizing the opportunity to impugn a long-time adversary, the *Cambrian* announced the denunciation under the heading: 'STRICTURE ON DR THOMAS WILLIAMS'S PAPER. Dispute over reproductive organs'. It quoted Lubbock at length: 'If the diagram from Dr. Williams's figure be now referred to, it will be seen how erroneous is the view it conveys of the generative system. The segments marked t.t. [in the diagrams exhibited] are said to be testicular, whilst the three intervening segments are said to be ovarian, whilst it is also asserted by Dr. Williams that the ciliated tubules in each segment, which can be seen in both diagrams, are connected with the generative system; which, indeed, he considers as merely modifications. That the real ovary has entirely escaped Dr. Williams is very evident. . . . Such is the paper in the 'Philosophical Transactions' of the Royal Society of London, in which several important organs of reproduction are not mentioned by its author, those that are drawn, are either imaginary or badly executed and misapprehended,. whilst the careful and accurate researches of two well known anatomists are styled 'confused and contradictory'. This being the case it is no longer possible . . . to entertain the view advocated by Dr. Williams . . . that the generative system of annelida is a modification of the ciliated tubules . . . which have a peculiar function and structure connected with excretion'.

Mr Lubbock conceded that the reproductive system of earthworms might not be of general interest, but he felt that he must be allowed to confirm the general accuracy of Dr. Herring's observations on the earthworm, and the inaccuracy of those of Dr. Williams.[36]

Early in 1864 Thomas Williams was again in difficulties at the RISW. In January the Council, of which he was now a member, had decided to offer the presidency – an appointment normally made with the greatest unanimity – to John Gwyn Jeffreys. But before Jeffreys could be formally approached, friends of Dr. Williams nominated him on grounds that a local president would be preferable to one based in England. Over Thomas Williams's protestations that he had not been party to the nomination, and that his supporters had not known that Jeffreys was the choice of Council, the *Cambrian* and John Lewis expressed their disdain. Lewis was 'shocked' that Williams would have let his name go forward before Jeffreys had been approached, while the editor considered his behaviour to be in the worst possible taste. As an FRS and a member of Council, fulminated the editor, his duty was plain. Instead of withdrawing gracefully, however, Thomas Williams had exacerbated an already fractious situation by 'invoking the meretricious aid of cut and dried memorials (solicited letters of reference) which are so cheap in the present day. Gentlemen', the editor continued, 'who have hitherto presided over our Royal Institution have never yet needed such outward pressure to ensure their elevation'. He concluded with a homily from *All's Well That Ends Well:*

> *The place is dignified by the doer's deeds.*
> *Where great pretensions swell, and virtue none,*
> *It is a dropsied honour. Honours best thrive,*
> *When rather from our acts we them derive.*[37]

Had Thomas Williams and his supporters allowed the Council to approach Gwyn Jeffreys the latter would, ironically, have declined the invitation. Thomas Williams's intervention meant that no formal approach to Jeffreys could be made before the annual meeting in June. Williams, presumably on account of the ill feeling it had engendered, had withdrawn his application before the meeting but in June Jeffreys was dredging in the Shetlands and he was elected, to his displeasure, in absentia. An appointment that twenty years earlier he would have prized had become 'a great bore'.[38] His interests were now in the deep seas, not in Swansea and its ailing Royal Institution, and when not dredging he divided his time between his homes in Hertfordshire and London

The election dispute was Thomas Williams's last public contretemps. In January 1865 he married, at the age of 46, Eliza Dennis at Hove in Sussex and the following month, when passing through London, he addressed the Medical and Chirurgical Society on the rate at which air flowed through the lungs. It was his last professional lecture. In March he sickened with what was diagnosed as typhoid fever from which, ironically, he had declared Swansea to be virtually exempt. He recovered but in May he caught a severe chill and then declined quickly. After an agonizing illness during which he was attended by several of the prominent physicians of the town, he died in May 1865. His local obituarists were tolerant. The *Cambrian*, which had conducted a twenty-year campaign against his excesses, limited its criticism to his arch demeanour, 'a certain amount of hauteur towards his professional brethren' and his marked eccentricities, 'his foibles and his faults'.[39] Popular in the town and with his patients, he was given a public funeral that left a crowded Wind St at 10 a.m., the procession led by the dissenting ministers of the town and one hundred tradesmen walking four abreast. Twenty-seven carriages followed in a cortege that ended at the High Street Station. Thomas Williams was buried beside his father in Llanedi, Carmarthenshire.

If Swansea and the RISW had been the making of William Edmond Logan, it could also be argued that they were the unmaking of Thomas Williams. In London, despite the licence allowed by the Guy's medical or debating society, there had been obvious restraints. At Guy's and at Grainger's Thomas Williams had been in the company of his peers and his excesses, for all his confidence and flair, would not have been tolerated for long. In Swansea, however, with the RISW long past its apogee and many of its weekly lectures given over to attention-seeking rhetoricians, the flaws of temperament that Richard Bright had discerned, proved fatal. By confining himself, in his professional lectures and publications, to subjects that he knew well he managed to preserve his national reputation. But by the end it, too, had begun to fray as specialised knowledge, much of it the fruit of Bright's 'slow, plodding, methodical groping', began to undermine Glendower-like speculation.

NOTES

1. Samuel Wilks and G. T. Bettany, *A Biographical History of Guy's Hospital* (London, 1892), 218-221.
2. Ibid., 428.
3. Quoted in Peter Thomas, 'Medical Men of Glamorgan: Thomas Williams of Swansea, 1818-1865', *Glamorgan Historian*, 9 (1973), 70-95.
4. Wilks and Bettany, 154.
5. *Cambrian* (June 1844).
6. For a list of his publications see T. I. Jones, 'The Contributions of Welshmen to Science, *Trans. Hon. Soc. Cymmrodorion* (1932-33).
7. Wilks and Bettany, 428-429.
8. R. Elwyn Hughes, 'Alfred Russel Wallace; some notes on the Welsh connection', 413.
9. His name was withdrawn in 1861 for non-payment of fees.
10. *Cambrian* (9 January 1848).
11. *Cambrian* (24 November 1848).
12. One of Bate's lectures bore the title: 'The History of Literature and the Progress of Civilization with respect to Physical Geography'.
13. *Cambrian* (8 Dec. 1848).
14. *Cambrian* (15 January 1849).
15. *Cambrian* (29 Dec. 1848).
16. Students who enrolled at Guy's before the founding of the University of London, October 1836, were excused the University's matriculation examination. Thomas Williams entered Guy's in 1837, so the accusation may have been unfounded. Williams held an M.D. from the University of London.
17. *Cambrian* (5 January 1849).
18. *Cambrian* (15 Dec. 1848).
19. *Cambrian* (15 January 1849).
20. Ibid.
21. Alison Winter, *Mesmerized, Powers of Mind in Victorian Britain* (Chicago, 1998), 58.
22. *Cambrian* (5 January 1849).
23. *Cambrian* (9 March 1849).
24. *Cambrian* (8, 15 June 1849).
25. Thomas Williams, *Report on the Copper Smoke and its Influence on the Public Health and Industrial Diseases of Coppermen* (Swansea, 1854).
26. *Sketch of the Relations . . .* 69-73.
27. 'On the mental and physical characteristics of the Various Races of Mankind, *Cambrian* (5, 12 February 1842; and *Sketch of the Relations . . .*, 27-32.
28. 'The Present Geographical Movement and Future Geographical Distribution of the English Race of Men', lecture, winter 1859/60. RISW box 47.
29. *Report on the Copper Smoke*, 87.
30. *Cambrian* (10 October 1854).

31. *Report on Copper Smoke*, 12-13.
32. Ibid. 97.
33. Ibid. 100.
34. *Cambrian* (8 December 1854).
35. *Cambrian* (21 Dec 1860).
36. *Cambrian* (30 Sept. 1864).
37. *Cambrian* (3 January 1864).
38. British Museum. Alder Norman Letters, #745, Jeffreys to Joshua Alder, 22 June 1864.
39. *Cambrian* (26 May 1865), *Swansea and Glamorgan Herald* (24 May 1865).

WILLIAM ROBERT GROVE FRS
1811-1896

Physicist, Jurist
Inventor of the Fuel Cell

In a 2001 press release, *The Birth of the Fuel Cell,* Don Prohaska, an engineer and fuel cell advocate from Boston, remarked that the inventors of the light bulb, the telephone, and the aeroplane are household names but who, he asked rhetorically, invented the fuel cell? He was responding to the worldwide burgeoning of interest in a technology that is widely predicted to revolutionize the production of electricity. According to Prohaska and others, the fuel cell will provide electrical power for cell phones, wheelchairs, vacuum cleaners, and even houses and automobiles. Prohaska also predicted that within relatively few years the name of its inventor, William Robert Grove, will be as familiar to us as those of Thomas Alva Edison and Sir Alexander Graham Bell.

Few large scientific reputations have suffered an eclipse as sudden as Grove's. The shadowing began even before his death. In a tribute to Grove, whom he described as 'Swansea's most distinguished son', S. C. Gamwell objected to a *Times* obituary that attributed to Dr. James Prescott Joule (died 1889) primacy for a critical perception that properly belonged to Grove.[1] The perception, that each of the various manifestations of force or energy in nature is convertible into any other, had been made by Grove in 1842, a full year before a similar conclusion by Joule. Not only this, but Grove's perception had been the germ for his book *The Correlation of Physical Forces*, one of the seminal works of nineteenth century science. As if to compensate for the *Times'* oversight, Gamwell noted a few paragraphs later that the incoming president of the RISW, Dr. Padley, intended to propose that Swansea build a suitable monument to honour, in Padley's words, 'this greatest Scientific Theorist of modern times'. No monument was ever built and its absence, like the *Times* oversight, is a measure of the waning of Grove's reputation.

William Robert Grove.

In 1892, the date of the tribute, Grove was still honoured as a theorist and as author of important discoveries in electro-chemistry, but his scientific days were well behind him. An official guidebook, compiled especially for the second visit of the British Association to Swansea in 1880, failed to record his name in a list of prominent Swansea men.[2] After his death in 1896 his reputation faded. No obituary ever appeared in the *Proceeedings of the Royal Society* and no monograph or biography was ever written.

Dr. Thomas Williams, author of a monograph on Gwyn Jeffreys, lauded him as one of Swansea's finest sons but he did not live long enough to write at length about Grove.[3] In 1985 Michael L. Cooper wrote a comprehensive Ph.D. thesis on Grove but it was never published and, even more telling, it was not (at the time of this writing) available in any Swansea library. In the RISW, and to some extent in the town itself, the names Vivian, Dillwyn and De la Beche still resonate but Grove is a veiled figure, known only to historians of science and a small number of engineers and physicists.

He was born in Swansea in 1811, the son of John Grove, a magistrate and deputy lieutenant of Glamorgan and, in 1838, mayor of Swansea. Like Jeffreys, he was a pupil of Evan Griffith at the Swansea Grammar School, and from there went to Bath for private tutoring and finally to Brasenose College, Oxford. Brasenose, which had no tradition in science, did not engage him and he left with only a pass degree. After Oxford he studied law at Lincoln's Inn and in 1835 he was called to the bar. He joined the Chester and South Wales circuits but ill health kept him from regular practice.[4] He returned to his family home, the Laurels, in Swansea and revived his boyhood interests in chemistry and physics. His grandfather had introduced him to astronomy, and his great uncle to chemistry, but he attributed his involvement in science to a child's story, *The Ghost,* in which a philosophical elder brother cures his younger brother of superstition by experimenting with phosphorous and electricity. Grove made an electrical device with an apothecary's phial when he was about twelve.[5] At the RISW, of which he was a founding member as well as a member of the General Committee, he lectured on optics, galvanism and electricity.[6] At his home, and presumably at the RI after the completion of its laboratory, he conducted experiments in electrochemistry and collaborated with Ben Hill, a talented scientist and inventor from Clydach who eventually became chief engineer on the Swansea Canal. Hill, like Grove, was a pillar of the RISW.

Electricity captivated Grove, as it did all physicists. Electrical phenomena had been investigated in the previous century, and electricity had been contained in a Leyden jar and made to pass through glass, but not until Alessandro Volta assembled his famous 'pile' in 1799 could it be produced as a continuous flow or current. Volta's battery consisted of a stack of coin-sized copper and zinc discs arranged in pairs (copper-zinc/copper-zinc) and separated by wafers of brine-dampened cardboard. The combination generated a steady electrical current that could be felt by placing a finger from each hand on the ends of the stacks. A number of stacks connected with metal strips produced a larger jolt. In a more elaborate experiment, the *couronne de tasses,* he took a number of vessels or cells containing brine or dilute acid and placed in each a zinc plate and a copper plate, the zinc being the negative and copper the positive pole. The plates were not allowed to touch but each zinc plate was connected to the copper plate of the adjoining vessel. A wire connected to the terminal plates at the two ends of the series channeled the resulting current.

Humphry Davy remarked that Volta's invention went off like an alarm bell among the experimenters of Europe. At Thomas Beddoes' Pneumatic Institute at Bristol, Davy built a massive electric battery from a hundred six-inch square double plates of copper and zinc that filled an entire room. Concluding that chemical changes in the zinc plates generated the electricity, Davy wondered if the reverse might also be true – that electricity might induce chemical changes. It was known that the fusion, or explosion, of hydrogen and oxygen gases created water. Could water, Davy wondered, be broken into its constituent parts by subjecting it to the power of an electric current? During his first electrochemical experiment, in which he passed an electric current through water, hydrogen appeared at one pole or electrode and oxygen at the other. With his battery, Davy also discovered that he could not only electrolyze water but also heat metallic wires. A platinum wire could be heated to incandescence, and a current, passed through rods of carbon separated by only a short distance, bridged the gap with an electric arc. Although he did not develop them, Davy had discovered two basic forms of electrical lighting.[7]

Grove's contribution to battery or cell development was to devise a combination of metals and liquids that greatly reduced the loss of voltage. In the simple early cells hydrogen bubbles collected at the poles, setting up a back voltage that rapidly weakened the current. The phenomenon came to be known as 'polarization'. To solve the problem, experimenters introduced liquid depolarisers that destroyed the hydrogen by oxidizing it into water. But the results were batteries of low voltage. By using nitric acid as his oxidizing agent, Grove discovered that he could produce a battery of much higher voltage. He described his experiment to the BAAS meeting at Birmingham in 1839. In a 'hastily constructed' battery, he placed a zinc (positive) electrode and dilute sulphuric acid in one compartment, and a platinum (negative) electrode and strong nitric acid in the other. The compartments were porous pots that allowed the easy passage of the electric current but contained the liquids.

The result was a battery of much higher voltage and, with low internal resistance, a stronger current than any previous battery. Grove modestly remarked that he had been fortunate enough to 'hit upon a combination which I have no hesitation in pronouncing much more powerful than any previously known'. But in the assessment of the science writer J. G. Crowther, his success had less to do with luck than with sound reasoning.[8] At the meeting Grove compared his battery to a rival battery by the German engineer Moritz Hermann von Jacobi. Size for size, and ignoring questions of expense, he calculated that his battery would produce two and a half times the power of Jacobi's. It was the most intense and powerful voltaic combination yet developed and, as the 'Grove Cell', it won its inventor a place in scientific eponymy.

Grove's battery was one of the highlights of the Birmingham meeting and it brought an invitation to lecture on polarization in the Voltaic cell at one of the Friday evening meetings at the Royal Institution, London.[9] At the end of the lecture he demonstrated how the current from a battery of Grove cells covering a space sixteen inches square and four inches high was strong enough to produce a powerful electric arc. Faraday, who at the time was experimenting with electromagnetism, assisted at the demonstration by holding an iron bar near the flame of the arc to show how the flame was attracted or repelled by electromagnetic effects. At a subsequent lecture at the London Institution, Grove illuminated the theatre with incandescent lamps made from filaments of platinum powered by the current from a battery of his nitric acid cells. Because of its strong current Grove's nitric acid cell was, from 1840 to about 1860, the favourite battery of the early American telegraph.

At the Birmingham meeting, Grove also met C. F. Schoenbein, a professor of physics and chemistry at Basle and the invited guest speaker from the continent. The two men would become lifelong associates and friends. After the meeting Schoenbein stayed with the Groves in London and had a Grove cell built by Francis Watkins, a London instrument-maker, for use in his laboratory at the University of Basle. Later in the year Schoenbein arranged for Grove's election as a corresponding member of the Philosophical Society of Basle and followed this, in 1844, by proposing that Grove be awarded an honorary doctorate by the University. It was, wrote Schoenbein, a 'feeble expression of the strong feelings of esteem and consideration which all members of that body entertain towards you'.[10] Working independently on electro-chemical reactions between liquids and metals in Voltaic cells, both men conceived of a cell in which the electric current arises as a result of chemical reactions between constituent gases instead of metals and liquids. Grove reasoned that if an electric current could divide water into hydrogen and oxygen, its component parts, then the reverse might also be true: that under particular conditions the fusion of hydrogen and oxygen might produce water and electricity.

Grove assumed he was now in unmapped country, and that he had gone, in his own words, 'a step further than any hitherto recorded'. In fact, however, he might have been a step behind Schoenbein who noted, in the January 1839 issue of the *Philosophical Magazine*, that the combination of hydrogen and oxygen (dissolved in water) created an electric current. In a postscript to an article in the February issue of the same magazine Grove indicated that he, too, had detected a voltage during the combination of hydrogen and oxygen in a galvanic cell. He ended the postscript with a remark that is now regarded as a prophesy: 'I hope, by repeating this experiment in series, to effect the decomposition of water by means of its composition'. In short, that he might combine the elements of water to produce an electrical current, and then use that current to convert water back into hydrogen and oxygen.

Whichever of the two men first concluded that electricity might be produced by combining hydrogen and oxygen, it was Grove who, over the next four years, tested the hypothesis in his laboratory. In a device which he called a 'Gas Voltaic Battery', he experimented with various combinations of gases. He described the experiments, thirty in all, in an 1843 article for the *Philosophical Magazine*. When the ends of two platinum electrodes were immersed in separate containers of dilute sulphuric acid, and the other ends in sealed containers of oxygen and hydrogen, a constant current flowed between the electrodes. The sealed containers held water as well as gases, and he noted that the water level in each rose as the current flowed. In order to increase the voltage, he linked several of these devices in series and produced what he described to as a self-charging 'gas battery'.

Unlike the wet-cell battery, which stored its energy internally, his gas battery (subsequently renamed the fuel cell) produced electricity continuously so long as it had a source of fuel.[11] It did not run down. Grove also experimented with other gases and succeeded in producing electricity from pairs such as oxygen and carbon monoxide, and chlorine and hydrogen, the latter fueling 'the most powerful gas battery'. Although hydrogen is the most abundant element on earth, it is rarely found in its pure form. In subsequent fuel cell systems the hydrogen was abstracted from hydrogen-rich fossil fuels and combined with oxygen to generate electricity and water. Although dependent on fossil fuels, a fuel cell is two to three times more efficient than a combustion engine which converts fuel to heat, then to mechanical energy, and finally into electricity.

Grove was no entrepreneur, but he was well aware of the commercial and industrial potential of his discovery. He wrote subsequently: 'If, instead of employing manufactured products or educts, such as zinc or acids, we could realize as electricity the whole of the chemical force which is active in the combustion of cheap and abundant raw materials, such as coal, wood, fat, &c, with air or water we should obtain one of the greatest practical desiderata, and have at our command a mechanical power in every respect superior in its applicability to the steam engine'. A steam engine wastes 60-85% of energy whereas the loss in a fuel cell is only 20-30%.

Grove's gas battery, however, was a classic example of the right invention made at the wrong time. It coincided with the development of the steam engine and the discovery of seemingly inexhaustible supplies of fossil fuels. With steam engines powered by coal or oil available to drive electro-magnetic turbines, Grove's gas battery lay virtually unused for more than a century. Only in the 1960s when NASA, the North American Space Agency, needed a supply of electricity for its manned Gemini spacecraft once it had left the ground, was its true worth realized. Conventional batteries were ruled out because of their weight and the

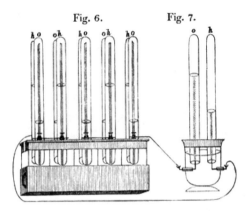

*Grove's drawing of an experimental gas battery,
the forerunner of the modern cell.*

toxicity that would develop over an eight-day flight. Problems of cost that had inhibited the development of earlier fuel cells were irrelevant because the spacecraft already carried liquid oxygen and hydrogen. Once in orbit, the astronauts could drink the fuel cell's water by-product. Since its adoption by NASA, fuel cell technology with its promise of clean emissions and an alternative to, or a more efficient use of, fossil fuels, has been the subject of intensive and sustained research by both industry and government.

Grove's electrical inventions guaranteed his election to the Royal Society, in 1840, and prepared the way, a year later, for his appointment as Professor of Experimental Philosophy at the London Institution. He was 29. At the Institution he had a laboratory and an assistant and was expected to convey, through lectures and demonstrations, the results of his research to an intelligent but untrained audience. In January 1842, a year after his appointment, he spoke at a soirée at the Institution. His theme was progress in science since the opening of the building in 1819. He began with the statement that the forces, or 'affections' of matter are interchangeable:[12]

> *Light, heat, electricity, magnetism, motion, and chemical
> affinity are all convertible material affections; assuming*

211

either as a cause, one of the others will be the effect; thus heat may be said to produce electricity, electricity to produce heat; magnetism to produce electricity, electricity magnetism; and so of the rest.

The following year he delivered a complete course of lectures under the heading 'The Correlation of Physical Forces'. Grove told the managers of the Institute that he hoped the course would 'possess a greater degree of originality and interest than any . . . yet delivered'. So satisfied were the managers that they insisted that the lectures be transcribed and published as a book. The *Correlation of Physical Forces* ran to six editions in several languages and remained in print for forty years. Each new edition was a revised and expanded version of its predecessor. Lay readers, for whom the book was intended, fell upon it.

John G. Hall of Montreal thought it was the most interesting scientific book he had ever read. George Eliot re-read the book in 1870 and noted in her diary 'I began Grove's . . . on the *Correlation of Physical Forces*, needing to read it again with new interests after the lapse of years'. Rose Mary Crawshay, wife of the Merthyr Iron King, William Crawshay, told Grove that his book, along with John Stuart Mill's *On Liberty* had been her bedside reading during the previous summer, confessing that 'many paragraphs I had read six times, not because of any obscurity in the wording, but because the thoughts were so new to me and so original'.[13]

From scientists the reviews were mixed. Mary Somerville, author of *On the Connexion of the Physical Sciences*, thought the book 'with its masterly demonstration of the principles of correlation' was 'one of the most remarkable and talented works that have ever appeared'.[14] F. J. Evans, the Admiralty hydrographer, considered the book to be 'one of the most remarkable of the present century and destined to exert a powerful influence on natural philosophy for some time to come'. Darwin's assessment, conveyed to Grove by his niece Frances Julia Wedgwood, was the most flattering of all. Grove apparently wrote to her requesting a small photograph of Darwin and she replied: 'I should like to have it inscribed with this [her uncle's] emphatic testimony of your work. 'The idea of the correlation of force was one of far greater scope than that of evolution, & I should add, than the Newtonian theory of gravitation'.[15]

Fellow physicists and chemists, however, made uneasy by the popular nature of the book, were more sceptical. Grove had no mathematics and had been unable to quantify the relationships between the elements. The Scottish physicist James Clerk Maxwell regarded the work as only a popular treatise designed to communicate some scientific principles in language intelligible to the educated layman. Furthermore, ideas about the interconvertibility of the elements were not new. Mary Somerville herself had noted that the analogies so far discovered between, for example, electricity and magnetism and light and heat, 'justified the expectation that all phenomena would ultimately be referred to the same agent'.[16] The reviewer for the *Cornhill Magazine*, however, thought to be the astronomer John Herschel, considered the book justified Grove's claim to be the first to articulate a general theory of the conversion of forces.[17] He noted that the work was based on lectures delivered in January 1842 and so predated the work of Mayer and Joule. Grove's primacy was also acknowledged by Herman Ludwig von Helmholtz, author of a celebrated paper, 'Conservation of Force', 1847, when speaking at the London Institution in 1861. Helmholtz allowed that Grove ought to be granted the distinction of having been the first to demonstrate that every force of nature was capable of bringing into action every other force of nature.[18]

In the preface to the fourth English, and first American, edition of *Correlation*, Grove answered his critics. He allowed that in science the same idea or ideas might occur at the same time to separate inquirers, and he cited the case of Joule whose 1843 paper on the mechanical equivalent of heat certainly bore on the issue of the convertibility of force in nature. But by not addressing the 'mutual dependence' of all the physical forces Joule's paper did not amount to a comprehensive theory. To those critics who accused him of merely synthesising existing ideas Grove made this stately riposte:

> *As I have introduced into the later editions of my essay abstracts of the different discoveries which I have found, since my first lectures to bear upon the subject, I have been*

regarded by many rather as the historian of the progress made in this branch of thought than as one who has had anything to do with its initiation.

Everyone is but a poor judge where he himself is interested, and I, therefore, write with diffidence; but it would be affecting an indifference which I do not feel if I did not state that I believe myself to have been the first who introduced this subject as a generalized system of philosophy, and continued to enforce it in my lectures and writings for many years, during which it met with the opposition usual and proper to novel ideas.[19]

He continued by expressing regret that family responsibilities had prevented him from backing his thesis with as much experiment as he would have liked, but he reiterated that the essay primarily was an exercise in the philosophy of science. He concluded the fourth edition with a disquisition on the necessity of theory:

To think on nature is to theorise; and difficult it is not to be led on by the continuities of natural phenomena to the theories which appear forced and unintelligible to those who have not pursued the same path of thought; which, moreover, if allowed to gain undue influence, seduce us from that truth which is the sole object of our pursuit.

Where to draw the line – where to say thus far we may go, and no farther, in any particular class of analogies or relations which Nature presents to us; how far to follow the progressive indications of thought, and where to resist its allurements – is a question of degree which must depend upon the judgement of each individual or each class of thinkers; yet it is consolatory that thought is seldom expended in vain.[20]

In 1846, the same year as the publication of *The Correlation of Physical Forces*, Grove received the Royal Medal of the Royal Society for his Bakerian lecture on Voltaic ignition and the decomposition of water into its constituent gases. But by 1846, as he intimated in his letter to Schonbein, he had returned to the law.

He now had a wife and four children to support and from now until the end of his career his scientific work would have to be conducted in tandem with his legal work. In 1845 he was elected to the Council of the Royal Society and appointed to a committee to advise on the screening of papers submitted to the *Philosophical Transactions* as well as on procedures for selecting candidates for the Society's medals and awards. The following year also found him on a committee charged with revising the charters of the Society and the rules for the election of fellows. Despite periodic efforts at reform, the Society was perennially in danger of degenerating into a club of cultivated, but not necessarily scientific, gentlemen.

Early in his presidency, Joseph Banks had to insist that membership be restricted to those with an interest in science. Determined to introduce more rigour into the procedures for admission, Humphry Davy, who was president from 1820-27, advocated the blackballing of unsuitable candidates. But neither Banks' nor Davy's strictures were effective. The membership continued to increase, and in 1827 Council appointed a committee to consider 'the best means' of limiting it. Its key recommendation was that by electing only four fellows each year the membership could, within a reasonable period, be reduced from more than 700 to 400. The Council welcomed the general thrust of the report but delayed consideration of the findings for so long that they eventually disappeared from the record.

The role of the new Charter Committee, as defined by Council, was to reduce the number of admissions and restrict these to accomplished scientists. Grove, who steered the Committee through the legal niceties of changing the charter, asked Faraday if he would be willing to join, but he declined on grounds of health. Faraday rejoiced, however, 'to hear of any attempt to reinvigorate the Society . . . Where is the honour of being one of 800 men of science?' At Grove's suggestion, the Committee recommended that the election of Fellows take place on one day – previously there had been four elections annually – and that no more than fifteen fellows be elected. Because a statute restricting the ordinary membership would have been illegal, Grove suggested that the Council choose the most eligible of the candidates and that the number chosen not exceed fifteen. In practice, the Fellows would not dispute the recommendations of Council so that the membership would be restricted, but not legally restricted. The reforms were regarded as the most important change in the administration of the Society since its foundation, transforming it, as the older fellows died, from a body of well-educated and cultivated men into a truly scientific body. In 1848 fourteen new fellows were elected, one withdrawing just before the election, and seven were unsuccessful.

Grove was seen as a, if not *the*, key figure in the reform movement. In *English Men of Science* (1874), Francis Galton would write: 'To have been elected a Fellow of the Royal Society since the reform in the mode of election introduced by Mr Justice Grove nearly thirty years ago, is a real assay of scientific merit'. In his presidential address in November 1896, the year following Grove's death, Sir Joseph Lister described Grove as 'one of the most active promoters of the reform of its [the Society's] constitution which took place in 1847'. Ten years earlier, in his presidential address, Huxley gave Grove the leading role. By fighting the 'battles of 1847' he and his supporters 'earned the undying gratitude of all who have the interests of science at heart'.

To maintain the momentum of the movement, the reformers realised that they would have to meet regularly to discuss Society affairs. The vehicle chosen, apparently on a suggestion from Grove, was a dining or philosophical club that would meet before the Society meetings. Membership would be restricted to authors of scientific papers and the number – to commemorate the year of the revised statutes – limited to 47. Grove was the Club's first treasurer, a committee member for thirteen years, and an ordinary member until 1892. Seven of the members were also members of Royal Society Council. The Club was variously described as the 'guardian angel' of all scientific societies, and as the 'most influential body in London'.[21]

The first task of the Club, and of the reformers in general, was to secure the chief offices of the Society. In November 1847 the junior of the Society's two secretaries announced that he would retire. The secretaries were at the hub of the Society's affairs, sitting on important committees, reading scientific papers submitted to the *Philosophical Transactions* and supervising its publication. Faraday and De la Beche, who was a member of the

Club, urged Grove to stand. Charles Lyell went further, proposing that the Council – as in the election of ordinary fellows – recommend Grove to the fellows. The lobbying for Grove elicited an immediate reaction from the more conservative members and from the natural scientists who saw the balance of power within the Society tilting irrevocably toward the physical sciences. S. H. Christie, the Society's senior secretary, was an experimental physicist and professor of mathematics at the Royal Military Academy. Alarmed at its prospective loss of control over the *Philosophical Transactions*, a large proportion of whose papers were written by anatomists, physiologists and biologists, the Committee of Zoology and Animal Physiology expressed its dismay to the Council, contending that one of the secretaries at least should be conversant with natural science. Among the Fellows, too, natural scientists outnumbered the physical scientists by three to one and there was already a preponderance of physical scientists in the Council.

At the Council meeting, May 1848, Lyell (as he explained in a letter to Grove) nominated Grove. Robert Brown, who argued that one of the secretaries should be a physiologist, proposed Professor Bell, but could find no one to second his motion. In the discussion that followed, the marine biologist Edward Forbes, who was an ardent reformer, spoke of the changes Grove would make if elected. Fearing a reaction from both neutrals and conservatives, Lyell and others rebuked Forbes for remarks they considered both untimely and inappropriate.

But they were too late. The conservative members and many of the natural scientists were so incensed that Brown's motion found a seconder and its adoption set in train a campaign to prevent Grove's election. In a letter to De la Beche, Edward Forbes, still unaware of his blunder, described the scene: 'As the Royal met yesterday I write to tell you what took place. Lyell brought forward your motion about Grove – Robert Brown moved an amendment that the secretary be [a physiologist?] but named no one . . . I quite see the force of Mr Brown's plea – but think in the present state of the society a year or so of Grove would so purge it of its impurities that we may waive physiological interests in the meantime with advantage'.[22]

Fellows who would normally have supported Grove, but who thought it unwise to waive physiological interests, wrote to Grove to explain why they must give their vote to Bell. Among them was W. B. Carpenter, the marine biologist. 'If *you* were a physiologist and Bell a reformer, I should have no doubt as to my vote. But it is because you are not a physiologist . . . that I find it difficult to see my way clearly. At present . . . the question of reform seems to me the paramount one; and I should have no hesitation in voting for you, if I did not perceive such a studied exclusion of the representatives of physiological science in the proposed list of Officers and Council'.[23] But not all the objections to Grove's candidacy were as reasonable. A wild rumour, spread presumably by supporters of Bell, held that Grove intended to exclude physiology from the *Transactions* and remove physiologists from the Society. It was patent nonsense but tempers were such that it was taken seriously by the physician Marshall Hall. 'It has been stated to me . . . that you have expressed yourself as desirous of severing physiology and physiologists from the Royal Soc. If this be correct, it is a shocking calumny; and I think it right to give you the opportunity of contradicting it . . . It is said that you expressed yourself in the manner stated, at the Philosophical Club'.[24]

A debate that divided the finest intellects in the country, and that had become acrimonious, inevitably spilled over into the public arena and the press. The *Cambrian* simply noted that Grove's candidature for the secretaryship was 'opposed by the natural history section, candidate Prof. T. Bell. Grove belongs to Chemical and Physical party'.[25] But the *Athenaeum*, in its editions of 18 & 25 November, 1848, carried thirteen letters on the debate, most of them favouring balance within the Society and opposing Grove and the physical scientists. One opposed Grove on personal grounds, allowing that his knowledge of French and his acquaintance with foreign scientists were distinct assets, but regretted that these were offset by an intimidating manner: 'I cannot forget that his conduct is somewhat too imperious to hold so important a situation, where he has to deal with his equals at all times . . . I shall vote for Prof. Bell – who follows science for its own sake, and whose affable manners and considerate conduct endear him to all Fellows of the Society'.

Under the whips of the two camps, the November 1848 meeting for the election of officers was the largest gathering of Fellows for many years. Gideon Mantell, the Sussex surgeon and palaeontologist whom Lyell had asked to attend, described the scene: 'Room crowded; between 200 and 300 Fellows present: a tumultuous and disgraceful scene; nothing could be worse. Several printed lists of candidates for Officers and Council were allowed to be issued, and inextricable confusion was the consequence. We waited till seven, but the result was not then announced, and I returned . . . to dinner'.[26]

But however chaotic the process of voting, the result was now predictable. Christie was re-elected as senior secretary but Bell won the vacant position by 134 votes to 108. Mantell, who did not learn of the result until the following morning was aghast: 'learnt that Mr Grove lost the appointment of Secretary! to the eternal disgrace of those who opposed him by such a man as Professor Bell, who though amiable and fond of Zoology, can scarcely be named for ability with Mr Grove'.[27] In victory Bell, who had distanced himself from the dispute, was magnanimous. At a subsequent dinner he proposed Grove's health, acknowledged his many gifts, and professed that only the perceived need for a representative from the natural sciences had persuaded him to stand.

For the reformers, the other crucial issue in 1848 was the election of a new president. In January 1848 Lord Northampton, who had been ten years in office, announced that he would retire before the end of the year. He also made it known that he thought Lord Churchill would make a suitable successor. The reformers' worst fears had been realised; Churchill had no strong scientific interests and he was said to be unexceptional. Grove, Faraday and others approached the astronomer John Herschel who declined to stand on grounds of distance from London and the pressure of work.[28] De la Beche and Charles Lyell, separately, approached Faraday who pleaded ill health to each entreaty. The reformers' main objective was a truly scientific president, not an aristocratic figurehead, and the most ardent of them wished to settle for nothing less. 'We must if possible', cried Edward Forbes, 'have a scientific president – not a peer – or there will be a revolt & barricades constructed scientifically in the antechamber at Somerset House'. Cooler heads, however, acknowledged that if a truly scientific president was out of reach then they might have to settle for a limited term of office. A president who proved unsatisfactory would not be in office for too long and more frequent elections would increase the chances of electing occasionally a scientific president.

In 1830 Charles Babbage, an earlier advocate of reform, had suggested a two-year term, as applied in the Geological and Astronomical Societies. De la Beche who was now half-way through his term as president of the Geological Society thought likewise. With Faraday and Herschel both declining to stand for the Royal Society presidency, De la Beche approached Sir Robert Peel who, if there had to be a nonscientific figurehead, would at least be an effective and appealing one. Peel, however, was none too pleased at being offered the role of stand-in president and he wrote a stinging reply. 'The Royal Society had better cease to exist than proclaim to the world that the members must take a politician as their President, on account of their disagreement, not on the principle of the superior advantage of selecting a man of science, but on the question of personal qualifications and preferences . . . If such jealousies as those which Sir H. de la Beche referred to were allowed to prevail, I was much more disposed to retire from the Royal Society than to solve the differences arising from such jealousies by accepting the office of President.' Eventually, the reformers settled for Lord Rosse, a scientific peer (astronomer) from Ireland who served for the next six years.

Grove's other great institutional commitment was to the BAAS. He was president of the Nottingham meeting in 1866, four times a vice president, and a Council member for all but three years between 1846 and 1866. Founded in 1831, the Association had been conceived as an instrument that would stimulate scientific research and raise the profile of science by bringing together, in a public forum, men and women with scientific interests. As the physicist Sir David Brewster, the driving force behind the Association, put it, the objective was 'to revive science from its decline, and the scientific arts from their depression; to instruct the government when ignorant, and stimulate it when supine [and] . . . to raise scientific and literary men to their just place in society.'[29] He saw the BAAS also as a means of integrating the various departments of science which, with the founding of specialised learned societies, were beginning to move apart. To meet the objective of presenting science to the public, the annual meetings of the Association would move around the country.

Grove served on a number of Association committees where he could apply scientific interests that embraced optics, astronomy and photography as well as physics and chemistry. He was a member of the committee that supervised the work of the Kew Observatory and when, in 1871, the responsibility shifted to the Royal Society, Grove simply changed hats. In his Swansea days, Grove had lectured on optics at the RISW. He was also a member of the BAAS's Lunar committee charged with preparing a large-scale map, six feet in diameter, of the moon. He had long been interested in telescopes, taking part in a notable discussion with James Nasmyth at the Birmingham Meeting in 1839. In the 1850s he spoke on methods of producing achromatic lenses at the Philosophical Club, and on methods of improving telescopes at the Astronomical Society.[30]

Grove was also an obvious choice for the Association's Patents Committee. When reviewing Charles Babbage's book on the decline of science in England (1830), Brewster cited patent monopolies and the payments demanded from patentees as reasons for the sorry state of scientific invention in the country. The patent abolition movement was linked to the free trade movement. Brewster raised the subject of patents at the very first meeting of the BAAS where it was agreed that a review of the patent laws would be an appropriate subject for the attention of the Association. But only when parliamentary amendments to the laws were undertaken, in 1852, did the Association strike a committee – of which Grove was a member – to review the new arrangements. Patent law was a significant part of Grove's legal practice.

By the mid 1840s Grove was well settled in London but he had not forgotten his debt to the RISW and Swansea. Just when the idea of inviting the BAAS to Swansea occurred to him is not clear, but a brief correspondence between Grove and John Henry Vivian suggests that the thought had also occurred to Vivian and been dismissed for want of a rail connection with England.[31] The first meeting of the BAAS, in September 1831, had been at York where John Phillips, Secretary of the Yorkshire Philosophical Society, had offered to accommodate the meeting. But for the next few years the annual meeting reverted to the university towns and the capitals: Oxford, Cambridge, Dublin and Edinburgh. It began to visit provincial towns again after 1836 but to bring the annual meeting to a small, remote town in Wales required a major act of persuasion. June and July, 1846, found Grove in south Wales, presenting briefs to the Summer Assizes, where he was able to gauge how much local support there might be for a visit of the BAAS.

In Swansea he conferred with Henry De la Beche, who was then mapping south Wales for the Geological Survey, with fellow members of the RISW, and with influential townspeople. Encouraged by the response, Grove approached Edward Sabine, the British Association's General Secretary, who thought Swansea might be a 'very desirable place' for a meeting, probably in 1849. (In 1844 the Reverend William Whewell, a former president, had advised Roderick Murchison, the general secretary, that 'there remain places that ought to be visited', and Swansea was on his short list.[32]

Oxford had been promised the 1847 meeting and Norwich was thought to be the front-runner for the succeeding year. By August, Grove, the RISW and the town had taken the decision to apply. Grove wrote to Schoenbein in Basel that he was soon to attend a meeting at Southampton to make application for Swansea and hoped that Schoenbein would meet him there. 'I hope you will come over to Southampton. I am going there to apply for a visit of the British Association to Swansea my native town. If I should succeed it will probably be for the year 1849 & should it please god we both live so long I will take no excuse from you for not coming there. You must accept a bed in my patrimonial abode'.[33] In public Grove was enthusiastic, but in private, as he intimated in a letter to George Grant Francis of Swansea, he rated the town's chances as only fair.[34]

During the second meeting of the General Committee at the Southampton meeting, the president, Sir Roderick Impie Murchison, acknowledged a letter from Grove informing them that a deputation appointed by the Swansea Corporation, the Royal Institution of South Wales, the magistracy, and the principal inhabitants of the town and neighbourhood would attend the meeting for the purpose of inviting the British Association to hold their annual meeting in Swansea at the earliest convenient date.

At the second meeting of the Committee, Grove, supported by De la Beche, read resolutions from the Corporation, the RISW, and principal inhabitants of Swansea. He then addressed the meeting, presenting, 'at great length', the attractions Swansea offered to a large body of visiting scientists. Inland were the coalfield and copper works, and beyond these a smiling countryside replete with fine houses, ruined castles and prehistoric sites. The town itself offered the facilities of a fashionable resort and a bay comparable to the bay at Naples.[35] It was a siren-like performance that two years later Lord Northampton would liken to the spell of a 'potent magician' who, 'like a representative of the Bard and Druid of ancient Britain, summoned us to the shores of the Bristol Channel'.[36]

Not all the members of the General Committee fell under Grove's spell but the general reaction was very favourable. At a meeting in London, in April 1847, the Council of the BAAS resolved that the 1848 annual meeting, Norwich no longer being a contender for that year, be granted to Swansea. The decision followed a report, by the Association's assistant general secretary John Phillips, on all aspects of the town's suitability. During the first week of April, accompanied by Grove, he had surveyed lodgings and meeting rooms and talked to townspeople. He advised the Council that he thought the town could support a 'moderate meeting' and noted that the existence of the RISW had weighed heavily in his decision.[37] On the first day of the Oxford meeting Grove attended a meeting of the General Committee and formally invited the BAAS to visit Swansea the following year. In spite of serious reservations about the suitability of Swansea, Sir Roderick Impey Murchison, president for the Oxford meeting, moved that the invitation be accepted. There were no demurrals. The Marquis of Northampton was voted president for the Swansea meeting and Grove one of the vice-presidents.

In spite of his resignation from the London Institution in 1845, and his increasingly heavy legal duties, Grove managed to keep abreast of developments in science and even do some original research. He gave the Royal Society's Bakerian Lecture in 1852 on the electro-chemical polarity of gases and in 1866 he was president of the BAAS's Nottingham meeting. His presidential address was on continuity in science. When Schoenbein learned, in 1840, that Grove contemplated reviving his legal career, he had tried to dissuade him. Grove's Voltaic cell, or 'pile', largely as a result of Schoenbein's promotion of it, had generated great interest on the continent. 'It must be most gratifying to you to learn', he wrote, 'that . . . I have received a great many letters from philosophers of all quarters in Germany and that there is only one voice of praise and admiration for your admirable arrangement . . . I tell you all these things not to flatter but to encourage you to continue the work which you have so happily begun and to dissuade you from reentering into the career of a lawyer. Nature has made you for being a philosopher and you ought to follow her calling'.[38] But family matters pressed heavily and Grove could only promise not to give up science altogether: 'I have nearly made up my mind to give up my professorship on the 25th March next. I find like you that money is actually necessary & as I have now four children I must put my shoulder to the wheel. I do not intend altogether to give up science whatever leisure time I have I shall devote to it'.[39]

Schoenbein replied that Grove's gift for science had come from a far higher authority than that which had granted his professorship at the London Institution and prayed that his genius would not allow him to abandon the paths of science and drown himself in 'the turbid floods of law'.[40] In spite of repeated apologias from Grove, Schonbein would not give up. In 1850 he wrote again: 'As far as I am able to judge you have been intended by nature to be rather a philosopher than a lawyer. How much could you do for science if less bothered by your professional business. There are so few original 'scutatori natura' so few who have a creative mind and the power of having views of their own'.[41] And again in 1858: 'I suppose you are deeply buried again in your professional affairs, but I am quite sure, that even amidst the bustle of official business, you will never lose out of sight the great and glorious cause of natural science and act now and then the part of the philosopher instead of that of a lawyer. Nevertheless I cannot help deeply lamenting it that you are prevented from exclusively devoting your time and mental powers to philosophical researches, for eminent as you no doubt are in the science and practice of law, I think by natural calling you have been intended to be before all a 'Naturforscher'. Original views and ideas are the heirloom of but a few privileged minds and those views and ideas are the ground from which alone spring up discoveries of a fundamental nature and consequently originate the real advancement of science'.[42]

Schonbein made his final appeal in 1864: 'You being an independent gentleman, why bother yourself any longer with the law business. Retire from that burdensome stage of life, enjoy the 'odium cum dignitate', to which you are fully entitled and your old love for science will revive conjointly with that placidity of mind so necessary to a successful philosopher. You are made for better things than carrying law suits'.

In 1855 the principal of Brasenose College also tried to divert Grove from the law by inviting him to apply for a vacant chair of chemistry. But the salary of £300 was far less than the amount he could earn as an ordinary barrister.[43] A move to Oxford would also have meant re-entering a world of refined jealousies and intrigues that, as a busy, practising lawyer he was remote from. Law and business, he commented in a letter to Schoenbein, were so demanding that they left little time or energy for self aggrandizement or, its corollary, the discrediting of rivals: 'Belonging to a profession where it is generally supposed chicanery reigns triumphant I have certainly not seen half so much intrigue or baseness as I have in the other sphere of my existence nor felt half so much selfishness'.[44] Yet, although he might not have missed the company of scientists, he missed the practice of science. He wrote to Schoenbein in 1853: 'The fact is that with 6 children a profession & odds and ends of property to attend to & occasionally a few moments directed to science I am whirled and worried so that my mind is frittered away & I am a nothing doing man – because I do so many things . . . I leave tomorrow for my misery, i.e. circuit'.[45] Other scientists also reproached him for giving up science for the law but his standard reply was that the support of a large family demanded a larger income than pure science could provide. Practical science might have supported him but he did not share the average Englishman's 'great liking' for it. In spite of his love of experiment, science, he insisted, interested him only 'as a means of extending our knowledge beyond its ordinary grasp.'[46]

As a barrister, he specialised in patent cases but these could only have amounted to a small proportion of his legal work. For disputes requiring some knowledge of chemistry or physics he was an obvious choice. In 1846/47 he helped Schoenbein acquire a patent for gun cotton – a smokeless and odourless explosive – and demonstrated its properties at the BAAS meeting at Southampton. Schoenbein licensed his gun cotton technology to an English entrepreneur whose operations ended with a factory explosion in 1847 that killed more than twenty employees. Schoenbein never worked on gun cotton again but Alfred Nobel is thought to have used his ideas when producing nitroglycerin and, subsequently, dynamite. In 1850 Grove acted for a group of Manchester gas manufacturers and industrial chemists, accused of infringing a patent for extracting paraffin oil from bituminous coal, and in 1854 for the photographer W. H. F. Talbot who spent much of the 1850s in litigation over his calotype and other patents. Talbot claimed that the collodion technique (invented, but not patented, by F. S. Archer in 1851) infringed his calotype patent of 1841.

Unwilling to let his patent lapse, Talbot allowed amateurs to use the calotype and collodion methods free of charge but insisted that professional portrait photographers using the collodion technique purchase a licence from him. The claim was challenged by Martin Laroche, a professional photographer, from whom Talbot sought £5,000 damages for infringement of the calotype patent. In the ensuing lawsuit, December 1854, Grove, who had experimented with photographic processes at the London Institution, represented Talbot, but reluctantly. He was familiar with the uncertainties of patent law and had reservations, 'strong opinions', about the restrictive nature of patents in general. In 1841 he had written to Schoenbein: 'We are in a sad restricted state in England regarding this & other scientific points from the innumerable patents. We scarcely can publish an experiment without risk of a lawsuit'.[47] According to J. D. Wood, an historian of photography, Grove did not encourage Talbot to enter court. At the end of the three day trial the jury acknowledged Talbot as the 'first and true inventor of calotype process' but ruled that Laroche, in using the collodion technique, was not guilty of infringing Talbot's patent.[48]

Grove's science also won him his brief at the trial of William Palmer, the 'Rugely Poisoner'. Palmer's trial was the most celebrated murder trial of the mid-nineteenth century. A former surgeon, he was accused of poisoning, with strychnine, John Parsons Cook. In November 1855 Palmer, who had abandoned medicine for the turf, attended the Shrewsbury races with Cook, a fellow gambler and racehorse owner. Palmer had heavy gambling debts and at the meet Cook's horse, Polestar, had won his race. After the meet Cook, attended by Palmer, became ill with severe retching and vomiting and died a few days later when staying at an inn in Rugely, opposite Palmer's house. The apparent cause of death was strychnine poisoning. Palmer was charged with murder and the subsequent investigation connected him with the suspicious deaths of a dozen other people.[49] Normally, Palmer would have been tried at an Assize Court in Staffordshire but the case excited such interest, and local feelings were so heated, that by special Act of Parliament the venue for the trial was moved to the Central Criminal Court, London: the Old Bailey. Dickens regarded Palmer as 'the greatest villain' ever to occupy that famous dock.

In another departure from standard practice, three judges were appointed. On each side of the bar were accomplished and, in a few cases, brilliant advocates who played to a packed courthouse of lords and commoners. The Earl of Dufferin, Earl Grey, The Marquis of Anglesea, the Earl of Derby, Prince Edward of Saxe Weimar, and the Duke of Wellington were among the recorded spectators. Lead counsel for the prosecution was the Attorney General Sir Alexander Cockburn. Grove, now a QC, had been appointed as scientific counsel for the defence. His role was to coach the leading counsel for Palmer, Mr Sarjeant Shee, and lead the witnesses for the defence.[50]

The trial itself was a great forensic contest between competing barristers and their teams of physicians and toxicologists. No man or woman in England had ever been tried for poisoning by strychnine and, to make the case even more singular, no traces of strychnine or other poisons had been found in Cook's body. The defence's strategy was straightforward: to posit natural causes for Palmer's death and by doing so disarm the prosecution's scientific and medical witnesses. Scientific witnesses for the defence suggested that Cook's symptoms might have been caused by tetanus, epilepsy, arachnitis, or angina pectoris. Most telling was the testimony of William Herepath, a distinguished professor of chemistry

Grove, the jurist.

and toxicology at the Bristol Medical School. Herepath testified that strychnine administered in sufficient quantity to kill a human being ought not to have escaped detection unless the body had decomposed. But neither Herepath nor the defence's physicians were able to convince the judges or the jurors and Palmer was duly convicted and hanged.

Grove's Swansea origins, his reputation as a scientist and, thanks to the Palmer trial, his high legal profile drew him inexorably into the south Wales copper-smoke disputes. In July 1858 Dugdale Houghton, the owner and leaseholder of several farms in the Neath Valley brought an action for damages against the Red Jacket copper works.[51] When first built (in 1849) the works had used a newly patented 'wet' or liquid method of separating copper from its ore. The process produced copper that was remarkably malleable and pure and, by reducing the number of calcinations and eliminating smelting, it did so by making far less smoke than the traditional 'dry' processes. The method, however, proved to be prohibitively expensive and after a short trial period the owners reverted to the old 'dry' methods and at the same time increased the number of furnaces and chimneys. The smoke passed over two of Houghton's farms, destroying crops and killing animals.

Houghton sought damages and, with Grove as his counsel, brought an action against Red Jacket.

At the trial, held in Carmarthen, they presented a formidable case that the defence answered with little more than rhetorical denials. Grove produced two telling scientific witnesses, William Herepath, the distinguished Bristol professor of analytical chemistry who had testified at the Palmer trial, and William Henry Michael M.D, then mayor of Swansea. Herepath, who declared matter of factly that he had probably conducted more tests on animal and vegetable substances than any other living chemist, examined the heads, organs and viscera of horses from Houghton's farms as well as samples of grasses, hay and ferns. The heads were swollen, the viscera and organs inflamed, and the lungs covered with large blood and water blisters. He attributed the injuries to the inhalation of sulphurous acid gas (the most toxic constituent of copper-smoke) and to the ingestion of grasses and hay impregnated with sulphuric acid.

William Henry Michael, a keen advocate of public health and smoke suppression, had been engaged by Houghton to monitor the effects of copper-smoke upon pristine farmland. He testified that until the Red Jacket works had reverted to the process of dry smelting the vegetation had been relatively undamaged, but once the chimneys began to send out dense clouds of smoke the vegetation was 'quite burnt up', as if hit by a Sirocco.

Unable to fault Houghton's farming practices, which had been a tactic used against farmers in earlier copper-smoke trials, the defence had to look for extenuating circumstances not connected with copper-smoke. On each side of the farms, near the mouth of the river Neath to the east and in the Crymlyn Burrows to the west, were large areas of marsh and stagnant water in which the atmosphere was thought to be miasmatic or epidemic. To explain the dangers of epidemic atmospheres the defence called Dr. Thomas Williams of Swansea. Williams asserted that the stagnant waters of the salt marshes and the Burrows created a 'sort of malaria' that induced ague and other fevers in the human population, and no doubt injured cattle and other animals. With a carelessness that would have disturbed Richard Bright, his tutor at Guy's, he offered that his conclusions were based on 'impressions' and 'general observations' rather than the study of particular cases. He had examined the animals brought as material evidence from Houghton's farms to Carmarthen and was convinced that their injuries were caused by dank and poor air, not copper-smoke.

Cross-examined by Grove, Williams was forced to admit that the farms were well managed but he asserted that some of the dried grasses had been reduced to that condition by the 'action of the weather' and, by inference, not by copper-smoke. To prevent further dissembling, Grove then quoted from Thomas Williams's *Report on the Copper Smoke* published four years earlier. Touched by the smoke, 'the hawthorn dries to a leafless skeleton, the evergreen dies, the apple, and the pear, and the plum, the ash and even the pachidermous oak shrink into saplessness'. He then turned to Williams's assessment of the equally damaging effects of the smoke and poisoned grasses upon animals. In his report, written for the General Board of Health, Thomas Williams had been concerned to defend copper smoke only against charges that it was damaging to human health.

Orchestrated by Grove, the combined testimony of Herepath and Michael, allied to Houghton's own careful detailing of the damages, was compelling and the court ordered damages in the amount of £450. It was the first successful suit brought by a farmer or landowner against a copper company. Constrained by costs, Red Jacket, however, did not revert to 'wet' methods of production. Smoke continued to pour from its chimneys and two years later Houghton sued again. The trial was at Swansea and Grove once again was Houghton's counsel.[52] With the Carmarthen trial as a model, the case ought to have been a walkover but Houghton, presumably with Grove's approval, demanded damages of £8,000 over three years for two farms that he leased for £250 annually. At the Carmarthen trial he had demanded damages of £864 for a similar period. At Swansea, Grove again called on Herepath and W. H. Michael but neither their testimony nor Houghton's recital of his farming practices could suppress the wrath of the judge, Sir George Bramwell.

While allowing that damages were due to the plaintiff, he regarded the amount requested as 'outlandish', 'most extravagant', 'enormously exaggerated', or 'rank', and 'of the most exorbitant character ever brought into a court of justice'. Grove's efforts to reduce the amount of the claim during the trial he regarded as too little too late and intimated that they were a ploy to avert the judge's displeasure. The jury expressed its displeasure by awarding risible damages of £150, one fiftieth of the amount requested and only one third of the amount awarded at the Carmarthen trial.

The debacle at Swansea had little apparent effect on Grove's reputation as a barrister. He was appointed to the Royal Commission on patent laws in 1863 and elevated to the bench in 1871, a year before being knighted. Among his legal colleagues and contemporaries, the consensus seems to have been that he was a better scientist than he was a lawyer. As a judge he had the reputation of being painstaking, accurate, and courageous in opinion. In patent cases, however, where his judgement ought to have been particularly valuable, his science may have been an impediment. On occasion, he appears to have been more interested in the technical merits of a patent than in its legality.[53]

Although he did no experimental work after 1870, Grove never lost his appetite for science, and he never tired of talking about it. Francis Galton recorded that the most striking intellectual conversation he ever heard was between Grove and Thomas Henry Huxley. Grove's taste, as the science writer F. J. Crowther remarked, was always for 'contemplative science', and the closer he approached the law, and the greater the distance from the laboratory, the stronger the tendency became. In a letter to his wife, Schoenbein wrote that 'Faraday and Grove . . . continually stood in fear of coming across something which would bring them in contact with the practical world'. Grove himself remarked that 'science to me generally ceases to be interesting as it becomes useful' and he disapproved of the ever-increasing list of 'artificial wants' that it brought in its train. Although his marshalling of the reforms at the Royal Society had been instrumental in professionalizing science, Grove himself was among the last of the great self-taught gentleman scientists. Intimations of the waning of reputation after his death would have disappointed him, but one senses that he would not have been dismayed by them. Yet what he might have regarded as a decent obscurity has, in effect, ended. In an August 2003 issue of the *New Yorker* magazine, Grove and the fuel cell, and the cell's probable applications, are the subjects of a featured article.[54] A scientist, for whom interest in discovery ended as soon as it became practical, has been the genesis of what advocates of the fuel cell confidently describe as the hydrogen age.

In the hope of reducing dependence on fossil fuels, and on inefficient methods of employing them, automobile manufacturers, electrical power producers, and governments throughout the world are investing heavily in fuel cell research and development. Iceland, which has no oil of its own and which is a popular testing ground for advanced technologies, has opened the world's first commercial hydrogen station. Grove may have been too retiring a figure to be, as Boston's Don Prohaska predicts, a suitable subject for a Hollywood biography but if the hydrogen age does dawn then he is assured of a place in the Pantheon alongside Edison and Bell. To close her *New Yorker* article, Elizabeth Kolbert quotes an exchange from Jules Verne's novel *The Mysterious Island*. A group of Union officers, escapees by balloon from a Confederate prison, have landed on a Pacific island. They pass the time by discussing, among other things, the Union's dependence on diminishing supplies of coal. One of the officers reassures the rest that there is nothing to fear: 'Yes, my friends, I believe that water may one day be employed as fuel, that hydrogen and oxygen which constitute it, used singly or together, will furnish an inexhaustible source of heat and light. I believe that when the deposits of coal are exhausted, we shall heat and warm ourselves with water. Water will be the coal of the future'.

NOTES

1. *Swansea Scientific Society Reports*, (1892-93), 34-5.
2. S. C. Gamwell, *Guide and Handbook to Swansea and its district*, (Swansea, 1880).
3. In a letter to Grove, written in 1847, Williams implored: 'May you long live that Swansea may boast of you as her son, and that your example may be exultingly cited to inspire and encourage others less gifted'. Quoted in Colin Matheson, 'William Robert Grove: Glamorgan Physicist and Judge', *Glamorgan Historian*, 9 (1973), 96-103.
4. Grove, who lived to the then considerable age of 85, described his condition as 'strong frame but weak and torpid liver'. He also had trouble with his kidneys. Quoted in Michael L. Cooper, 'William Robert Grove (1811-96): a gentleman of science' (Open University Ph.D. thesis, 1987), 21.
5. Francis Galton, *English men of science* (London, 1874), 153-4.

6. He was appointed a member of the General Committee at the first general meeting of subscribers to the RISW, 1 June 1835. *Cambrian* (7 August 1896).

7. Oliver Sacks, *Uncle Tungsten* (London, 2001), 118-122.

8. J. G. Crowther, *Statesmen of Science* (London, 1965) 84-6.

9. The Friday evening meetings, initiated and introduced by Michael Faraday, were designed to inform mixed audiences, of specialists and non-specialists, of recent developments in science. For Grove it was the beginning of a forty-year relationship with the Royal Institution, as lecturer and legal and administrative adviser.

10. Schoenbein to Grove, 22 January 1844. Ulf Bossel, *The Birth of the Fuel Cell* (Oberrohrdorf, 2000).

11. The term 'fuel cell' was coined by the chemists Ludwig Mond and Charles Langer in 1889 when, using air and industrial coal gas, they attempted to build the first practical gas battery.

12. Cooper, 278.

13. Grove and his wife Emma were frequent visitors to Cyfarthfa Castle, Merthyr Tydfil. Mrs Crawshay, who was the only female on the eleven-member Merthyr School Board, and the Groves were strong advocates of women's rights.

14. Cooper, 289. Cooper points out that her book, about methods connecting the physical sciences rather than the unification of forces, is not a precursor of Grove's. In the preface to the first edition, however, she did suggest that 'an occult connexion' between heat, light, electricity and so on would probably be revealed eventually.

15. Cooper, 290.

16. Mary Somerville, *On the Connexion of the Physical Sciences* (London, 1834).

17. Reviews were often anonymous but the reviewers were sometimes identifiable. Cooper, 291.

18. Cooper, 373.

19. Correlation of Physical Forces in *The Correlation and Conservation of Forces: A Series of Expositions*, ed. Edward L. Youmans (New York, 1865), preface, 5.

20. Ibid., 198

21. Cooper, 189.

22. NMW, De la Beche Papers, 570, Edward Forbes to Henry De la Beche.

23. Cooper, 195.

24. Marshall Hall to Grove.

25. *Cambrian* (24 November 1848).

26. From the journal of Gideon Mantell. Quoted in Colin Matheson, 100. Lyell was so keen to elect Grove that he both wrote to and visited Mantell.

27. Thomas Bell was Professor of Zoology at King's College, London. He is considered to have been a good Secretary. From 1853-61 he was president of the Linnaean Society.

28. In an earlier attempt at reform during the 1830 leadership election, Herschel had been defeated by the Duke of Sussex, the youngest son of George III.

29. Cooper, 235.
30. Cooper, 243-44.
31. Cooper, 245.
32. Louise Miskell, 'The Making of a New Welsh Metropolis: Science, Leisure and Industry in Early 19th Century Swansea', *History,* 88 (2003).
33. Grove to Schonbein, 16 August 1846, Bossel 116.
34. UCWS, G. G. Francis letters, Grove to Francis, 18 August 1846.
35. *Hampshire Independent* (12 September 1846).
36. *Athenaeum* (12 August 1848).
37. Cooper, 247.
38. Schoenbein to Grove. 17 April 1840, Bossel 86.
39. Grove to Schoenbein, 30 January 1844, Bossel 101.
40. Schoenbein to Grove, 18 February 1844, Bossel 102.
41. Schoenbein to Grove, 23 November 1850, Bossel 128.
42. Schoenbein to Grove, 12 February 1858, Bossel 138.
43. As a judge (Grove was elevated to the bench in 1871) he would earn at least 5000 a year, a fortune at the time.
44. Grove to Schonbein, 8 October 1857 Bossel 136.
45. Grove to Schoenbein, 1 March 1853, Bossel 134.
46. Crowther, 100.
47. Grove to Schoenbein, 26 October 1841, Bossel, 90.
48. R. Derek Wood, *The Calotype Patent Lawsuit of Talbot v. Laroche 1854,* originally published to mark the opening of the Talbot Museum at Lacock, and published privately by the author, 1975.
49. The investigation into the death of Cook connected Palmer with several other mysterious deaths. These included an illegitimate child who had recently visited Palmer, his mother-in-law, from whom he inherited property, a Mr Bladon to whom Palmer owed gambling debts of £800, and his wife whose life, six months earlier, he had insured for £13,000.
50. W. Hodge, *Trial of William Palmer* (London 1952); George H. Knott, *Trial of William Palmer* (Canada Law Book Co., Toronto, 1912).
51. *Cambrian* (6, 13 August 1858).
52. *Cambrian* (27 July 1860).
53. Crowther, 98.
54. Elizabeth Kolbert, 'The Car of Tomorrow', *The New Yorker* (11 August 2003), 36-41.

THE 1848
BRITISH ASSOCIATION MEETING

Once the enthusiasm generated by the success of the Southampton meeting had subsided, and the bubble of Grove's rhetoric lost some of its air, questions were raised about Swansea's suitability as a venue for the eighteenth annual meeting of the British Association. However impressive the credentials of the RISW and its leading scientists, a railway-less town in Wales seemed to some of the more prominent members of the Association an unpromising setting for what they now fondly disparaged as their Wisdom Meeting or Parliament of Science.

The most severe critic was the Oxford geologist William Buckland. Anticipating a striking success for the Oxford meeting in the coming year, he looked askance at Swansea with which he was familiar from his association with Dillwyn and the RISW. His loyalty to the RISW, however, of which he was an honorary member, did not extend to the town. He expressed his views of the latter to Roderick Impie Murchison who, somewhat tactlessly, conveyed them to Henry De la Beche. De la Beche had also represented Swansea at the Southampton meeting. Buckland, wrote Murchison, 'is "toto caelo" opposed to a meeting at Swansea *now*. He says that access to it will keep away the great mass of the association & that until a rail be established it ought not to be mentioned – that [it] is a beggarly, wretched, stifling, stinking place without one decent lodging in it. In short, he is convinced that it would be a failure . . . What is to be done? I am now striving to get Norwich to compete in order that we may have some choice. But this is *entre nous*; young Grove is a capital fellow & if the Swanserians were like him and Dillwyn success would be certain'.[1]

Professor John Phillips, palaeontologist for the Geological Survey and one of the architects of the British Association at its founding in York in 1825, was also disgruntled even though, as the Association's assistant general secretary, he had declared Swansea a suit-

The Royal Institution, Swansea, 1848.

able venue for a 'moderate' meeting. In June, two months before the meeting, he wrote to De la Beche: 'I am forced to take a run down to Swansea for 4 or 5 days to help set matters agoing, and a great plague it is. I do not wonder at your feeling a little weary of our Parliament of Science, which can only meet in the summer, & which interrupts your business'.[2] Had Swansea been more to his liking Phillips, one suspects, might have felt less put upon. His temper was not improved by a long journey by train and mail coach from York; he arrived at the Mackworth Arms with 'a troublesome cough'.[3] Phillips usually allowed himself two weeks in a town immediately before the meeting, but in the case of Swansea he hoped to be able to spend a whole month in residence. Other commitments prevented this, but during one of his visits he and the Swansea antiquarian Grant Francis suggested that the streets be named. Slates, painted white and edged and lettered in black, were nailed to the walls. Not only were they an aid to visitors, but when George Clarke of the General Board of Health came to Swansea in 1849 he proclaimed them an indispensable adjunct to sanitary improvements.

Less forthright than Buckland, Phillips intimated his disapproval of Swansea as a venue by advocating, in a letter to the General Committee, that in selecting venues for the annual meeting it should not restrict itself only to those towns or cities that presented a formal application. The letter was read in the lecture theatre of the RISW during the customary meeting of the General Committee on the day preceding the opening sessions. Phillips's ideal location, which hardly needed spelling out, was an accessible town or city in a district or region where they might pick up new members and not lose friends from a distance. He urged that the decision should not be delayed beyond the Swansea meeting but as Birmingham – regarded by all as a thoroughly suitable venue – had been promised the 1849 meeting the Committee decided that no immediate action was necessary. The thinly disguised misgivings about Swansea did not, of course, escape the press. *The Cardiff and Merthyr Guardian* noted: 'It was very evident from the tone of remarks made by some of the officers . . . and the principal personages who were present . . . that they had anticipated a failure'.[4] Even the president for the meeting, Lord Northampton, intimated in his presidential address that the Association had been lured to Swansea by Grove's oratory.[5]

Local members and supporters, however, despite a number of 'croakers' in the community, had few doubts about the appeal of Swansea and the RISW. In May 1847 Dillwyn informed De la Beche that some of his neighbours had already sent out invitations for the Wisdom Meeting, '15 months hence', with no expectation that they would be declined.[6] Six months later he was even more optimistic: 'Arrangements for the Wisdom Meeting are proceeding with considerable spirit throughout this neighbourhood & it seems likely to come off with more *eclat* than I first expected'.[7] The local organizing committee had been given fair warning of the challenge ahead by John Phillips: '[Swansea] is not so large a place, or so richly environed as to be able to support a meeting of the Association, except by the united strength of public opinion'. To strengthen public opinion and maintain a sense of urgency, the committee billed the meeting as 'the most important event in the recent history of the Principality'.[8]

Visitors began to arrive on the Tuesday and it was soon evident that there would be a decent showing. Special steamers arriving from Bristol, and the flys (small carriages) and omnibuses – the latter drawn by four post horses – bringing them into town from the Mumbles Roads, were encouragingly full. By Thursday, the day of the first sessions, more than eight hundred had registered, five hundred fewer than at Oxford but a respectable number given the difficulties of access and the date of the meeting – early August, the height of the holiday season for scientists as well as the general population. Torrential rains might have silenced, or at least muffled, the 'excellent' German band hired, against John Phillips' advice, to greet registrants on their way into the RISW, but the rain did not dampen spirits. By evening even sceptical reporters were enthusiastic: 'Swansea', reported the *Literary Gazette*, 'has been graced by an opening Congress of more than expected numbers, of much brilliancy [and] of much talent and science'.[9]

Of the scientists associated with the RISW only the geologist William Logan, now director of the Geological Survey of Canada, and unable to abbreviate the short survey season allowed by the Canadian climate, did not attend. Lewis Weston Dillwyn was chair of the zoology and botany section, John Henry Vivian of mathematics and statistics, and Henry De la Beche of geology. Grove, Vivian, De la Beche and Dillwyn were also vice presidents of the meeting. Richard Phillips, an honorary member of the RISW, was chair of the chemistry section. Gwyn Jeffreys was the local treasurer and Thomas Williams was a member of the local organizing committee. Most of Britain's prominent scientists had registered as well as at least fifteen from abroad, among them Professor Julius Plucher, a physicist and mathematician from Bonn, Per Adam Siljestrom, a physicist from Sweden, the French photography pioneer Francois Jean Claudet, Professor Henry Darwin Rogers, a geologist from Pennsylvania, the Danish archaeologist Peter Wilhelm Forchammer, and G. Mateucci a physicist from Italy noted for his researches in electricity. Of the more than eight hundred registrants almost two hundred were women. The RISW had encouraged female membership from its inception.

Among the notable absentees was Grove's friend and associate C. F. Schoenbein. Although obligated, as president of the Basel Philosophical Society, to attend a similar scientific conference in Switzerland, he did not escape a friendly rebuke from Grove: 'Why did you not come to Swansea. You constantly come to British Association meetings & yet you avoid the native place of your friend Grove where there is as much practical chemistry to be seen as in any place in Europe . . . We had Faraday Graham Phillips Percy Playfair & all the chemists here but no Schoenbein. You ought to be 'hoist with your own petar[d]' i.e. blown up with gun cotton'. Another notable absentee was the geologist Roderick Impie Murchison who, having failed to interest Norwich in the 1848 meeting, presumably had taken Buckland's censure of Swansea to heart. Murchison attended the same Swiss meeting as Schoenbein.

Several of the prominent scientists and chief officers of the BAAS stayed in private houses. At Singleton there was a house party of nineteen that included the president of the BAAS, the Marquis of Northampton, and a former president, Sir Robert Inglis. At Sketty Hall, the home of Lewis Weston Dillwyn, there were six guests, at Penllergare, the home of his son John Dillwyn Llewellyn, four, and at Bryn y Môr, the home of the banker Robert Eaton, six. William Robert Grove stayed with his uncle Thomas Grove at Dan y Coed. John Phillips declined all invitations and took rooms in Adelaide St. near the RI because he would be on call throughout the meeting. The chemist Richard Phillips stayed with relatives in town. The remainder stayed at hotels, boarding houses and private houses. For those staying in rooms without any services, 'ordinaries' (breakfasts, teas and dinners) were available at the Assembly Rooms, around the corner from the Royal Institution.

For the meeting, every suitable public building near the RISW had been commandeered: the RI itself for the chemistry section and a reception room; a girls' school opposite for mathematics and physics; the town hall, then on the harbour front, for geology and ethnology; the Assembly Rooms for statistics and zoology and botany; and an adjacent chapel for mechanics. Unlike the university towns, which had lecture halls, dining rooms, messengers and porters, everything in Swansea, as the *Cambrian* remarked, had to be 'fitted up'.

Several of the RISWs scientists presented papers. Thomas Williams, playing to his strength – as always in the company of his peers – gave a paper on the structure and function of the bronchial organs of annelidae and crustacea. As well as chairing the geology sessions, De la Beche delivered the *piece de resistance* of the meeting, a two-and-a-half hour lecture on the geology of the South Wales Coalfield. Gwyn Jeffreys read a paper on a genus of gasteropod inhabiting British waters. Dr. John Percy, a chemist with strong associations with the copper industry, read a paper on the chemistry of smelting processes. Faraday, who attended the session, contributed to the discussion. Dillwyn, who was a vice-president of the meeting, distributed copies of his monograph on the flora and fauna of Swansea.

Saturday was a day for recreation, field excursions and demonstrations. There was a wide choice: in town were the Dillwyn pottery, copper works, and the South dock and the copper-ore yards, while farther up the valley were coal mines, tin and iron works. A large group visited the Ystalyfera iron works and, following a marquee lunch at the Lamb and Flag in Ystradgynlais, the party divided. Some descended an anthracite mine at Abercraf, others walked in the limestone hills above, and still others visited the site of Logan's trees, *Sigillariae*, at Cwm Llech. Geologists and palaeontologists sought out the cliffs and caves of Gower while zoologists dredged in the Bristol Channel from the *Osprey*, the yacht Gwyn Jeffreys would use on his Shetland expeditions. The mollusc catch, which included 'a beautiful *velella limbosa*', was displayed on the following Monday at the sectional meeting for zoology. For lighter palates there was an excursion to Penllergare, the estate of John Dillwyn Llewellyn, where the highlights were a champagne buffet and a demonstration on the upper lake, conducted by Benjamin Hill, John Dillwyn Llewellyn and William Robert Grove, of a rowing boat powered by a Grove cell.

In 1841 Hill and Grove, in collaboration with John Dillwyn Llewellyn, had built an electric motor capable of propelling a boat. In a letter to Schonbein, August 1842, Grove wrote that he had been experimenting with a boat capable of speeds up to three miles per hour when carrying several hundredweight. Lewis Weston Dillwyn was privy to the experiments: 'Drove in the afternoon to meet John at Lewis's laboratory to try a small electric galvanic apparatus invented by Mr. Hill for propelling boats instead of steam. It worked beautifully, and John is constructing a larger machine for an experiment with his boat on the lake at Penllergare'.[10] The 1848 motor consisted of stationary and rotating electro-magnets wrapped in continuous coils of copper wire whose ends were connected to a Grove battery. The rotating magnet drove a screw propeller at the stern of the boat. With five passengers on board, the boat managed a speed of only 3.5 miles per hour.[11]

Unimpressed by the speed, the geologist Leonard Horner thought it a 'pretty experiment' that was never going to have practical application.[12] On Friday and Saturday evenings the Vivians opened their house, gardens and grounds to the attendees. At dusk on the Friday evening Lieutenant Carte demonstrated how rockets with lines attached could be used to rescue sailors on shipwrecked vessels. Singleton Park oaks stood in for stranded vessels. On the following Monday, watched by Lord Northampton and hundreds of spectators, he substituted a moored schooner in Fabian's Bay for a wreck, and fired a rocket and line across its deck. The line was fastened, a lifebuoy drawn across, and two sailors were brought safely ashore.

In spite of poor and indifferent weather and, compared with Oxford, a low attendance, the meeting was judged to have been a great success. Britain's principal scientists came in force and, in a few cases, offered fulsome praise. Edward Forbes thought the meeting 'an admirable one both in men and matter' while Horner, in a letter to Grove, looked back 'with unmixed pleasure to the meeting at Swansea', trusting that he would not have 'a single feeling connected with the meeting that is otherwise than entirely satisfactory'.[13] Swansea's hoteliers, boarding-house owners and merchants were grateful for the influx, and a few days after the end of the meeting they held a public dinner at the Assembly Rooms in Grove's honour. When Grove rose to respond to a vote of thanks he was greeted by loud and sustained cheering.

Although a heartening success, the meeting was a swansong for the RISW which had reached, if it had not already passed, its apogee. When writing of the progress of geology in Wales, F. J. North expressed regret that the RI had not continued in the way it had begun: 'had [it] done so', he ventured, 'Swansea might have become one of the greatest of the provincial scientific centres'.[14] But by the middle of the century most of the figures who had founded and energized the institution were either aging or living elsewhere. Dillwyn and Vivian were in their sixties, Logan was in Canada, and Jeffreys, De la Beche and Grove were in England. Changes within science also militated against the survival of small, private and municipally supported institutions serving a lay membership.

As the sciences became more specialised they quickly moved beyond the grasp of the generalist, and for research and development they required government support. By the middle of the century, the terms 'natural history' and 'natural philosophy', Michael

Faraday's objections notwithstanding, were near-anachronisms. The physical sciences were the first to leave the generalist's realm and by the last quarter of the century, if Thomas Henry Huxley was representative, they had no wish to be identified with naturalists or natural historians. 'The word 'Naturalist' unfortunately includes a far lower order of men than chemist, physicist, or mathematician . . . every fool who can make bad species and worse genera is a 'Naturalist'.[15]

By 1850 even geology, which had been the core science of the philosophical societies, had lost much of its popular appeal. Unlike their predecessors, the new professional geologists, working alongside palaeontologists, had no need to rely on amateur collectors for fossil specimens. For determining the age and sequence of rocks, the quality or beauty of the fossil did not matter; the *Geologie des Dames*, which had been driven largely by aesthetics, was finished. By mid-century, too, the general stratigraphy of Britain was well understood and there would be no more Lias cliffs and Mary Annings to light the public imagination.

As geology became more painstaking and prosaic, and its language more technical, public interest plummeted. In America, Charles Lyell, who was a great popularist as well as a great geologist, was still able to attract large audiences but in Britain geology had lost most of its public following. In the postscript to a letter to De La Beche, Andrew Crombie Ramsay quoted the following '*morceau*' from an 1841 issue of the *Examiner*. 'We are informed that Mr Lyall [*sic*] is now lecturing on geology at Boston to 1,500 persons, 2,000 or more are unable to obtain tickets, which have been bought at a guinea each Extra. – All this while at our great and ancient seat of learning, Oxford, Buckland lectures on the same interesting subject to an audience of three'.[16]

With the departure of its gifted scientists, and the gradual appropriation of science education and field and laboratory research by government-supported institutions, the RISW assumed the role of a run-of-the-mill provincial philosophical society. Gwyn Jeffreys' ambition to establish in Swansea a school of science offering advanced and systematized instruction did not survive his move to London.[17] As early as 1849, the *Cambrian* noted a growing reliance on local lecturers and at its lowest pass, in the 1860s, the lecture theatre became a stage for attention-seeking rhetoricians.[18]

To raise the profile of the Institution, Gwyn Jeffreys, in 1864, and William Robert Grove, from 1886 to 1888, were elected to the presidency but both were London-based and they could be figure-heads only. Unable to call on 'leading minds', as had been possible in 1848, the way forward for the RISW, the *Cambrian* suggested, lay in popular lectures in scientific and historical subjects for an essentially middle class audience.

This signaled a humbler role for the RISW that it has maintained to the present: no longer a place for leading edge science but, through lectures and museum exhibits, a venue for public education and, thanks to its splendid nineteenth century library, historical research. By 1880, the year of the second visit of the BAAS to Swansea, the Royal Institution could not play its former substantive role, but as an icon in the cultural life of nineteenth century Wales it was, as it remains, peerless.

NOTES

1. NMW De la Beche Papers, 1020. Murchison to Henry De la Beche, 9 Feb. 1847
2. Ibid., 1639. John Phillips to Henry De la Beche, 23 June 1848.
3. Margaret Walker, 'The British Association in Swansea in 1848', *Gower Journal,* 22 (1971), 14-19.
4. *Cardiff and Merthyr Guardian* (26 August 1848).
5. *Athenaeum* (12 August 1848).
6. NMW. De la Beche Papers, 461. Dillwyn to De la Beche.
7. NMW, De la B Papers, 462. Dillwyn to De la Beche, 14 Dec. 1847.
8. RISW 83/3. Memorandum from Location Committeee to inhabitants of the Town and Neighbourhood of Swansea and Neath.
9. *Literary Gazette* (12 August 1848).
10. Dillwyn, Diary 9 January, 1841.Ben Hill described his motor in an article 'Electric Magnetic Machines' written for an 1841 issue of the *Proceedings of the London Electrical Society.*
11. *Cambrian* (18 August, 1848).
12. Michael L. Cooper, 'William Robert Grove', 253.
13. G. Wilson and A. Geike, *Memoir of Edward Forbes* (Cambridge 1861), 443; Cooper, 254.
14. F. J. North, 'From the Geological Map to the Geological Survey', 102.
15. Simon J. Knell, *Culture of English Geology,* 286.
16. F. J. North, 'History of Geology in South Wales', 74.
17. David Dykes, *The University College of Swansea* (Stroud, 1992), 33.
18. *Cambrian* (8 June 1849; 3 June 1864).

BIBLIOGRAPHY

MANUSCRIPT AND UNPUBLISHED SOURCES

Scientific Correspondence of Joshua Alder and Alfred Merle Norman 1826-1911, 7 Vols., British Museum (Natural History).

Sir Henry Thomas De la Beche Papers, National Museum of Wales (Geology).

F. J. North, unfinished manuscript biography of Sir Henry Thomas De la Beche, National Museum of Wales (Geology).

Sir William Edmond Logan Papers, McGill University Archives.

Diaries of Lewis Weston Dillwyn, 1818-1852, 36 Vols., Private Collection.

Calendar of the Dillwyn Diaries, 3 Vols. University of Wales, Swansea.

Michael L. Cooper, 'William Robert Grove (1811-96): a gentleman of science' (Open University Ph.D. thesis, 1987).

Letter Files, Royal Institution of South Wales.

OTHER WORKS

Bailey, Sir Edward, *Geological Survey of Great Britain* (London, 1952).

Boorman, David, *The Brighton of Wales, Swansea as a fashionable seaside resort 1780-1830* (Swansea, 1986).

Bossel, Ulf, *The Birth of the Fuel Cell* (Oberrohrdorf, 2000).

Buckland, William, *Reliqiuae Diluvianae* (London, 1823).

Clarke, John M., *James Hall of Albany, Geologist and Palaeontologist, 1811-1898* (New York, 1978).

Deacon, Margaret, *Scientists and the Sea 1650-1900* (London, 1971).

Dillwyn, Lewis Weston, *The natural history of British Confervae*, 16 Fasc. (London, 1802-1814).

Dykes, David, *The University College of Swansea: an Illustrated History* (Stroud, 1992).

F. J. North, 'From the Geological Map to the Geological Survey', *Trans. Cardiff Naturalists Soc.*, 65 (1932), 42-115.

Flett, J. S., *The First Hundred Years of the Geological Survey of Great Britain* (London, 1939).

Fox, Caroline, *Memories of Old Friends* (London, 1882).

Gabb, Gerald, 'The Dillwyn Family in Mumbles', *Gower Journal* 51 (2000) 20-31.

Galton, Francis, *English men of science* (London, 1874).

Gay, Hannah, 'East End, West End: Science, Education, Culture and Class in Mid-Victorian London', *Canadian Journ. History*, XXXII (1997), 425-53.

Geikie, Sir Archibald, *The Founders of Geology* (London, 1905).

Geikie, Sir Archibald, *Landscape and History and other essays* (London, 1905).

Gilmour, John, *British Botanists* (London, 1944).

Green, J. Reynolds, *A History of Botany in the United Kingdom from the earliest times to the end of the 19th Century* (London, 1914).

Harrington, Sir Bernard, *Sir William Logan* (Montreal, 1883).

Harris, J. R. 'Copper and shipping in the eighteenth century', *Economic History Review*, 29, (1966), 550-68.

Hawks, Ellison, *Pioneers of Plant Study* (London, 1977).

Hodge, W., *Trial of William Palmer* (London, 1952).

Hughes, R. Elwyn, 'Alfred Russel Wallace; some notes on the Welsh connection', *British Journ. Hist. of Science*, 22 (1989), 401-418.

Hyde, H. A., 'Lewis Weston Dillwyn as a Botanist', *South Wales and Monmouth Record Soc.*, 5 (1963), 6-8.

James, Frank A. J. L., *Correspondence of Michael Faraday* (London, 1991).

Jeffreys, J. Gwyn, 'On the Marine Testacea of the Piedmontese Coast', *Annals Mag. Natural History*, Series 2, 17: 155-188; repr. in *Gleanings in British Conchology* (London, 1858).

Jeffreys, John Gwyn, *British Conchology*, 5 Vols. (London, 1862-69).

Jeffreys, J. Gwyn, 'Preliminary Report of the Biological Results of a Cruise in H.M.S. *Valorous* to Davis Strait in 1875', *Proceedings of the Royal Society*, 173, 1876, 177-237.

Jenkins, Elis, 'Swansea Porcelain', *Glamorgan Historian,* 6 (1970), 116-147.

Jenkins, Elis, 'William Weston Young', *Glamorgan Historian*, 5 (1969), 61-97.

Jones, T. I., 'The Contributions of Welshmen to Science', *Trans. Hon. Soc. Cymmrodorion* (1932-33).

Knell, Simon J., *The Culture of English Geology*, 1815-1851 (Aldershot, 2000).

Knott, George H., *Trial of William Palmer* (Canada Law Book Co., Toronto, 1912).

Kolbert, Elizabeth, 'The Car of Tomorrow', *The New Yorker* (11 August 2003), 36-41.

Logan, W. E., 'On the Characters of the Beds of Clay immediately below the Coal Seams of South Wales', RISW, 5th Annual Report, 47-51.

Matheson, Colin, 'John Gwyn Jeffreys, a Famous Glamorgan Naturalist', *Glamorgan Historian*, 8 (1972), 29-35.

Matheson, Colin, 'Lewis Weston Dillwyn as a Zoologist', *South Wales and Monmouth Record Soc.*, 5 (1963), 9-11.

Matheson, Colin, 'William Robert Grove: Glamorgan Physicist and Judge', *Glamorgan Historian*, 9 (1973), 96-103.

McCartney, Paul J., 'Henry De la Beche – a new kind of geologist', *Amgueddfa*, 21 (1975), 13-28.

McCartney, Paul J., *Henry De la Beche: Observations of an Observer* (Cardiff, 1977).

McClintock, David, *Companion to Flowers* (London, 1968).

Mills, Eric L., 'Edward Forbes, John Gwyn Jeffreys, and British dredging before the Challenger Expedition', *Socy. Biblphy. Nat. Hist.* 8, 4, (1978), 507-536.

Miskell, Louise, 'The Making of a New Welsh Metropolis: Science, Leisure and Industry in Early Nineteenth Century Swansea', *History*, 88, 289 (2003), 32-52.

Nance, E. Morton, *The Pottery and Porcelain of Swansea and Nantgarw* (London,1942).

North, F. J., 'The Red Lady of Paviland', *Glamorgan Historian*, 3 (1966), 123-137.

North, F. J., 'From the Geological Map to the Geological Survey', *Trans. Cardiff Naturalists' Soc.* 65 (1932), 42-115.

North, F. J., 'Further Chapters in the History of Geology of South Wales', *Trans. Cardiff Naturalists' Soc.*, 67 (1934), 31-103.

Painting, David, *Amy Dillwyn* (Cardiff, 1988).

Rees, Gareth, 'Copper sheathing: an example of technological diffusion in the English merchant fleet', *Journal of Transport History*, 1 (1971-2), 85-94.

Report of the Royal Commission into the State of Large Towns and Populous Districts (London, 1845).

Ridd, Tom 'Swansea's Parks and Public Libraries', *Glamorgan Historian*, 6 (1970), 105-115.

Ross, J. R., *Letters from Swansea* (Llandybie, 1969).

Rudwick, Martin J. S., *The Great Devonian Controversy* (Chicago, 1985).

Rudwick, Martin J. S., *The Meaning of Fossils* (London, 1972).

Russell, Colin, 'In the Service of Government', *Chembytes – e-zine, Royal Soc. Chemistry*, 2001.

Russell, Sir Arthur, 'John Hawkins, F.G.S., F.R.H.S., F.R.S., 1761-1841, 'A Distinguished Cornishman and Early Mining Geologist', *Journ. Royal Inst. Cornwall*, New Series, 2, 2, (1954), 98-106.

Sacks, Oliver, *Uncle Tungsten* (London, 2001).

Sharpe, Tom, 'Henry De la Beche and the Geological Survey in Swansea', *Gower Journal*, 36 (1985), 5-12.

Sharpe T. and McCartney, P. J., *The Papers of H. T. De la Beche (1796-1855)*, National Museum of Wales (Cardiff, 1998).

Somerville, Mary, *On the Connexion of the Physical Sciences* (London, 1834).

'Soranus' (Dr. Thomas Williams), *The Science and Scientific Men of Wales* (Tenby, 1855).

Stearn, William T., *John Lindley: 1799-1865, Gardner-Botanist and Pioneer Orchidologist* (Portland, 1995).

Stewart, Averil, *Family Tapestry* (London, 1961).

Swainston, Stephanie and Brookes, Alison, 'Paviland Cave and the 'Red Lady', the history of collection and investigation' in Stephen Aldhouse-Green, *Paviland Cave and the Red Lady* (Bristol 2000) 19-47.

Swansea Scientific Society Reports, (1892-93), 34-5.

Thomas, Janet, *Swansea as a Fashionable Watering Place 1787-1820* (Swansea, 1983).

Thomas, Peter, 'Medical Men of Glamorgan: Thomas Williams of Swansea, 1818-1865', *Glamorgan Historian*, 9 (1973), 70-95.

Thomson, C. Wyville, *The Depths of the Sea* (London, 1873).

Tomos, Dafydd, *Michael Faraday in Wales* (Denbigh, 1977).

Torrens, H. S., 'William Edmond Logan's Geological Apprenticeship in Great Britain 1831-1842', *Geoscience Canada*, 26, 3 (September 1999), 97-110.

'Tubal Cain', *The Mineral Basin of Glamorgan and Adjoining Districts* (Merthyr Tydfil, 1835).

Turner, Dawson and Dillwyn, Lewis Weston, *Botanist's Guide through England and Wales*, 2 Vols. (London, 1805).

Vivian, John Henry, 'Observations on the processes for making the different Preparations of Arsenic', *Trans. Royal Geol. Soc. Cornwall,* 1 (1814), 61-76.

Vivian, John Henry, 'A sketch of the plan of the Mining Academies of Freyberg and Schemnitz', *Trans. Royal Geol. Soc. Cornwall,* 1 (1814), 70-77.

Vivian, John Henry, 'Remarks on the Salt Mines of Wielitska in Poland, and of Salzburg in Germany', *Trans. Royal Geol. Soc. Cornwall,* 1 (1814), 155-167.

Vivian, John Henry, *Results of Experiments made at the Hafod Works by Messrs. Phillips and Faraday, July and August, 1822.*

Vivian, John Henry, 'An Account of the Process of Smelting Copper', *Annals of Philosophy*, 69-95, 1823.

Vivian, Stanley, *The Story of the Vivians* (Truro, 1989).

Walker, Margaret, 'The British Association in Swansea in 1848', *Gower Journal,* 22 (1971), 14-19.

Walker, Raymond, 'The Dillwyns as Naturalists: Lewis Weston Dillwyn (1778-1855)', *Minerva* XI (2003), 20-42.

Wallace, Alfred Russel, *My Life; a record of events and opinions* (London, 1905).

Wilks, Samuel and Bettany, G. T., *A Biographical History of Guy's Hospital* (London, 1892).

Williams, Thomas, *Report on the Copper Smoke and its Influence on the Public Health and Industrial Diseases of Coppermen* (Swansea, 1854).

Williams, Thomas, 'The Present Geographical Movement and Future Geographical Distribution of the English Race of Men', lecture, winter 1859/60. Royal Inst. South Wales.

Wilson, G. and Geike, A., *Memoir of Edward Forbes* (Cambridge 1861).

Winder, G. C., 'Logan and South Wales', *Proceedings Geol. Assoc. Canada,* 16 (1965), 103-121.

Winter, Alison, *Mesmerized, Powers of Mind in Victorian Britain* (Chicago, 1998).

Woodward, Horace B., *History of the Geological Society of London,* (London, 1907).

OTHER BOOKS FROM GLYNDŴR PUBLISHING

WWW.WALESBOOKS.COM.

Full Reviews appear on the website

Books by Terry Breverton

An A to Z of Wales and the Welsh
ISBN 0715407341 296pp (Christopher Davies Ltd. 2000)
'*the first Welsh encyclopaedia!*' 'an important addition to the Welsh reference bookshelf', '*A massive treasure chest* of facts and figures covering thousands of years of history, which no collector of books on Wales can overlook', 'the A-Z has many surprising as well as predictable entries and is clearly the result of a passionate interest in post-devolution Wales combined with impeccable research . . . an inportant addition to the Welsh reference bookshelf', 'this book is great fun', 'a *comprehensive anthology and compendium of Welshness*', 'the author wants the world to know what Wales has to offer . . . alongside the Cool Cymru actors and pop stars, there is a wealth of information on more traditional Welsh culture, history, legend, art, literature and so on.' £14.99

The Secret Vale of Glamorgan
ISBN 190352900X 230pp (Glyndŵr Publishing 2000)
Millennium Award
'Terry Breverton belongs to that rare breed of Welshmen who stake their livelihood on trying to publish books in which they passionately believe. His imprint Glyndŵr Publishing/Wales Books has already made its mark on the Welsh publishing scene by bringing out substantial and handsomely produced books on Welsh subjects, particularly local history. He was born in the Vale of Glamorgan, to which he has returned after many years as a management consultant in Britain and overseas. He is the author of several useful books such as "An A-Z of Wales and the Welsh" and "One Hundred Great Welshmen". What drives him as a publisher is the belief that the Welsh people have been deprived of their own history. He aims to provide the information that will make them proud of their country. If that means he has to lose some money, he thinks it's well worth it. Among his most recent books is "The Secret Vale of Glamorgan" which shows a local man's pride in the history and culture of his

native patch, combined with a historian's delight in tracing the past and relating it to the present. For anyone born or living in the Vale, this book should be essential reading. There are chapters on Cowbridge, St Athan, Gileston, Aberthaw, Flemingston, and all the places in between, together with a wealth of information about the area's most famous son, the wayward genius Iolo Morganwg.' £13.99

The Book of Welsh Saints
ISBN 1903529018 606pp hardback (Glyndŵr Publishing 2000)
'this book is *a really extraordinary achievement*: a compilation of tradition, topography and literary detective work that can have few rivals. I have enjoyed browsing it immensely, and have picked up all sorts of new lines to follow up' – Rowan Williams, Archbishop of Canterbury; 'impressive', 'the book is full of fascinating information . . . a must for anyone interested in the history of the Church in Wales, indeed for anyone interested in learning the glorious heritage bequeathed to them from the time when Wales was the only Christian country in the world,' 'Another work from the prolific pen of Terry Breverton who is blazing a trail in producing bodies of knowledge about Welsh heritage and history. The Book of Welsh Saints is *an enormous work of research and will provide a welcome and ready book of reference* to the men and women who in Tad Deiniol's words "created Wales". The much-bandied term "The Dark Ages" may well have meant just that east of the Severn, but to us this period is the Age of Saints. And there are hundreds of them – over 900 in fact – monks, scholars, warriors, missionaries. Breverton places Arthur firmly in the context of Welsh history and shows how the seminal folk legends of European romance and literature originate in Wales. We see Wales at the very heart and very root of western Christian civilisation, a pre-eminent position from which it was thrown down by greedy, rapacious invaders who not only usurped its legacy but traduced its memory with sickening arrogance and chilling contempt', 'An *impressive* work', 'Wales certainly seems to have not only the oldest surviving language in Europe, but also the oldest Christian heritage; for in the first millennium it was accepted by Rome as the "cradle of the Christian Church". The unique historical importance of Wales has for too long been neglected until now. An important book in putting the record straight is "The Book of Welsh Saints", 'The book is *a veritable gold mine of information*, 'The Book of Welsh Saints' is an excellent publication – conscientious, clear, intelligent and, where necessary, modern', a lovely book', 'The Book of Welsh Saints is more than a compendium of folk tradition and mythology. Like all books, it has an agenda: it is just that Breverton is more explicit about his aims than most. What

he is imploring us to undertake is nothing less than a revitalisation of our spiritual culture. His programme spirals out from the revival of the cults and feast days to encompass farmers' markets, Welsh kilts, locally produced crisps and Welsh theme pubs. He directs his anger against the bland 'MacDonaldisation' of our popular culture and the corrosive political neglect which has pushed Wales to the margins of democratic life and the bottom of the UK household income statistics', 'a remarkable achievement. The amount of work and study you have put into it almost beggars belief, and I found it *utterly absorbing'*, 'The book also confirms that King Arthur was Welsh, despite many claims from other parts of the UK that the legendary king is part of their folklore. Mr Breverton said more than 100 Welsh saints from the 5th and 6th centuries were associated with King Arthur and the Knights of the Round Table.The book reveals that the legends of the Holy Grail, Tristan and Isolde, The Fisher King, the Black Knight, Camelot, Sir Gawain, Sir Lancelot, Avalon and Queen Guinevere stem from Wales. Mr Breverton says "The book sets Arthur absolutely into his Welsh context, with direct links to over 100 6th century saints, predating the medieval romances, and I wish to explore this subject further." £24.99

100 Great Welshmen (First Edition)
ISBN 1903529034 376pp (Glyndŵr Publishing 2001)
Welsh Books Council *'Book of the Month'*
'a revealing volume illustrating the great and good with Welsh connection . . . *painstaking research'*, 'Now he (Breverton) wants to ensure that his discoveries are shared by releasing a fascinating compendium of short biographies celebrating some of Wales' most venerable sons. 100 Great Welshmen is a revealing volume illustrating the great and the good with Welsh connections, either by birth or family ancestry . . . From heroes of Waterloo and computer engineers to lethal pirates and golf champions, Breverton has attempted to include them all, and that's no mean feat given our colourful heritage,' 'Now and again a book comes along that answers most, if not all your questions about your Welsh heritage. Who are the Welsh, who are their military heroes, political leaders, writers, poets, kings, princes, saints, historians, explorers, men of industry, famous actors, athletes and religious leaders? The amount of research that went into the making of this book is astounding, it seems the author left no stone unturned in order to ferret out information concerning his subjects. He has produced *a veritable gold mine of a book* that you can dip into again and again. 100 Great Welshmen will make you proud of your Welsh heritage by remind-

ing you that the little country of Wales has contributed so much to the modern world in so many areas,' 'Hwyl and Hiraeth, heritage and history, people and places, myths and imagination all come together in Terry Breverton's comprehensive anthology and compendium of Welshness. He starts by asking the question "What is Wales?" and then goes on to show us. The book is, as Breverton says, a sort of "Hitchhiker's Guide to the Galaxy" that is Wales and declares modestly that his background is more modest than academic. We have just what's needed in this unashamedly proud-to-be-Welsh work. Everything from "Assassination" (Owain Llawgoch) to "Zulu Wars" (Rorke's Drift) is covered with few stones unturned. *A massive treasure chest of facts and figures covering thousands of years of history, which no collector of books on Wales can overlook,'* 'This book is great fun . . . ' Letter to Author – 'I hope you don't mind me writing to you, but I was compelled to. I have just brought the book '100 Great Welshmen'. I have been unable to put it down and have read every last word in the Appendix. Astounding and inspiring work that put me to shame. I had very little knowledge of my heritage, but I have now vowed to re-educate myself. With such associations now being set up, I hope that our future in Wales and our language is about to flourish. Thank you for inspiring hope. Diolch yn fawr, Mared'. £18.99. **Second updated edition, 2005, is ISBN 1903529158 £14.99**

100 Great Welsh Women
ISBN 1903529042 304pp (Glyndŵr Publishing 2001)
'Perhaps the most prolific Welsh author today is T.D. Breverton, of Glyndŵr Publishing, in the Vale of Glamorgan, South Wales. This astonishing worker has recently produced such practical reference books as 'An A-Z of Wales and the Welsh', 'The Secret Vale of Glamorgan', 'The Book of Welsh Saints' and '100 Great Welshmen' (Volume I of Eminent Britons), as well as published important books by other Welsh authors. Now Terry has done it again. His latest book has finally arrive to fulfil the enormous gap in our knowledge of the enormously important, but sadly unheralded contribution of women, not only to Welsh society and Welsh history, but to Western civilisation itself. Titled '100 Great Welsh Women' (Part II of Eminent Britons), it gives short biographies to those of the fairer sex who deserve to be added to out pantheon of Welsh heroes', 'These (referring also to '100 Great Welshmen') are not necessarily books that you want to read from cover to cover, but to browse in, following your nose, as one section leads to another in a serendipitous sequence that throws up some pleasant surprises. Both are really

extraordinary achievements by a single author whose industry and enterprise seem to show no bounds . . . Terry Breverton is to be congratulated', 'This most invaluable addition to every bookshelf and library begins with the little-known Saint Almedha (5th-6th century) and ends with Jane Williams (19th century). In between, you can read of such modern notable Welsh women as singers Charlotte Church, Shirley Bassey, and Petula Clark; of world-class athletes such as Tanni Grey-Thompson; of such historical characters as Nell Gwynn, mistress of Charles II, or Saint Helena, the mother of Constantine the Great; of Catherine Zeta Jones, whose recent wedding to Michael Douglas caused such a stir; and so on. The book is *an absolute must for all those who value their Welsh heritage*, and for all those who wish to see Welsh women accorded their rightful place in history . . .', 'Famous figures stand alongside equally illustrious but lesser-known names. Entrants enjoy a detailed biography, which flags up their links to Wales, and it is *a fascinating read*. His list includes the obvious, such as Shirley Bassey and Catherine Zeta Jones, alongside the more surprising, such as Kylie Minogue, and the obscure, such as Princess Nest, and Helen of Wales', 'Breverton's breadth, generosity and sheer enthusiasm about Wales are compelling. However, one is left feeling that his potential readership may be confined to the Welsh, those with Welsh ancestry, Kylie-obsessives or someone like myself, about to marry a hugely accomplished Welsh museum director – come to think of it, quite a large potential readership after all!' 'The result of another extensive trawl through time, it celebrates the history and achievements of Welsh women through the ages', 'Breverton's two well researched and entertaining volumes are *a delightful tour-de-force* and *an astounding achievement* by a writer who seems to be ever so prolific. It was a huge task even in its contemplation'. £16.99

The Welsh Almanac
ISBN 1903529107 320pp hardback (Glyndŵr Publishing 2002)
Welsh Books Council *'Book of the Month'*
'Terry Breverton's ongoing series of Welsh history books continue to enthuse as my library steadily increases with his work. And the latest, The Welsh Almanac is one of the most enjoyable to date. In fact, I'll go so far as to *say it's a must for anyone with a drop of Welsh blood in them*. Continuing his solo mission to make Wales' proud history more accessible or for that matter readable, in comparison to the huge dusty tomes hidden in darkened libraries, The Welsh Almanac is yet another success. Filled with fascinating facts and figures, Breverton explains that the rationale behind the publi-

cation is two-fold. On the surface it is for Welsh people to remember their loved ones' birthdays, anniversaries, important dates and events. There is also an A-Z section annexed, so that addresses and telephone numbers can be entered. But on the other hand it is to record information about famous Welsh people and events upon each of these days. For each day there is also a quotation, usually from a Welsh source, tying in with people and events of the day,' '*A tremendous undertaking and a very worthwhile and absolutely fascinating addition to the library of Welsh history*,' 'Every day has space for the reader's own notes and a few apt quotations to add interest to the page. So this is a *Book of Days* in which people can record important dates in their personal histories and see them in the context of Welsh history. It's useful for jotting down birthdays and anniversaries, especially those one tends to forget, and *will take its place on the shelf with other works of reference*', 'All in all, it is a prodigious work, chock full of facts and figures from every age of Welsh history. One example will hint at the wealth of information contained within this fascinating book. On the 1st of January, Welsh people can celebrate not only Dydd Calan (New Year's Day), no fewer than six saints, the birth of the first Welsh language newspaper, a Welsh defeat of a Norman army, and Welsh team victories in rugby football and so on. The entries for each day are accompanied by a quotation that ties in with the people and events of the day. This wonderful book, attractively priced at £16.99 . . . ' £8.49 (**Special Offer**, from £16.99)

The Path to Inexperience
ISBN 1903529077 160pp (Glyndŵr Publishing 2002)
'Terry Breverton is well known as a tireless recorder of Welsh achievements in many fields. In this poetry collection, he allows us a glimpse of the tumultuous feelings that drive him. A tortured energy rushes through this book. There is bitter anger, a keen sense of injustice, national pride, compassion, fear of loss. The images whirl. He jokes and parodies, he gets drunk on words; and there are quieter moments too. Sometimes he gives us a long 'found poem' like his 'inventory' of statistics about the suffering of the miners of South Wales, where the plainly stated facts are the agonised poem; or his final 'partial list of endangered species' with their evocative and often musical names. It is good to know that out of this turmoil have come – and are still coming – books so positive in their celebration of Wales, its people, history religion and arts,' '*magnificent, compassionate and moving . . . "Chalice" will surely help Aberfan to stay in our memories.*' £5.99 (**Special Offer**, from £10.99)

Glamorgan Seascape Pathways – 52 Walks in the Southern Vale of Glamorgan
ISBN 1903529115 144pp (Glyndŵr Publishing 2003) *ARWAIN Award*
'fascinating . . . useful to anybody interested in the topography, geography and history of the southern Vale of Glamorgan,' 'Yet another publication to add to the ever-growing Breverton library of Welsh history – this time a very interesting ramble across the South coastline... Ramblers will love it, and armchair devotees can easily imagine the beauty from the descriptive passages, or maybe it will be enough to inspire them to drop the TV dinner and take a stroll', 'Terry Breverton believes in giving value for money, but it is still amazing how much info he crams into a slim book like this. There are practical details about the main walks, which stretch west from the Gwent levels to Cardiff Bay and on to Gileston. But there are also stacks of local history, ancient and modern, about the buildings and landscapes you see along the way, which makes this good for armchair travellers too. This coastline deserves more recognition.' (**Special Offer**, £6.99 from £10.99)

The Book of Welsh Pirates and Buccaneers
ISBN 1903529093 388pp (Glyndŵr Publishing 2003)
Welsh Books Council *'Book of the Month'*
'an immense work of great scholarship . . . effectively, a study of the whole genre of piracy . . . exemplary, yet the writing is light and accessible . . . wonderful, fascinating detail and essential reading' . . . *'absolutely fascinating.'* £17.99

The Pirate Handbook – A Dictionary of Pirate Terms and Places
ISBN 1903529131 388pp (Glyndŵr Publishing 2004) Welsh Books Council *'Book of the Month'*
'This *wonderful source book* is an absolute "must" for anyone who is interested in nautical matters . . . if you ever wondered where phrases like "hit the deck" and "let the cat out of the bag" come from, then this is undoubtedly the place to look . . . the amount of detail and depth is *phenomenal* . . . this book is a vitally important addition to the canon of literature about naval history,' 'a lot of fun.' £9.99

Black Bart Roberts – The Greatest Pirate of Them All'
ISBN 1903529123 254pp (Glyndŵr Publishing 2004)
'the true story of John Robert, the most successful pirate of all time, who took over 400 ships in just three years, and brought trans-atlantic shipping to a standstill', *'a must reading* for anyone inter-ested in pirates and American nautical history – first-hand accounts,

court documents and maps accompany *a fascinating story* of piratical history on the High Seas,' 'based on an impressive list of books to tell the story of Black Bart. If you like pirate stories and tales of the High Seas, get a copy!' 'Long ago just the whisper of his name was enough to strike terror into the hearts of all who sailed the high seas. Dressed in his crimson jacket and hat, bloodthirsty Black Bart was a terrifying figure that ruled the oceans from the West Indies to the coast of North Africa. So why is it that no one has heard of the Pembrokeshire pirate who took 400 ships and had half the British navy determined to hunt him down and hang him? Historian and author Terry Breverton is about to put the record straight with his latest book, which chronicles the Welsh pirate's lost history." Blackbeard, who is much more well known, was nothing but a rank amateur compared to Black Bart" said Mr Breverton, a lecturer at the University of Wales Institute of Cardiff. "He was the most successful pirate in history. He would attack anything – he basically declared war against the world."£8.99

OTHER AUTHORS WITH GLYNDŵR PUBLISHING

The Dragon Entertains – 100 Welsh Stars – Alan Roderick
ISBN 1903529026 230pp (Glyndŵr Publishing 2001)
'*a celebration of Welsh talent* in all its vibrany variety', 'this is the book to reach for the next time someone tells you that Wales has not nurtured any great talent in the worlds of entertainment or show-biz.' £5.99 (**Special Offer**, from £11.99)

A Rhondda Boy: The Memoirs of Ivor Howells – Ivor Howells, edited by Owen Vernon Jones
ISBN 1903529050 144pp (Glyndŵr Publishing 2001)
'a charming evocation of the childhood of a 93 year old Welshman. Son of a miner, Rhondda born and bred, Rhondda educated apart from his degree years at Aberystwyth, Ivor Howells spent all his professional life as teacher and headmaster in Rhondda schools.' £6.99

From Wales to Pennsylvania: The David Thomas Story – Dr Peter N. Williams 2003
ISBN 1903529085 112pp (Glyndŵr Publishing 2002)
'. . . the story of the man who emigrated from Ystradgynlais, to transform the American iron industry and make America an economic

superpower . . . Dr Peter Williams takes us back to the days of mass emigration to the United States. The terrible conditions at home, which sparked the Chartist Riots, are described, to put into context the reasons for this difficult transatlantic flight. Through Dr Thomas's correspondence with Wales, Dr Williams shows us the Welshman's immense contribution to the industrialisation and economic growth of America.' £8.99

Glyn Dŵr's War: The Campaigns of the Last Prince of Wales – Gideon Brough

(ISBN 1903529069 Glyndŵr Publishing 2002)
'The Great Liberation War is THE defining moment of our nation's history. Had it not been for Owain Glydwr and the men and women who stood at his side against overwhelming odds, there would be no Welhs nation today. You will find all the details here,' '*A massive undertaking* indeed for a 30 year old, first-time author, but one which Brough, who himself boasts an impressive militart background, has tackled with immense confidence and success.' £13.99

The Man from the Alamo: Why the Welsh Chartist Uprising of 1839 Ended in a Massacre – John Humphries

(ISBN 190352914X Glyndŵr Publishing 2004)
'. . . *one of the fastest-selling books in Welsh publishing history*', 'the remarkable story of two men sentenced to hanging, drawing and quartering. Zephaniah Williams ended up a respectable business-man after being transported to hard labour in Tasmania. John Rees ('Jack the Fifer' escaped from the Alamo to probably fire the first shot at the Westgate Hotel, before escaping back to join the great California Gold Rush', '*an amazing story*, full of meticulously researched new facts, from the former editor of the Western Mail.' £9.99

FORTHCOMING BOOKS

Admiral Sir Henry Morgan: the Most Famous Buccaneer of Them All – Terry Breverton (May 2005) – what more is there to say? Breverton has recently given an academic paper at Gregynog to an international conference, pointing out the little-known fact that Morgan was one of the greatest 'generals' in history, a genius at defeating overwhelming odds.

William Williams and the First American Novel – Terry Breverton (2005) – Breverton went to Indiana to transcribe the original 'The Journal of Penrose, Seaman' and has appended a biography of its author, the amazing yet unknown William Williams, polymath, marooned buccaneer, artist, theatre-builder, poet, writer of America's first novel, who taught Benjamin West to paint. Williams has been called 'the first flower of American culture' and the factional novel based upon his being marooned on the Miskito Coast is probably the first anti-slavery book

Cave of Heroes – Various Writers, edited by Terry Breverton with Rhys Parry (2005) – a children's featuring all of Wales' greatest heroes, their stories told by the best Welsh writers of the day. Hopefully a Welsh edition will appear in 2006.

Wales at War at Sea: Memories of World War II – Terry Breverton with Phil Carradice (2005) – at last the untold contribution of those who served at sea and in Welsh docks – to be followed by books recounting the stories of those who served in the air and on land.

General Scallywag – Gringo Revolutionary – John Humphries (2005) – the former editor of the Western Mail has done it again, following the amazing success of his The Man from the Alamo – this is the true story of a Welsh anarchist who fought with Zapata and Pancho Villa, was Hollywood's first all-action hero, and a World War I hero.

Ramblings of a Patagonian: 'When You Going Back, Then?' – Rene Griffiths (2005) – if you like off-the-wall reminiscences, this is the biography of a Patagonian troubadour and film actor who spends half his life in Cardiff and half on his ranch in the foothills of the Andes. Very humorous, and utterly absorbing in his perspective of two vastly different cultures.

Another 100 Great Welshmen – Terry Breverton (2006) – featuring many men who should have been in the original 100 Great Welshmen

A Song of Patagonia – William Casnodyn Rhys – the memories of one of the first settlers in Y Wladfa, the most socally advanced settlement in the world.

WHERE TO BUY

All of the Above Books are Available from The Welsh Books Council, Unit 16, Parc Menter Glanyrafon, Llanbadarn Fawr, Ceredigion SY23 3AQ, or from its **website www.gwales.com**, or from **any good bookseller**. Please support your local bookseller. If your bookseller states that it cannot get any of these books, they are on all the relevant ordering databases, so take your custom elsewhere. Alternatively, **send a cheque** with order to Wales Books (Glyndŵr Publishing) at Porth Glyndŵr, Higher End, Sain Tathan, Bro Morganwg CF62 4LW. There is no postage on orders in the British Isles, but £6 per book is charged for overseas orders. Visit our **website www.walesbooks.com** to download an order form, if you wish. The web pages feature a Welsh Quiz, addresses for over 400 Welsh Societies around the world, and reviews on all our books. Please let us know any additions or alterations to societies.

Our American Publishing Partners are **Pelican Publishing Company**, PO Box 3110, Gretna, New Orleans LA 70054, with the **website www.pelicanpub.com**. In process of publication are Terry Breverton's 'Admiral Sir Henry Morgan' (Spring 2005) and John Humphries' 'The Man from the Alamo' (Fall 2005). In 2004 Pelican published Terry Breverton's 'Black Bart Roberts' and 'The Pirate Dictionary' in 2004, and it is hoped that all of Glyndŵr Publishing's output will be available in the USA via Pelican over the forthcoming years.